IN THIS WORLD AND THE NEXT

IN THIS WORLD
AND THE NEXT

SELECTED WRITINGS

by

I. L. PERETZ

Translated from the Yiddish by

MOSHE SPIEGEL

NEW YORK · THOMAS YOSELOFF · LONDON

Thomas Yoseloff, Inc.
11 East 36th Street
New York 16, N. Y.

Thomas Yoseloff Ltd.
123 New Bond Street
London W. 1, England

Printed in the United States of America
American Book–Stratford Press, Inc., New York

Acknowledgment

The translator wishes to express his appreciation to Melech Grafstein for graciously granting permission to reprint in this volume the articles on Peretz by S. Niger, David Pinski and Melech Grafstein, A. Mukdoni, A. A. Roback, and Sholem Asch, which appeared originally in *The Jewish Observer*.

M. S.

Translator's Preface

O N NOVEMBER 23, 1952, the thirty-seventh anniversary of the great author's death and the centenary of his birth, the area on New York's Houston Street between First Avenue and Avenue A was officially named the I. L. Peretz Square. This was American Jewry's homage to an illustrious son of the world's Jewish-speaking people, a tribute paid to the man who had preserved for Jews in the New World the epos of their East European brethren who had perished in the Nazi holocaust.

Itzchok Laibush Peretz was born on May 18, 1852 (some authorities give the year as 1851), in Zamosc, Poland, and died in Warsaw on April 3, 1915.

Though raised in the orthodox tradition, he had also absorbed worldly knowledge. He was an *iluy*, a prodigy, being advanced enough at the age of six to begin the study of the Talmud. He took to heart the dictum of Pinchosel, his teacher: "The things that matter most are the cultivation of one's own intellectual powers, the ability to commune with oneself. . . . A disciple should turn to his *rebbe* for help only when perplexed or in doubt."

On the one hand, he had absorbed the dialectics and the *pilpul* of the sages, their ancient code of laws and ethics, their preoccupation with the hereafter, their search for the secrets of the spirit and the meaning of God. On the other hand, Michal the fiddler had once handed him a key to a well-stocked, multilingual library stored away in a neglected attic—an event that marked a turning-point in his life. The boy could grope his way through Polish somehow, but when it came to French and German he had to resort to grammars until he had acquired a working knowledge of these languages, and he then proceeded to burn the midnight oil as he pored over the "heretical," dusty volumes of secular knowledge.

Peretz was thoroughly familiar with the milieu of the orthodox

7

Jew who clung tenaciously to the ritual of his ancestors, intolerant of any changes; at the same time he was swayed by the impact of the *Haskalah,* the progressive movement of Enlightenment.

As was customary in that era, Peretz's father arranged a match for his son, when the latter had turned nineteen, with Sarah, the daughter of Gavriel Yudah Lichtenfeld, a well-to-do and scholarly merchant. As a young married man he tried his hand at several business enterprises; among other things, he became a partner in a small brewery. But within a few years he had lost his assets. His marriage was no more fortunate, and at twenty-four he was divorced. At twenty-five he married Helena Ringelheim and his second matrimonial venture proved a most happy one.

He turned to private tutoring, but still devoted himself to the study of law; he passed the bar in 1877 and, for a decade, had a thriving practice in his home town. In addition to his legal work for the local townsmen his counsel was also sought by the Polish gentry, but in 1887 his license was revoked by the Czarist authorities.

At about the same time Jan Block, a wealthy apostate Jew, felt impelled to refute the anti-Semitic slurs and accusations that the Jews had monopolized the wealth and resources of the country, and he sponsored an economic survey. The unemployed Peretz was assigned to cover a specific area in this statistical work, and the commission afforded him an excellent opportunity for the study of a vast diversity of Jewish types, as well as for the observation of the widespread poverty of the Jewish masses. The data and impressions thus gathered were to prove a rich source of material for his stories.

In 1890 he secured a position as a secretary to the *gminah,* the Jewish Community of Warsaw—a position he was to retain for the rest of his life. His salary, though increased from time to time, barely provided the comforts for his family of three (Lucian, his only son by his first marriage, was to be a cause of great concern to him later on).

When Peretz appeared on the literary horizon, Yiddish letters of the Haskalah period were marked both by didacticism and uncertainty. Though he experimented with Polish, Hebrew, and Yiddish, it was the last that was to become his chief literary medium. In 1877 he published a slender volume of Hebrew poetry (which included some verses by his first father-in-law). But it was his poem "Monish" (published in *Die Yiddishe Bibliothek,* in 1877) which demonstrated that Peretz was a literary craftsman.

While his compeer, Mendele Mocher Seforim, was still enmeshed in the Haskalah movement, Peretz managed to break away from it. Although both Mendele and Sholom Aleichem concentrated on the *shtetel,* or small town, for their backgrounds, Peretz's treatment of his milieu arouses universal interest. Mendele excelled in satire and in portraying nature; Sholom Aleichem was gifted in the genre of humor, in distilling human suffering into peals of wholesome laughter as well as into sardonic grimaces, but it was Peretz who rose to symbolic heights in psychological analysis, in his Hasidic tales as well as his folkloristic ones. He avoided the broad canvas of the novel, but in the short story, whether it dealt with the devout Jew, the illiterate menial worker, the woman breadwinner, the *zaddik* (the spiritual leader of a Hasidic following), or the perplexed young intellectual who had lost his bearings, Peretz, the literary craftsman, emerged with lyrical pathos, uncanny insight, and dramatic force.

At the turn of the century East European Jewry underwent another of its persecutions. Jews were restricted to the Pale of Settlement and subjected to innumerable indignities and oppressions, yet at the same time were subject to military service. Jewish communities were ravaged by pogroms; their humble folk, their hearts overburdened, flocked to their miracle-working rabbis, seeking comfort and intercession from their God. "If I forget thee, O Jerusalem, let my right hand forget its cunning," they chanted. "Let my tongue cleave to the roof of my mouth, if I remember thee not; if I set not Jerusalem above my chiefest joy."

Some of the Jewish youth, lured by various cults and doctrines, turned to assimilation or to the revolutionary movement in its various forms. Others, losing faith in the advent of the Messiah, made their way to the Holy Land where they plunged into the arduous pioneer life. Still others fled to America, where the Statue of Liberty proclaimed:

> Give me your tired, your poor, your huddled masses
>   yearning to break free
> The wretched refuse of your teeming shore.
> Send these, the homeless, tempest-tossed to me;
> I lift my lamp beside the golden door.

9

The abortive uprising of 1905 against Czar Nicholas II left a great many of the Jewish youth apathetic. They had pinned their faith on *lèse majesté*, on opposition to autocracy, on revolution. Peretz both admonished and comforted those who had lost their bearings and whose hopes had been dashed. "My people have been singled out for ignominy and derision, for anguish, grief and attack. But that is why they are impelled toward the uttermost horizon of human emancipation, toward triumph over brute force. . . . My people have been stigmatized with the mark of Cain, and doomed to a life of wandering—cursed, yet blessed. . . . They pay dearly for the least advance in the fight for liberation—but rarely, if ever, are they commended for their sacrifices. . . . The weakest and least of nations, you will be liberated last of all. . . . As long as blood is shed, or fervent hope is crushed, or wings are clipped—that blood, that hope, those wings shall be yours! You will be redeemed last of all, when mankind shall rise above worldly things and the encrustations of custom, when human worms will be regenerated into soaring eagles. . . . I go with my people. My soul is imbued with the refulgence of its banner, and my rallying-cry is: 'Fellow-Jews, join hands! The road ahead is fraught with danger; make common cause with your nation!' "

Peretz scourged the avaricious, the sanctimonious, and the tyrannical elements among his fellowmen. He infused courage into the humble, the meek, the long-suffering. He castigated the fawners, the cringers. Only the *intelligentsia* of the People of the Book were well versed in classical Hebrew, the Holy Tongue. And so Peretz spoke to the untutored masses in everyday-Yiddish, a medium familiar to them. "God gave me a radiant soul; it wasted its sacred fire in lighting penny tapers in the rainbow-hued gardens of pleasure. And the fire of my soul became extinguished," he remarked in one of his short stories.

This translator recalls a childhood incident in his native town of Ostropol in the Ukraine, just prior to World War I. It was a Sabbath afternoon; he was sitting on the earthen ledge that hugged his thatched house, alongside of his father, who was looking through a Yiddish daily. (There was a mere handful of newspaper readers in the entire community, who clubbed their subscriptions.) A number of bearded Jews in long shabby gabardines and weather-beaten headgear, their hands clasped behind them, were strolling leisurely down the street. They were returning from the House of Study where a *maggid*, or preacher, had held forth in homilies and parables on Job's text: "Wherefore do the wicked live, become old, yea, wax mighty in power?" The plain un-assuming townsmen clustered about us, eager for worldly news: "What's going on in the outside world?" they asked. And then followed the inevitable query: "Anything new by Peretz or Sholom Aleichem?"

Though influenced by masters of European literature such as Chekhov, Gorky, Ibsen, and Heine, Peretz neither imitated nor tried to follow them. He absorbed their skill and techniques, just as he had been inspired by the prophets of the Bible, thus enriching his talent and individual manner. He relied on meta-phor and allegory. His Yiddish is interspersed with Biblical Hebrew.

Peretz maintained that Yiddish literature had to be the voice and conscience of a harassed people. "It must be the millennial reservoir of faith and hope, the living forces that sustain us and inculcate our children with the thought that to be a persecuted Jew is to have destiny conferred upon one."

Peretz's modest residence at #1 Ceglana Street in Warsaw came to be a Mecca for budding authors, confused intellectuals, baffled youths at the parting of the ways between orthodox traditions and the ineluctable march of events.

During the first year of World War I the Russian troops took flight before the victorious German Wehrmacht. The Russian Commander-in-Chief, as a face-saving measure, made the local Jews the scapegoats and ordered them expelled at short notice and with but few belongings. Many of the sorely-pressed families flocked to Warsaw where the Jewish leaders—Peretz among them—made every effort to alleviate their plight. Food, shelter, and medi-cal attention were provided for the unfortunate; Peretz was also instrumental in founding a children's home. But the gigantic task and the sight of the suffering men, women, and children plunged him into sorrow and undermined his sensitive heart. On April 3, 1915, Peretz's voice was silenced. A hundred thousand sorrow-laden, weary Jews followed the coffin of the distinguished man of letters who had championed East-European Jewry, and millions of Jews throughout the world joined in their mourning.

MOSHE SPIEGEL

Contents

CONTENTS

IN THIS WORLD AND THE NEXT

Four Generations and
Four Wills

WHEN REB ELIEZER, son of Haikel, passed into eternity, the following note was found under his pillow:

"It is my wish that my children should own the timberland together.

"After my demise let them erect an enclosure around the cemetery and repair the roof of the synagogue.

"My collection of sacred writings is to go to my son Benjamin, who is of marriageable age—may God grant him long years and many; my other sons and my sons-in-law received their inheritance as wedding presents.

"Let my wife, may the Lord prolong her days, live in the house as she has done up to now, separately from the children, and let her take in some poor orphan girl, so that she will not lead a lonely life. On holidays, let her pronounce the benediction over the bread and the wine.

"And may she receive the same share as the rest of my heirs.

"Apart from this—"

The rest could not be made out. The note had evidently been thrust under the pillow before the ink had time to dry, and the letters were smudged.

Reb Benjamin, son of Eliezer, wrote at greater length:

"My hour has struck and I shall soon be found worthy of returning the soul given in my keeping to Him Who is Sovereign over all souls. Man trembles before His Name and His Judgment, whereas I am leaving this world without fear but with great faith in His mercy, and I believe that He will act in my case not according to the full rigor of the law but as His great mercy bids Him.

I know that I have not justified the trust of the Lord, and that my soul, during its stay with me, has become stained and marred."

We omit his confession and his admonitions to his children and read on:

"My feet are turning to ice, my consciousness is growing ever dimmer, and yesterday something extraordinary befell me: while I was deep in the reading of a sacred book I dozed off and dreamed of something very vague. The book fell out of my hand, and when I awoke I immediately grasped that this dream was not in vain, that I was being called. . . .

"Concerning my actual merits in this world, I shall say nothing for the present. That is something the Lord will repay me for a hundred and twenty years from now. I shall be found worthy of beholding the fruits of these actions when I appear before the face of the All-Highest. May His will be fulfilled! Amen.

"That which I am now leaving behind was never mine and, as God sees me, I leave all this without any regret.

"I leave no instructions as to how the inheritance is to be divided, inasmuch as I am convinced that my family, may the Lord prolong their days, will live together in peace, divide my property in accordance with law and justice, peace and accord, and will not, God forbid, confiscate anything from one another.

"I demand that my family—my wife, my sons, and my sons-in-law, may the Lord prolong their days—set apart two tenths from the estate. Immediately after my death, let them take exact inventory of my personal belongings as well as my land, the household furnishings, promissory notes, and moneys due on verbal agreements. Let the first tenth be distributed to the poor, in my name, for the salvation of my soul.—Out of what is left, that is, from their own shares of the inheritance, let them set aside a second tenth in their own names, also for the benefit of the poor, in keeping with my custom of tithing out of my gains those who have nothing.

"And, over and above these two tenths, let them contribute another three per cent, in case they should be incorrect in their reckonings.

"Both tenths must be distributed among poor strangers—by no means among relatives. As to how much should be given to the poor relations, let them decide that for themselves; they must, however, make such gifts not out of the above sums, inasmuch as sacrifices must not be made for one's own gratifications; and in any case giving to relatives is the same as giving to one's self.

"On my memorial stone let them engrave only my name and the name of my father, blessed be his memory—nothing more.

"And I ask my sons and my sons-in-law not to indulge themselves too much in the vanities of this earth and not to become merchant princes, for the more princely the merchant the sooner does he cease to be a Jew. Let them not seek enterprises in distant lands, or scatter their capital to the four winds, for the Lord helpeth only where it is His will to do so, and His blessing can descend upon small enterprises as well as upon great ones.

"I particularly ask this of my dear son Jechiel, inasmuch as I have noticed that the inclination toward a princely way of life is very strong within him.

"I also ask my children to keep up the custom of giving away before every New Year a tenth of the profits for the benefit of the poor and if, at any time, there should be no gains, God forbid— even if, worse yet, there should be a loss—let them distribute alms just the same, for the loss will undoubtedly be a trial sent by God.

"I ask especially that each day they should devote a little time to the study of the Talmud and, at the very least, to the Beginnings of Wisdom.

"Let them pay a visit to some saintly sage once a year, if not oftener.

"Let the women, on Sabbaths and feast days, read the Kav-Haioshor and the Tseneh-Urena. On the anniversaries of my death, let the whole day be devoted to reading the Torah, and let the women distribute alms. This above all: let such charity be bestowed without any blowing of trumpets. . . ."

When Moritz Bendetsohn, son of Benjamin, died, they found a note written in Polish:

"A telegram must be sent to my son in Paris, and my burial is to be delayed until his arrival.

"I donate ten thousand for the benefit of the Society for Assisting the Poor; the interest from this fund must be distributed among paupers annually on the anniversary of my death.

"I bequeath ten thousand for the maintenance of a hospital bed, with the stipulation that the bed must bear a tablet with my name.

"Let alms be distributed at my funeral.

"Send contributions to all the institutions of Hebrew learning. Let the pupils and the religious instructors of these institutions follow the procession after my coffin.

"Engage a *daion*, [great scholar] or some other learned Jew, to recite the mourner's prayer over me.

"Order the monument from abroad, identical to the model which I have left.

"Transfer whatever sum is necessary to the Society for Assisting the Poor, and let it undertake the maintenance of my grave and monument.

"The firm is to bear the name of Bendetsohn's Son.

"And in regard to—"

We omit an inventory of the estate, the list of debts to be collected, and detailed instructions as to how the business was to be carried on.

"I, 'Bendetsohn's Son,' am leaving this world, not out of joy, not because of melancholy, but out of sheer emptiness.

"A great sage was Aristotle, who said that nature abhors a vacuum. The universe is a frightening machine. Every wheel carries out its own work, has its own designations. A wheel may get out of order or wear out before its time—and then it ceases to be a part of the machine and *passes from being into nothingness*.

"I can no longer go on living, because there is nothing here for me to do. I am no longer fit for anything because I have lived out my time. I have drained from the bottom of the cup those delights which were intended for me; I have touched everything with my lips and have drunk my fill of everything.

"They taught me many things, but never taught me to live without burning the candle of life at both ends.

"There is nothing in the world that could hold or attract me. I lacked nothing, and nothing held any value for me. Everything came to me easily without grief or effort—everything was there for my taking. Things and people—men and women.

"All fawned upon me—but I did not have a single friend. Women kissed me willingly, but I had no need of them.

"I inherited riches, and those riches increased and multiplied without me, without the slightest effort on my part. They grew —until they were greater than my own self.

20

"My heart often wept: if there were just one thing I wanted, if I were forced to work, just once! Yet the doctors prescribed excursions, games, sport. . . . This was not life but a travesty on life —falsified life, falsified work.

"Many lands have I beheld, but not one of them was *my* land; many parts of the world enchanted me, yet not a one of them did I come to love.

"I spoke glibly in many languages, yet had no *feeling* for any of them; I played with words as a juggler plays with spinning balls.

"I changed my nationalities and languages like gloves.

"All the world was mine, but I was too small to embrace it or to reign over it.

"And that which I might have acquired by myself came to me all ready made. Everything was done, everything was bought and paid for. And that which had not yet been completed was finished off by my wealth. Everything: the smile on the face of a friend, the kiss from beautiful lips, the prayer for my dead father. At best, I paid for one thing or two. But when it came to giving, to bestowing gifts: that was something I had never been taught to do.

"That which was insignificant became for me even more insignificant; that which was enormous became crushing. There really was nothing to live for.

"I am dying because I am sterile, in spirit as well as in body. There is nothing within me that can live and give life. I have long ceased to live and to enjoy life. Life has now become unbearable to me.

"They did with me as a peasant does with a porker: they fattened me up. But the peasant kills the porker when it becomes sufficiently fat, whereas they forced me to bring about my own death, and I lack the courage not to submit.

"The arsenic is on the table: the last drink that will intoxicate me—and I shall never awaken to sober up.

"Should I make arrangements about my estate? Whatever for? It was a curse to me.

"Have I anybody to thank?

"No: I have paid everybody—for everything.

"I have even paid in advance for this last drink. . . ."

The Supreme Sacrifice

MANY AGES AGO, in the city of Safed, which is in the Holy Land, there lived a well-known Jew, a trader in precious stones. He was an extremely wealthy man, not one of the *nouveau riche*.

He lived in a palace of his own, this Jew. The palace, whose windows faced the Sea of Kinneret, was surrounded by a great garden luxuriant with every conceivable kind of fruit tree and crowded with song birds. This garden flourished with fragrant flowers, pleasing because of their beauty, and with herbs gracious in their healing virtues. Its wide paths were strewn with sand that glinted like gold; the tops of the trees intertwined, casting shade over the paths. There were restful bowers throughout the garden and many looking-glass ponds on which resplendent white swans glided.

This rich man owned many asses and camels; he also owned a ship, with a captain and a full crew at his command.

All of Israel should fare no worse!

Nor was this Jew miserly when it came to dowries, provided he could become an in-law to renowned rabbis, heads of seminaries or great sages of the Holy Land and Babylon. When he married off his sons, he gave each a patrimony in cash, in addition to such sums and gifts as are usual at a wedding. He was left in his old age with but one daughter, Sarah, his youngest and most beloved. He guarded her jealously; she was a maid of great beauty, of rare goodness and piety. For her this Jew picked out a bridegroom from among the scholars in the seminary at Babylon, a young man by the name of Hiyah, who was a genius.

In recommending the young scholar to the Rabbi of Safed, the Dean of the celebrated Yeshiva of Babylon called him the crown of his head and the crown of the Seminary and also pointed out that he was a descendant of one of the noblest families of Israel. In fact, this young man was reputed to be of royal origin, a descendant of the Kings of Judaea, even though his genealogical records were said to have been destroyed during one of the mass slaughters of Jews in Babylon (when his father and mother as well as his brothers and sisters had all been slain, and Hiyah had escaped only by a miracle). Reb Hiyah, because of his great modesty, never spoke of his origin, and therefore no one had any real knowledge concerning him.

It suffices to say that when people saw him in the street they were stunned by the perfection of his features. More than one man had, upon meeting him, recited a benediction to the Creator of marvels and beauty, for his face testified, better than any witness could, to his kingly origin: it could not be denied that the Divine Presence had cast its glory over him.

After the marriage, Hiyah came to live with his father-in-law and settled down to studying the Torah. However, he did not devote himself for long to his beloved studies, for his widowed father-in-law departed this life within a few years, and the young man had to assume direction of the decedent's business affairs and to travel with precious wares through distant lands. And thus Hiyah became a trader, a merchant-prince in his own right.

But he did not forget his studies. As he rode through the desert, someone in the caravan would lead his camel by its reins while Reb Hiyah held some sacred volume in his hands. Aboard ship, he had a cabin all to himself where he pursued various studies, both overt and occult. He also found time to learn secular sciences from the old sheiks whom he met on his travels. In this way, he acquired the medical art and began to understand the roaring of beasts and the noises of birds; he even learned something of astrology.

His charity knew no bounds. Upon arrival at any place, the first thing Reb Hiyah would do was to distribute among beggars a tenth of all the profits he had accumulated during his travels. The ransoming of fellow-Jews likewise cost him a great deal of money.

There was also another way in which Reb Hiyah aided the Jews. His dealings in precious stones put him in close touch with kings and their grandees, and through his honesty and intellect he found favor in the eyes of the nobility. They trusted him implicity and acceded to his requests. Reb Hiyah came forward as an intermediary in every crisis, scotching intrigues with his eloquence, releasing men from dungeons or delivering them from chains or bastinado. On more than one occasion he had snatched men from the hangman's noose or from a mosque, where fanatics held them prisoner while they attempted to make Moslems out of them.

When Hiyah was away, Sarah, his wife, represented him in matters of charity in the city of Safed, as behooved a truly pious woman who held the trust of her husband. And Reb Hiyah was at peace, knowing that every hungry man who knocked at the door of his house would depart with a full belly and that their only daughter, Miriam, would be brought up in the spirit of piety and benevolence.

Their house was always filled. Men of learning, distinguished rabbis touring to raise funds for their yeshivas, frequently visited at the home of Reb Hiyah's wife, and she would receive them graciously, showering them with her hospitality and only asking in return that they pronounce benediction upon her daughter.

And the blessings of the righteous were realized: Miriam was a wonderful child, a gift from heaven. All of Safed admired her. "Reb Hiyah's daughter glows like a little sun," they said; "She is as serene as a summer's day"; "She is blessed with the charm and loving kindness of Queen Esther." The little girl took after her mother and was growing up to be a beauty.

But the ways of the Lord are beyond all knowing. The words of Solomon the Wise were not in vain: *The man whom the Lord loveth He likewise chastiseth.* For at times the Lord sends evil to test a man of righteousness, to ascertain how profound, how great and strong his faith is. And so it happened that the righteous Sarah fell seriously ill. Reb Hiyah received the sad news during his travels and immediately dropped all his affairs to hasten home. He sped over deserts and seas, with all sorts of obstacles to detain him—the asses and camels would founder in the desert for lack of water, or storms would rise and destroy his ship. But the deeds of Reb Hiyah were great in the eyes of Heaven, and, having surmounted all obstacles, he arrived home to find his wife on her deathbed.

On recognizing him, the righteous woman raised herself up, despite the pain, and gave thanks to the Creator of the Universe Who had heard her ardent prayers and given her the opportunity before her death of bidding farewell to her faithful husband.

Then she consoled Reb Hiyah, assuring him of her acceptance of the judgment of heaven and the torments of death.

The saintly woman asked him to take care of their only daughter, who had been carried out of the room in a faint. Reb Hiyah promised her that he would be both father and mother to their daughter, that he would allow no harm to come to her, and Sarah, in turn, promised not to forget them in the Kingdom of Heaven, to pray for a worthy bridegroom for their daughter. She promised that, if difficulty arose, she would try, if Heaven permitted, to appear to Reb Hiyah in a dream and show him the right path.

Then, having bid farewell to Reb Hiyah, Sarah once more uttered the *Shema Yisroel* [Hear O Israel, the Lord our God, the Lord is One!], opened her eyes for a final look at her husband, asked that her greetings and blessings be conveyed to her daughter, reminded him once more that the judgment of the Lord must be accepted with faith and love and meekness, sank back on her pillows, stretched herself out, and turned her face to the wall— and her pure soul went up to heaven.

Barely had the thirty days of mourning passed after his wife's death when Reb Hiyah liquidated his various enterprises, selling his precious stones almost for nothing, and vowed to devote himself henceforth to the study of the Torah and to the service of the All-Highest. He established a Yeshiva in his mansion, called forth from Safed and its environs youths who were known for their zeal in study, and proceeded to enlighten them daily on the sacred writings. They paid eager attention to his discourses. The poor students Reb Hiyah maintained at his own expense, assigning two or three lads to a room, furnishing them with clothes, as if they were of his own flesh and blood, and even issuing them pocket money, so that the young men might afford themselves certain pleasures and not be ashamed before their well-to-do fellows.

Whenever one of them reached his eighteenth year—the age for marriage, according to Jewish tradition—Reb Hiyah would send for the matchmakers and, having chosen for him a suitable bride, would make sure that a means of support commensurate with his merits were guaranteed him. Furthermore, he would provide the dowry, the wedding garb, gifts, and at least half the expenses incidental to such an event. Also, he would usher the youth to the wedding canopy and carry out the ceremony in accordance with the Mosaic law.

For his daughter Miriam, he was seeking a bridegroom who would be of an equal station to his, one over whom God and men would rejoice. He wrote on one occasion to a relative of his, the spiritual head of the Yeshiva in Babylon with whom he was in constant correspondence, both on questions of scholarship and personal affairs. He wrote in the ancient tongue, which loses a great deal of its beauty in our translation:

"Through the sanction of the Lord—may His Holy Name be blessed!—I have cultivated a beautiful garden [a Yeshiva] with different kinds of trees, bearing all sorts of fruit [disciples]. Whenever this fruit or that becomes ripe and succulent [when the disciple is worthy of entering upon matrimony], I seek out a worthy person [a good father-in-law] and I have him utter a benediction over it [the wedding]. If the Lord will guide me, there will emerge a citron without any blemish, and I shall take it for my only daughter, Miriam—may she live long!"

But when the spiritual leader at Babylon wrote back asking: "Can it be that there is not in your Yeshiva a scholar worthy of her?"—Reb Hiyah gave him to understand that the matter did not have to do exclusively with scholarship. "Learning," Reb Hiyah wrote in reply, "is like unto water. Not all waters flow out of paradise [not every man busies himself with study to the glory of God]. One exerts himself out of pride, desiring to surpass and overcome his companions. Another does so for the prestige and glory to be derived from study, his intention being not so much to honor the Torah as to have the Torah honor him. A third one turns to learning through ambition, out of love for philosophizing, rejoicing not so much over the Word of God as over the novelties he invents, admiring his own forensic, the fruits of ineffectual mind. For the sake of mental exercise, a person like this is always ready to garble the meaning and the words of the Torah. Others regard learning as the means to carnal happiness: a prosperous father-in-law, a well-stocked board, a rich inheritance. True enough, although at first they may undertake their studies to their own glorification, gradually they may give themselves over to studying in the name of God and His Glory, but just the same a blemish remains upon the soul for all time! Now, there are many good citrons in my garden, but what I seek is a special one whose inner substance fully corresponds to its exterior. But it is not so easy to determine the inner substance of a man. There is always a doubt. . . ."

The spiritual leader at Babylon, having acknowledged that Reb Hiyah was in the right, nevertheless answered as tersely as ever:

"Seek and thou shalt find! Have faith!"

But how was one to seek?

"It should be easy to recognize a man by his eyes," Reb Hiyah would say. "The soul is imprisoned within the body, as if in a dungeon. But the Lord, in His compassion, has constructed two small windows in this dungeon: the eyes, through which the soul may look out at the world and at the same time may show itself to the world. And so it should be possible to recognize a man by his eyes. But regrettably the little windows have curtains: the eyelids have lashes. And if a man has within his soul a shortcoming, he veils it, just as a bride veils herself. And when the soul looks out upon God's world, the man, seemingly out of modesty, lowers the curtains. . . .

"It is easier, therefore, to recognize a man through his voice!" Reb Hiyah would conclude, and would elaborate on the idea in this fashion:

"A man is like unto a vessel of clay: with little effort both can turn into dust. Even as a vessel holds water, so may a man hold learning within himself without losing a drop, but only if the vessel is whole. But how is one to be positively sure the vessel is whole, just because the eye cannot detect a leak. One must tap the vessel and listen to the sound it emits. If the sound is clear and reverberating all is well! If not—the pot has a flaw. It is the same with man.

"The voice of the man who is not whole will ring with overtones; it will rasp or quaver, but will never produce a pure, clear sound, for he is devoid of a real voice.

"But, after all, a man is not an inanimate vessel. When a man is put to the test, knowing his voice will betray him, he simulates the voice of another. At times one hears the faraway song of a bird and thinks it is such and such a bird singing. Yet when one draws near the fraud becomes apparent, for it is only a parrot."

Therefore, Reb Hiyah pursued the following course: he taught in the early afternoon, and at dusk he would let his disciples out into the garden. There they would stroll in the shade of the trees, plucking the fruits and blessing the Creator or breathing in the fragrance of the flowers and the scent of the grass and shrubs. As they strolled about, they would review what they had learned, discuss the study of holy things, or indulge in friendly conversation among themselves. Meanwhile Reb Hiyah would withdraw into his own chamber and study occult science. The windows of his room faced the garden and were curtained with heavy silk to shut out the sun. From time to time, Reb Hiyah would take off his glasses and place them on the volume before him, which he then covered with a cloth of fine weave on top of which he deposited his snuff-box. Then he would approach a window, stand behind the curtain, and listen to the voices of his students as they strolled about the garden in pairs or in small groups. They talked freely as they walked and had no one to fear or any reason to disguise their voices.

Reb Hiyah could not catch the gist of what they were saying, nor had he any desire to do so. Only the sounds of their speech floated up to his room, not their words.

But when a long time had passed and Reb Hiyah still had not found one genuinely pure voice, a profound sadness overcame him. And one day he poured forth his sorrow to the Lord:

"Sovereign of Heaven!" he called upon Him. "The birds in the garden, if they have but the breath of life in them, sing glory unto Thee, and my disciples, having soul and cognition, attain awareness of Thy Word. Wherefore, then, is the voice of Thy little birds so clear, so whole and pure, as though they were pouring forth all their soul in their song, whereas my disciples—"

But he did not finish: he did not want to utter disparagement against his disciples. His sadness would not leave him. From time to time new students would enter his seminary and there would be the sound of new voices in the garden—but still not one of unique excellence.

One day Reb Hiyah called his daughter Miriam near him, and with great love and tenderness he questioned her:

"Daughter, do you ever visit the grave of your mother?"

"Yes, father," she answered, having kissed his hand.

"What do you ask of her, my daughter?"

"I pray to her for your health, father!" said Miriam, raising her clear eyes to him. "You are so downcast at times—and I do not know how to cheer you. Mother—may she rest in peace—knew how."

"I am well, glory be to God," said Reb Hiyah, patting her velvety cheek. "There's something else, my daughter, which you should ask of your mother —"

"And what may that be?"

"You will go to her grave, my daughter, and ask her to do her best that my plans for you may be fulfilled."

"I will do so, father," Miriam replied.

One day, as he sat in his room, Reb Hiyah heard loud voices in the corridor. There were two of them: one, raised in anger, was that of the supervisor; the other was a youthful, unfamiliar voice—probably that of a newly arrived scholar. And it was this second voice that made a powerful impression on Reb Hiyah. It was the voice he had long sought, the one for which he had prayed to the Creator. He shut his book and listened closely. But the pleading young voice had ceased and only the reproachful, angry tones of the supervisor could be heard.

Reb Hiyah rapped on his table. The door opened, and the supervisor entered, excited and apprehensive, assuming a submissive pose near the doorway. His face was pale, his eyes were bright with anger, and his nostrils quivered.

"Wrath," Reb Hiyah reminded him, "is a sin."

"Nay, Rabbi!" the supervisor gasped. "This is too much! What impudence the youth has!"

"Just what is the matter?"

"It isn't much he wants—merely to enter the Yeshiva!"

"Well, what of it?"

" 'Do you know the Talmud and the Commentaries pertaining to it?' I asked him. 'No,' said he.—'Do you know the Mishnah, the basic premises of the Talmud?'—'No.' Then I asked him, in jest: 'Well, have you gone through the En Yakov [the Talmudic legends]?' He hadn't done that either! At this point I actually burst into laughter. 'Do you know how to pray, at least?' The lad began to weep. He knew how to recite the prayers, he said, but had forgot the meaning of the words! 'Where do you think you are going then, foolish one?' He wants to enter the Yeshiva. 'Why?' He wants, said he, to ask Reb Hiyah for permission to attend the Yeshiva and hear the word of God—and then, if the Lord is merciful, he will recall everything!"

"That means that he had the knowledge once but has forgotten!" sighed Reb Hiyah. "He has probably been ill, the poor fellow. Why, then, are you so angry?"

"How can one help but be angry? 'Very well,' I said, 'I'll admit you to the Yeshiva.' But all he had on was sackcloth, all tattered and girded with coarse rope; and he was carrying a home-made staff fashioned, obviously, from the withered branch of an almond tree. So I said to him: 'Very well, young man, I'll admit you to the Yeshiva. But you will have to change your clothes. Have you anything to wear?' No, he had no intention of taking off his sackcloth, he said. 'Leave your stick, at least!' He didn't want to; he must not let that stick out of his hands, he said, at any time—night or day; he does not let go of it even in his sleep!"

Reb Hiyah realized at once that the youth was a penitent sinner and ordered the supervisor to bring him in.

The young man who entered and hesitated near the door was wan and emaciated, clad in sackcloth and girded with a rope. He carried a staff of almond wood. Reb Hiyah signaled him to come closer and greeted him, without allowing him to fall on his knees nor kiss his hand. "My son, why do you keep your eyes lowered?" asked Reb Hiyah. "Are you concealing your soul from me?"

"Yes, Master!" answered the youth. "Mine is a sinful soul. . . . I feel ashamed of it."

"Man ought not to consider himself evil," Reb Hiyah admonished. "I command you to lift up your eyes!"

The youth obeyed.

After a look into his eyes, Reb Hiyah shuddered: he had seen a curse in them.

"There is a curse in your gaze, my child," said Reb Hiyah. "Who has cursed you?"

"The spiritual leader in the Jerusalem Yeshiva."

"When did this happen?" asked Reb Hiyah, who knew that the great sage had passed away recently.

"It's two months by now," replied the youth.

That was correct, Reb Hiyah reflected; at that time the old scholar had still been among the living.

"Why did he curse you?" he asked.

"That is something I have been ordered to confess to you."

"It is well. What is your name, young man?"

"Hananiah."

"So be it, Hananiah," said Reb Hiyah, getting up from his seat. "Let us go now and say the evening prayer, after which the supervisor will show you to your place at the table. After supper, go into the garden; I will come to you there and hear your story."

Taking Hananiah by the hand, Reb Hiyah led him to the House of Worship.

How young he is, Reb Hiyah thought as they walked along. What a voice. . . . And he is repentant. But there is a curse in his eyes. The ways of the Lord are past all knowing.

Late that night Reb Hiyah walked in the garden with the youth. From time to time, the older man looked up imploringly at the heavens, seeking some astrological sign, but the sky was leaden with clouds: it was a night without a moon, without any stars. What light there was came from windows of the house. Reb Hiyah led Hananiah to a remote arbor, where, after they had seated themselves, he was the first to break the silence:

"And it is said in the Scriptures," he began *"D'aga b'lev ish—yeshinah."*

"What does that mean, Master?" asked the youth.

Reb Hiyah translated for the youth, who repeated after him:

"D'aga—sorrow, *b'lev*—in the heart, *ish*—of man, *yeshinah*—let him speak thereof: let him pour forth the bitterness of his heart before another."

And, although the young man understood only the translation, not the original words, his pale face glowed with joy.

Great pity for the youth overwhelmed Reb Hiyah.

"P'sach picho b'ni," said he. "Open your lips, my son. *V'ioiru d'vorechu*—and may your words be glowing. Repent, my child."

And Hananiah began his strange confession.

He had been born in Jerusalem; his mother, a rich widow, dealt in spices. She had only two children: Esther and Hananiah, the girl being the older of the two.

And the mother naturally had greater love for the male child, since he would be the one to recite the *Kaddish* prayer in her memory. Then, too, Hananiah had shown signs of genius since early childhood. Although Esther had already passed her sixteenth year, the mother showed no concern over her and was not seeking a bridegroom for her. Whenever her neighbors reminded her of this, she always had a ready answer: "My daughter is still not to be numbered among the old maids!" She devoted herself completely to her son, engaging the finest teachers for him. Since she was a distant relative of the dean of the Jerusalem Yeshiva and had entry into his house, she would frequently, on the Sabbath, bring her son to the Rabbi's wife who, in turn, would ask her husband to check the boy's progress.

The old Rabbi loved Hananiah, and the mother, as she stood on the other side of the door, would often hear him singing her son's praises. Peeping through a crack in the doorway, she would see the eminent Rabbi patting her son's cheek or giving him the choicest apple from the Sabbath fruit bowl, and she rejoiced.

The mother rejoiced still more when she learned that the headmaster was anxious to have the lad enter the academy. However, she could not bear to be parted from her darling child, and wished to keep him with her at home. This way, she could leave the shop in the care of a neighbor whenever she pleased and run home to kiss him.

She engaged a well-known scholar to tutor the young man at home and in so doing made a grievous mistake.

The teacher belonged to the pseudo-scholars who busy themselves with the word of God not in the name of the Lord but only to magnify and glorify their own names. And he caused Hananiah as well to stray from the path of truth. Making his mind keen only through casuistry and sophistry, the instructor developed in him the ability to dispute all things and sowed in the soul of Hananiah the bitter seeds of vainglory. And it did not take the boy long to master this art. But it was not with this art that the words of God first ran forth on Mount Sinai.

People, however, did not understand this and sang Hananiah's praises loudly.

As for the mother—well, what does a foolish Jewish woman know? She grew more and more enchanted with him.

After a while Hananiah informed his mother that he no longer needed any instructors—and she was in ecstasy.

And Hananiah, now on his own, kept following the false path. He launched into arguments with other boys from the Yeshiva, overcoming them easily, humiliating them, making them look like fools. When these arguments finally came to the attention of the spiritual leader, he deemed them childish mischievousness and remarked that such things were the first manifestations of genius. He merely suggested that Hananiah's mother should be told, in his name, to punish her son slightly. The mother, said he, had the right to do so.

But instead, she showered the lad with kisses and gave him a valuable gift because of his achievements.

Hananiah, understanding that everyone was pleased with him, became more and more impudent. He frequented the synagogues and Houses of Study and showed off his art. If he noticed a scholar poring over a book, he would approach and put a question to him concerning the text being studied. After hearing the answer, it would take him only a moment to demolish it, but he would persist until the other would lose his head entirely, at which point Hananiah would demonstrate to all assembled that the scholar did not have so much as a glimmering of what the Talmud was all about.

A student at the seminary might be delivering a recitation, or some scholar might be lecturing to the student body—well, the speaker would barely finish when Hananiah scrambled up on the dais, pulverizing the orator, making hash of his discourse, tearing it apart like a cobweb, and showing up everybody's ignorance.

New complaints were made to the spiritual leader, who left instructions that Hananiah's mother should flog him. But she, proud of the young man's successes, pampered and spoiled him still more, and Hananiah kept right on. When he discovered that the mother was neglecting her duty, the headmaster said that he did not wish to punish the boy himself, since he excelled in his studies, and that only his mother had the right to do so. However, in view of his mother's bedazzlement, he ordered Hananiah brought to him.

The boy strutted in proudly and began immediately to contradict the old man's remarks. The spiritual leader, who was known for his humility, did not interrupt him or become angry, but satisfied himself by saying:

"Listen to me, Hananiah! What all your knowledge amounts to is the ability to demolish the arguments and ideas of others by saying 'No.' You have not yet understood the entire Torah, for the Torah harbors not only denials but affirmations: Thou shalt!

and Thou shalt not!—and you have claimed only the denials for your own. The other half you have not absorbed. Try, for instance, to affirm something. Say something positive —"

Hananiah remained silent. This ability of which the old man spoke was something he did not have. His strength lay only in tearing down, not in building up.

"That is something my teacher did not cover!" he rationalized.

"Your teacher, Hananiah, is dead," the old man informed him. "Your teacher is now burning in the flames of hell. Even his scholarly achievements did not save him from the torments of Gehenna. He will go on suffering until such time as you, Hananiah, reform and pluck forth from your heart the evil he has sown there. Take pity, Hananiah, upon yourself and upon your teacher. Study for the Glory of God —"

Hananiah rushed to the cemetery to find out if his teacher had really died and was informed that the teacher had been buried only the day before. They pointed out the grave to him, and when he drew near, he saw that the mound was already overgrown with nettles and thorns. He realized that this was an omen and vowed to reform.

But it was not to be.

At that time, there was a certain butcher who lived in Jerusalem. Because the rabbinical court suspected that he was selling meat not duly certified for consumption, a man of learning had been sent to this butcher's shop as an observer. The observer tried to carry out his assignment faithfully, and one day the infuriated butcher threw a cleaver at his head. The victim escaped death only by sheer luck, and the rabbinical court forbade Jews to buy meat from this butcher. In revenge, the butcher made accusations to the authorities against the rabbinical court. Its members were seized, thrown into prison, and sentenced to flogging and subsequent exile. The butcher went unpunished, and the people were relieved that the malicious fellow had quieted down and was no longer bent on vengeance.

Having closed up his shop, the butcher became a usurer. He had always been a miser, was not master over his coppers. He often went without food, and although his clothes were nothing more than rags, he refused to give them to a beggar because there was always the chance he might sell them to some old clothes dealer. He even got himself some dogs, so that no beggar could come anywhere near his house.

He had only one child, a daughter by the name of Hannah. His wife, a righteous and pious woman, was so angered by his evil nature that she had prayed the Lord to seal up her womb and withhold sons from her, for she believed that sons take after the father in character and inclinations. As for reforming her husband, she found this beyond her strength. She suffered in silence, but when her endurance was taxed—her husband used to beat and torture her—she begged the Lord for an early death, took to her bed, and gave up her soul. Before the end she had managed to persuade her kin to bury her at their expense, so that her husband would not know even the whereabouts of her final resting place.

Thus the butcher was left a widower. And since no upstanding woman would consider marrying such a scoundrel, he lived on with his daughter, Hannah. He loved her fiercely and guarded her closely. He would have denied her nothing, although he loved money more than his very soul. Hannah, however, did not wish to avail herself of his riches. Her mother had willed that she should accept nothing from her father except bread and water. She did not want expensive clothes: of what use were they to her when she dared not venture out of the house for fear of hearing how people vilified and cursed her father!

However, the more Hannah refused to accept from him, the more her father wished to give her. He decided that there was one thing which his daughter would not spurn—a scholarly husband.

And so, as soon as she reached marriageable age, the father began seeking a bridegroom for her—one who would command the envy of all the world. Promising the matchmakers huge sums of gold, he instructed them to search, while he himself made the rounds of the seminaries in Jerusalem. He worked long and hard, but could find no one who wanted to become his son-in-law—for people knew nothing of the good qualities of the bride.

Malice consumed the rich man, and his wrath boiled over when a matchmaker advised him to abandon vain hopes and marry his daughter to an ordinary young man. This matchmaker even dared to suggest a candidate—a young, honest carpenter, a neighbor who, having fallen in love with the girl, would not object to taking her without a dowry. So great was the wrath of the father that the matchmaker had a most difficult time getting away from him in one piece.

Finally the rich man conceived the idea of sending two match-makers to distant parts. Having selected two learned, but poor, men, he gave them enough money for two years' travel, promising to maintain their families while they were away, and sent them off to places so remote that his ill fame could not possibly have reached there. Between them they covered all of the Holy Land, but in vain.

The thing was easily understandable: the emissaries spoke of the dowry, of clothes and gifts, but never mentioned the prospective father-in-law. They allowed questions concerning him to go unanswered, having no desire to lie. And so people surmised what the catch was and turned them down.

The period of time the rich man had allotted for the search was up, and the two emissaries were returning empty-handed. Beset with fears, they halted at the gates of Jerusalem. In fact, had it not been for their wives and children, they would never have come back to the city. The rich man, they knew, would not believe them and would think that they had not served him faithfully. He would deal harshly with them—he was likely to turn them over to the Gentiles to be tortured. And so they trembled fearfully at the gates.

Suddenly they were approached by a poor lad, clad in white sackcloth with a rope for a girdle, a piece of almond-wood for a staff. The young man greeted them and asked them if they were thirsty. He said he was a hermit and that he could lead them to a spring. He had nothing, he said, and therefore could not bring water to them. They thanked him and began to question him: who was he and from where did he come. The boy said that he was an orphan and that he lived in the desert.

"Have you no desire at all to study the Word of God?" the two learned men asked him.

The young man told them that the Word of God could be studied even in the desert. Every night when darkness descended, he said, an old sage appeared before him. The ancient's eyes glittered like stars and his white beard glistened like snow. Each time he came, the ancient sat down close to the orphan, teaching him Holy Writ and the Talmud and its Commentaries. It occurred to the matchmakers to test his knowledge—and they soon perceived that the orphan was a genius. They asked him why he had left the desert and come to the city. And the youth told them that the sage had bidden him farewell the evening before and, having said that he would come no more, pointed out to him the road to Jerusalem where bride and good fortune awaited him and where he would be able to continue studying and serving the All Highest.

The matchmakers rejoiced.

"Come with us, young man," they said. "We will show you the house of your future father-in-law."

And the orphan accompanied them.

"Pay no heed to his appearance," said the two men of learning when they presented him to the rich man. "You are looking at a genius. The prophet Elijah himself has taught him the highest wisdom of God."

The father believed them and immediately arranged a feast, announced the engagement, and set the wedding for two weeks later. He was in a hurry for fear of the evil eye and too much idle talk. He provided his prospective son-in-law with decent clothes and kept the sackcloth and the staff, thinking he would sell them.

The townspeople began to gossip. " 'Tis the vicious hound that gets the best bone," said some. Others ascribed the girl's good luck to the goodness of her mother. Still others maintained that the ways of the Lord were unfathomable.

The two weeks passed peacefully [Hananiah went on with his confession], and the day of the wedding arrived. For the sake of his daughter, the miser had been most generous and arranged a banquet to which the entire town was invited. Since rumors of the bridegroom's genius had reached far and wide, even the foremost citizens and the scholars from the academies of Jerusalem came to the wedding.

The bridegroom delivered a lecture to the young men in the presence of the local scholars and the judiciary. In another room preparations for the wedding ceremony were going on. The musicians began to play, while the Grand Rabbi and the headmaster of the Yeshiva, who were to escort the bridegroom to the canopy, waited with lit tapers. But the bridegroom had not yet concluded his lecture. Wisdom seemed to flow from him and spread through the air like incense. Those present were spellbound, including Hananiah, who for once was not even looking for discrepancies. On the contrary, he was rejoicing over the bridegroom's success because at last he had found someone worthy of sharing his studies. His ardent admiration for the newcomer impelled him to rise, approach the bridegroom, and kiss him. He actually started to do so, but, as he was elbowing his way toward the speaker, he heard someone say that the bridegroom was a far more profound scholar than he, Hananiah. The individual to whom this remark was addressed commented that Hananiah was not fit to lace the bridegroom's sandals.

Something clutched at his heart, a bleeding wound gaped within his breast as though a serpent had stung him—the Serpent-Tempter himself! And, drawing himself erect, Hananiah broke into a torrent of abuse; venom poured from his lips and the very air reeked fire and brimstone! Even as he spoke, he suddenly became conscious of his transgression in rising against the holy teachings of the prophet Elijah and in hurling defiance against the Torah itself. It was the Word of God which he assailed, the very Torah itself that he was sending to perdition!

Fear took hold of him. With all his strength, he tried to restrain himself, yet could not do so. Against his will, the words escaped him, the Power of Evil spoke through his lips. He saw that the bridegroom, pale with horror, was swaying in his seat.

A commotion sprang up throughout the house. The father, beside himself with fury, was dashing back and forth through the hall, shouting all the while that he had been swindled, that he had no need of a genius for a son-in-law—away with him! Like a raving madman, he threw himself upon the two men of learning who had been his emissaries; he beat them and drove them out of his house. He attacked the musicians and began to smash their instruments with his bare hands. He dashed up to the bride, who was seated in the center of the hall, and snatched the wedding veil off her head. He tore the clothes from the bridegroom's back and threw him out into the street all but naked, hurling after him his old sackcloth and his staff. The guests of honor departed in haste.

Hananiah alone remained. He stood there, stunned, not moving a muscle, and heard the rich man shouting: "The food must not be wasted. Bring the carpenter here! Hold the canopy!"

With supreme effort Hananiah tore himself from the spot and dashed out of the house. In the street, he saw the spiritual leader of the Yeshiva, who stopped him and said:

38

"Hananiah, you will now forget everything you have ever learned!"

"At that very moment," Hananiah went on with his confession, "something snapped in my head, and I was left completely stripped of all knowledge. Falling at the feet of the master, with my soul repentant, I began to beg for help.

" 'God knows if it is possible to help you,' " sighed the spiritual leader.

"I began to weep and sob, whereupon he pointed to the bridegroom, who stood huddled in a corner, not knowing where to go or to whom to turn in this city of strangers.

" 'First of all,' " said the master, 'go to him and ask his forgiveness.' I told him I was afraid. 'Go,' the master repeated. 'Persuade him to go to your house. I shall come there, too.'

"I went toward the disgraced groom. He ran to meet me, saying: 'I forgive you! I forgive and fully excuse you. This maiden was never destined to be my wife.' "

"I would have preferred execution to his kindness. Yet the youth had placed a hand on my shoulder and was calling me his friend.

" 'What sort of companion can ignorance be to a genius?' I cried out in bitterness.

"The youth was amazed at my tone. I told him about the master's curse, and he consoled me: 'When my former mentor (referring to Elijah the Prophet) appears again, I shall plead for you.'

"I set out with him for my mother's house, going through the torments of hell on the way. I could not understand a word he was saying. My heart wept with longing for the Torah; my soul was bleak and desolate. We entered my house. Sobbing I fell upon my mother's breast:

" 'Mother, God has punished us. . . . Your son has been transformed into an ignorant beast—'

" 'Who has put the evil on you?' asked my mother, turning pale.

"I told her of my misfortune, pointing to the disgraced bridegroom. My mother wrung her hands, shedding bitter tears. Esther, my sister, was weeping softly in a corner.

"Suddenly the headmaster of the Yeshiva entered and spoke to her:

" 'Go to the kitchen and prepare something for the scholar,' and he pointed to the groom. 'And, if fortune should smile,' he added, 'he will go under the wedding canopy with you.' Esther glanced sorrowfully at him and his humble appearance but still went to the kitchen. 'This is no time to weep,' said the headmaster to my mother. 'You yourself are to blame—you gave not a thought to Esther, but pampered your son instead. It was not right—not right at all!' My mother wept harder.

" 'No use weeping!' the master said 'This is a time for action!'

" 'What action?' asked my mother.

" 'But will you obey?'

" 'I will—I will!' my mother answered.

" 'First of all, give Esther in marriage. Here is her destined bridegroom!'

" 'This young man in rags?'

" 'This young man was found worthy of hearing the Word of God from the lips of the Prophet Elijah! Is this the way you obey?'

" 'Forgive me, Rabbi! I submit—I obey!'

" 'As for thy son,' the spiritual leader went on, 'he will have to undergo the torments of exile. Let him wander about until such time as the Lord, through His unutterable compassion, takes pity upon him. There will come a day when you will rejoice when you gaze upon him, but that will be only in due time. Esther is still your first child. . . . As for you,' he turned to me, 'there might possibly have been no redemption for you at all after your great transgression—but for your good fortune this marriage will take place, and by the Will of God. The matter turned out for the best, for the bridegroom as well as for the bride!'

" 'For the bride as well?' my mother was amazed. And the master answered her:

" 'Know, then, that Leah, the daughter of the evil butcher, is herself a woman of great righteousness, and that her late mother also pleaded for her before the Lord, and a man of great righteousness was designated to be her bridegroom—one of the six and thirty mystic men of devotion through whose prayers the Universe is sustained. He is the same carpenter whom the rich man dragged under the wedding canopy, fearing that the wedding feast would grow cold. But I beg of you: keep my words in the utmost secrecy, until the carpenter himself deems it needful to reveal himself—'

" 'O, the miracles of God!' exclaimed my mother, somewhat consoled.

" 'Now, my dear children,' the master turned to me and the bridegroom, 'exchange clothes! As for you,' he said when I had complied, 'leave the city at once. Take this staff with you and guard it closely; hide it at night at the head of your bed. I shall pray that the Lord may give His help to thee, that this staff shall burst forth into bloom. Then your soul, too, shall blossom forth, and you shall remember the Great Wisdom of God once again. Only then will you have the right to cast off this sackcloth. Go, without bidding farewell to anyone!'

"My sister entered the room, bearing food. Noticing that we had changed clothes, she let the plate fall from her hands and it broke with a ringing sound. The master called out: 'Congratulations! I congratulate both bridegroom and bride!'

"I heard no more—I was on my way."

Having left the city behind him [Hananiah went on with his tale] he had wandered out into the desert—without bread or water. But it was not of bread or water that he was thinking. He lived on whatever he found. He was in constant peril, threatened on all sides by wild beasts, serpents, and scorpions. But they left him unscathed; growling and hissing, they made way for him. Hananiah realized that the beasts had no power over him, that he was condemned to total exile. Once he heard as if someone had uttered it clearly: "This man belongs to—" but could not hear the rest.

And so, he wandered day and night, grieving for his youth that was passing him by without study, without knowledge, without a glimmer of light in his soul. If he could hear only one word of God! If he had a prayer-book with him. . . . But he could recall not a word of prayer—not one word!

Once, his head strewn with sand, he stood on one foot to intensify his torments and cried out to heaven: "Torah! Torah!" Over and over, he cried this one word to the heavens, until the sun went down, until he dropped nearly unconscious with exhaustion and fell asleep. But even in his sleep he moaned and cried out: "Torah! Torah!" And the master of the Yeshiva rose up before him, wearing a shroud and a crown of gold, and said to him:

"Arise, Hananiah—the hour of your redemption approaches! The Lord has heard your prayer, and the prophet Elijah has come to your defense. Arise, and go wherever your eyes lead you. When you come to the town of Safed, go to the house of Reb Hiyah, the good of heart; repent before him and ask him to accept you as one

41

of the scholars in his seminary. He will not refuse you. When you have reached your eighteenth year, he will find your destined wife and will pray for you—and his prayers always resound before the Throne of the All-Highest. Marriage, of itself, and the ritual of the seven blessings cleanse a man of his sins. And your salvation will come. On the morning of the eighth day after thy marriage, your staff will burst into blossoms and your soul shall flower.

"And you will recall learning—all except the evil part; you will deliver a recitation before Reb Hiyah, and your words will be constructive and not destructive. And Reb Hiyah will rejoice over you. But whether your years will be many, I know not—"

The master vanished.

"On awaking early in the morning I set out on my way. And now I am here, Rabbi."

Hananiah had finished. The poor lad was condemned to an early death, he concluded. . . . Meanwhile Hananiah lifted up his eyes to the Rabbi's and voiced his heartfelt plea in a tremulous voice.

"Master, will you accept me among your disciples?"

There is a desert within his soul, Reb Hiyah thought. Not a word of Torah, yet the very harp of King David seems to sing in his throat. . . . But, aloud, all he said was:

"Go to sleep, my child. Tell the supervisor to show you your place, and come to me tomorrow morning for an answer. Go, my son!"

Reb Hiyah remained alone in the arbor, gazing through the small window at the heavens. He wondered: Could this be *the* man? But the heavens were drawn over with clouds and told him nothing.

The reason for Reb Hiyah's difficulty in giving Hananiah an immediate answer was apparent in their conversation the next morning:

"Hananiah, my son," he said to him after having called him into his chamber, "there are no objections on my part to admitting you to the Yeshiva, but—"

A shudder ran through Hananiah's body:

"Rabbi," he exclaimed, "allow me to sit as far away from thee as possible, somewhere on the last bench, in the darkest corner. All I want is to hear you instructing your disciples. . . . Just let me listen—"

42

"I have already told you I have no objection," Reb Hiyah calmed him. "There is only one thing I fear: the disciples are, after all, a youthful lot; they may, God forbid, make fun of you. Besides, I must speak the truth—they are all men of learning, whereas you, for the time being, are not. . . . And the contempt of the learned man for the unlearned is great. You will suffer because of them—that is what I fear!"

But Hananiah replied joyously:

"So be it! Why, Master, I want to suffer, I must endure this by way of atonement. The more humiliation, the more suffering, the sooner will the curse pass from me—"

"That may be so," said Reb Hiyah. "But, I am afraid lest they may transgress—which God forbid. It is said in the Talmud: *Hamalbin p'nei haveroi borabim—*"

"What does it mean, Master?" Hananiah asked, his eyes sparkling.

"It means: He who offends a companion before the people is deprived of the Kingdom of Heaven!"

Hananiah said joyfully:

"Rabbi, when I have atoned for my sin, and the curse passed from my soul, I shall nevertheless be deprived of the Kingdom of Heaven and shall study the Torah solely for the Glory of God, without hoping for any reward. May God grant it!"

Reb Hiyah's heart absorbed Hananiah's words as if they were fragrant oil.

"Yet what of them—what of my disciples?" he asked. "How can I let them sin and lose the Kingdom of Heaven?"

"But suppose that I forgive them—forgive them beforehand?" Hananiah asked after a short silence.

"That is possible!" Reb Hiyah decided and, taking Hananiah by the hand, led him into the academy where he indicated to him a seat apart from the rest of the disciples.

Reb Hiyah began expounding the Word of God, glancing, from time to time, at Hananiah. He noticed that the youth was sitting with his eyes closed, listening intently to the lesson, flushing with pleasure when he caught a word or paling in terror when he lost the thread of the lecture, or obviously griefstricken when he failed to grasp the tenor of the lecture. All this visualized for Reb Hiyah the image of a camel in the desert, tormented by thirst yet at the same time overjoyed on hearing the distant murmur of a clear rill.

At times, the master observed his students discussing Hananiah among themselves or pointing at him. Words of abuse reached Reb Hiyah's ears: ignoramus, simpleton, boor. He was greatly disturbed but refrained from any remarks when he saw how Hananiah, his eyes uplifted, gazed with love and respect at the classmates who insulted him, as if they were engaged in virtuous deeds.

During the discourse students put questions to Reb Hiyah, which he answered, and learned debates would ensue. Hananiah alone kept silent, sitting there as if he were voiceless. And the delight with which he listened to every word made his whole face beam. When the lectures were over, he would be the last to leave; then, he would wander by himself along the garden paths or perhaps make his way to a neglected arbor among the oleanders where he would sit down, in solitude, to pass the hours until the evening prayers.

One day the supervisor came to seek Reb Hiyah's advice as to whether or not he ought to apologize to Hananiah.

"What, again?" asked Reb Hiyah. "Have you given him another scolding?"

"God forbid!" exclaimed the supervisor. Then he began to tell Reb Hiyah how, on more than one occasion, as he walked by the arbor, he had heard Hananiah repeating the words of the holy text, along with the translated version, or fervently lifting up his voice to heaven, and crying: "Torah! Torah!"—pleading as the starved plead for bread.

"And I realized," the supervisor went on, "that I was beholding a repentant sinner, an extremely repentant sinner, and now I am uneasy because I offended him, when he first came to beg admittance to the Yeshiva. What if I should be punished in heaven —"

Reb Hiyah advised him to refrain from any apologies, because he knew that Hananiah had to endure the torments of humiliation. But, inwardly he rejoiced greatly because people were beginning to take Hananiah seriously, and he was doubly happy when he noticed that many of the students were showing respect for the newcomer.

And he devoted a great deal of thought to the possibility that

44

Hananiah might be his son-in-law, but always added with regret: "Still he is really very unschooled!"

On one occasion Reb Hiyah set out for the arbor before dusk to question Hananiah about his progress with his studies. "Do you understand the text yet?" Reb Hiyah asked him.

"Not yet, Master. I have not yet been found worthy of that, but each time I hear it, it sounds clearer and more and more of its words remain in my memory."

Reb Hiyah said nothing and sighed.

Hananiah asked him:

"Master, did you once happen to tell me the word *Yesihena*—which means '*let him tell it.*' This word has remained in my memory; it glows in the darkness of my soul like a brilliant jewel. Allow me to speak —"

"With pleasure!" said Reb Hiyah.

"Master, something wonderful is happening to me! From the very first days of my stay here, when I used to listen to a lecture with closed eyes, afraid to miss a word, it seemed to me at times as if I were wandering through the desert, parched from thirst. Yet in the distance I heard the murmur of a spring, a clear inviting sound, a herald of joy and happiness. And I felt that the graciousness of God was guiding me to this spring. I was going toward the spring, and the spring was coming forward to meet me, for I knew what this spring of living waters was—after all, there was a time when I had tasted its waters, until an evil man confused me and persuaded me to reject the living waters in favor of stagnant and poisoned waters which, to my undiscriminating taste, seemed the very dew from heaven. But now once more, I sense the help of God, and again I am on the road to living waters, and the spring is helping me in my search, and the hope that I shall reach the spring is growing stronger within me. Although I must tread upon rocks overgrown with thorns, nevertheless I walk on with joy. And, even as fast as I move toward the spring, the spring moves forward to meet me—"

"Amen—and may God help you!" Reb Hiyah blessed him.

"Sometimes, when I sit in the arbor, I fall into deep thought and see myself as a cage full of birds singing praises to the Glory of God. But then I see an evil wizard coming to cast a spell over the little birds, and the birds then break into other songs—songs of defiance against God. The common people do not notice any change, and they praise the birds and their songs as of always. But a man of great righteousness who is passing by stops to listen to the birds and immediately detects their wantonness and passion. This man approaches the cage and says: 'Rather than sing of such things, it would be far better if you birds were dumb!' And a harsh wind blows its cold, malignant breath upon the birds, and the birds become mute. They cannot move and fall to the bottom of the cage, where they lie with their little wings twisted, their tiny beaks closed, and their eyes shut, as if they were dead. . . . But when I listen to you, each sound stirs this bird or that inside me, and they open their eyes and begin to sing, in faint and weak songs that are pleasing to God. And gently they flap their tiny wings, and it seems as if they will take wing at any moment—"

"So you see, Hananiah, the Lord is evincing His grace toward you," Reb Hiyah calmed him. But Hananiah did not want to be soothed.

"All this," he went on in a plaintive tone, "takes place in the daytime only. But hardly does the sun go down when the shades of night lie heavy upon my soul, and everything dies in silence inside the cage. The birds that had just begun to flap their wings become paralyzed. . . ."

"Go to the House of Worship, my son," said Reb Hiyah, greatly moved, "and say the evening prayer. I shall stay here and pray for you."

Hananiah looked at his master with deep gratitude and love, and he left the arbor.

Reb Hiyah began to intone his evening prayer. Then he decided to go out into the garden and pray for Hananiah under the open sky. As he stepped out of the arbor, he noticed two serpents twined around two oleanders that grew side by side. The heads of the serpents were bent toward each other, their poison fangs all but touching, as they hissed. The Rabbi knew all the living creatures in his garden: those that flew high under the heavens as well as those who lurked in the branches of the trees; those that crept over the leaves of low shrubs and clods of upturned earth as well as those that multiplied in the thick grass. He knew immediately that one of the serpents lived in his garden but that the other was a newcomer.

46

Determined to find out why the viper had come out here, Reb Hiyah stood in the shadows of the arbor and listened closely. He heard the serpent from his garden ask the newcomer why it was here and heard the viper hiss in answer:

"I have come to poison a man."

"Your attempts will be in vain," the local serpent smiled. "I have lived here a long time: when I first came here I was as evil as evil could be, and I stung the students. But soon I stopped, for Reb Hiyah, the headmaster of the Yeshiva, had learned the healing art from the chieftains he met on his travels in the far-off lands where he went as a trader. From remote islands, he had brought back all sorts of herbs for snake bite. We sting, and he heals. Convinced that my efforts were in vain, I ceased—"

"Nonsense!" answered the newcomer. "The herbs help only when a snake bites of its own will, out of the hatred which originated in God's curse for the sin Adam committed in Eden. It is God's nature to prepare a cure for every disease. And therefore, the Sovereign of Heaven, before creating the poison fang of the serpent, gave orders to the soil of remote islands where the serpents increase and multiply to bring forth all sorts of healing herbs. However, I have no fear of them: I have come not through my own will, and it is not through my malice that I shall sting but by the command of the Angel of Death, who has sent me to execute a man condemned to death—"

"A condemned man—here? Here, in the house of the learned men of righteousness?" the first serpent was amazed.

"It is Hananiah whom I seek, Hananiah who often comes alone to the bower nearby and who has been condemned to death at the Seat of Judgment."

"For what reason?"

"He once insulted a man of learning, a disciple of the prophet Elijah. He insulted him before the world on his wedding day. Hananiah has already received his punishment in part: the headmaster of the Yeshiva at Jerusalem put him under a curse and ordered him to wander through the desert, clad in sackcloth and girded with a rope instead of a belt. He was also to carry a staff, a withered stick which, the headmaster had told him, would blossom forth when he regained his learning."

"Which means never!" remarked the local serpent.

"That is something still unknown," answered the newcomer,

47

"for there was no assent to this sentence in heaven! The Angel
of Death claimed that the punishment was too light, that he
should be deprived of the Kingdom of Heaven. But the Angel of
Highest Wisdom opposed this suggestion. They compromised on
the following: in expiation of his sin, Hananiah must marry the
daughter of a pious family and, on the eighth day after the marriage, he is to die. Half of the sin will be redeemed by the marriage and the seven blessings said during the ceremony; the other
half will be washed away by death. But since a daughter of Israel
will be an innocent victim, a widow in the prime of her life, it
has been decided that her womb shall be blessed by a male child
who shall grow up to be a great man of learning, a light unto
all of Israel. . . ."

The viper grew tired, for it had not delivered so long a speech
in all its life, and concluded with a request for its friend to lead
it to water. The two slid down the oleanders and crawled away.
Reb Hiyah was overcome with horror.

A great decision confronted him. If he did not bring Hananiah
to the wedding canopy, he would be transgressing against the decision of the Seat of Judgment, and the boy would never regain
his learning. But, by marrying him off, he was delivering him
over to execution. And how dared he make a sacrifice of a Jewish
daughter? How dared he make her a widow on the eighth day
after her marriage?

Reb Hiyah awaited an answer from heaven—but heaven was
silent. His heart began to throb! Something inside him said:
"Hiyah, sacrifice your daughter—your only daughter, Miriam.
. . . Father Abraham would never have hesitated—"

Yet it is not easy to sacrifice the happiness of one's only daughter. He remembered that his wife had promised, on her deathbed,
to appear to him in a dream and resolve his doubts. Reb Hiyah
lifted up his eyes to heaven and began to pray for such a dream.

While he prayed the clouds vanished from the sky, and millions
of stars appeared, twinkling gently and graciously.

Reb Hiyah's prayer had been heard. As he sat in his room one
evening, after fasting all day, he dozed off, and at once his wife
appeared before him, the righteous Sarah, looking as she did on
the day of her death. She regarded him tenderly and lovingly with
eyes that gleamed as they had in life and placed her right hand
on his shoulder.

"Grieve not, Hiyah!" she said. "The happiness of our daughter glows like the very sun. Rely upon her."

Reb Hiyah wanted to question her, but she had vanished. He felt someone shaking him. He opened his eyes and beheld his daughter Miriam. She was standing before him, with her right hand on his shoulder, and was saying:

"Forgive me, father, for awaking you. The sun has long since gone down, the moon has risen and the stars are all aglow. It is time to eat, father—"

Reb Hiyah saw in this something like a continuation of his dream. Tenderly he took her hand and, pressing it to his bosom, said:

"Daughter, I shall not touch food until I learn the whole truth." He saw that she had turned all red but went on: "It is the way of the world that a girl will open her heart only to her mother. But because you are an orphan, and because I am both father and mother to you, you must tell me the whole truth, keeping nothing back—"

And Miriam hid her face on his chest and whispered softly: "Ask, my father."

And he said to her:

"The years go by, and I am no longer young. My beard is as white as the snow on Mount Hermon. What will happen, my child, when I am called up before the Seat of Judgment—in whose care am I to leave you?"

"Speak not to me of such things, my father. I shall always carry out your will."

"Miriam, could you be more righteous than Mother Rebecca?" The girl smiled in denial. "When Eleazar, the servant of Abraham, came to take Rebecca as a wife for Isaac, as it is told in Holy Writ, they asked Rebecca whether she desired to follow after Eleazar. She was not ashamed, and said, 'Yes, I shall go!' "

"Ask me, my father, and I shall answer."

And he asked her:

"Tell me the truth, Miriam: Whom amongst my disciples would you take for your husband?"

"Hananiah!" Miriam answered softly: so softly that only a father's ear could catch the name.

"How did he catch your fancy, daughter?" Reb Hiyah asked in wonder. "Have you spoken with him?"

"God forbid!" she answered quickly. "And besides, would he ever have replied to a woman?"

"Then, how has he captured your heart?" asked Reb Hiyah, smiling. "Tell me!" But, seeing that she could not summon the courage to do so, he said: "I order you to tell me!"

She confessed to her father that Hananiah had attracted her from the very first moment, by his voice that poured into one's soul like a fragrant oil and by his strength—

"His strength?" Reb Hiyah could not conceal his surpise.

"Of course, he must have strength! To walk about in sackcloth among the students, neither ashamed nor afraid of their comments, he must possess strength!"

"Is that all?" asked Reb Hiyah.

"And also through the kindness that shines in his eyes, and the sadness in them that clutches at one's heart—"

"Child, he is a repentant sinner. A grievous sin lies heavy on his soul!"

"The Lord must forgive him!" answered the girl. "I once happened to be passing by the arbor and heard him praying. Can it be, my father, that such earnest prayers go unheard?"

"The Lord is merciful, daughter!"

"I do not know his sin. But his repentance is great! There is so much grief written on his face, so much despair! We cannot help but pity him."

"And do you feel only pity for him, my daughter?"

"I did in the beginning, father. If I were in your place, father—I once thought—I would pray for him day and night. Then I began to think that if I were his sister I would give up my soul for him. And suddenly—father—for you have asked me to tell the whole truth—warmth flooded my heart, and I knew that only a loving wife can help him! You have asked me, therefore I am telling you everything! And once, father, I had a dream. It was on a holiday—Lag Boimer [the 33rd day of the Omer]. You and your students had gone for a sea cruise. Hananiah went, too: you had invited him. And through the window I saw how dejected he was. . . .

"I was left alone. I became bored staying by myself in the house, and felt very depressed. I went down into the garden. Everything was quiet. I set out for the flower beds. The flowers were languishing, their heads drooping with the heat. I lay down near a row of white lilies to gaze at the sky and I dozed off. It was then this dream came to me:

"There was a dove flying in the sky—a gentle, white, sad dove. And behind the dove, unseen by it, soared a sable bird with a long, sharp beak; it was bent on capturing the dove. I felt sorry for the dove and began to shout; the dove did not hear me and flew on, but the sable bird was frightened off and disappeared for a few moments. Then it appeared again, flying at great speed. It was about to seize the dove. I cried out again, and again the sable bird vanished in fright—only to appear once more. A wild scream escaped my lips. This time the dove heard me and swooped down. It asked me: 'Why do you scream, maiden?'—'I scream,' I answered, 'to drive off a sable bird which you cannot see and which would deprive you of life—'

" 'It does not want to do so, but it must slay me. I am condemned to death. And it will deprive me of life, unless someone sacrifices himself for my sake. And that,' the dove added sadly, 'is something no one will undertake.'

" 'I will!' I called out to the dove. 'I am ready to do so—'

" 'And you will not go back on your word?'

" 'No!' said I—and I gave him my promise.

"The dove swooped toward me, looked into my eyes with love, and flew away.

"On awaking, I understood the meaning of the dream: Hananiah is the dove. Only a loving wife can help him. . . . And I have consecrated myself to that sacrifice!"

Reb Hiyah asked:

"But what if Hananiah's death is imminent? What if he is only to father a son, a great man, and depart this world in the prime of his life?"

"It does not matter how many years may be destined for him, as long as they are blessed!" answered Miriam.

"But what if his destiny is only to father a great scholar, a genius, while his own life is numbered not in years but in days, just a few days after the marriage?" asked Reb Hiyah, his eyes moist with sadness.

"Then, let there be only a few days—but let those days be blessed!"

"And you agree to be left a young widow?"

"A widow blessed by God!"

Reb Hiyah said no more. This was destiny, he realized.

But the girl placed her hand on her father's shoulder, lifted her eyes, and whispered:

"I hope, however, that the death which threatens him will be remanded. I would sacrifice my life for his sake—"

"How, my daughter?"

"As yet I do not know, for I do not know what his sin is. Later, he will tell me everything."

By now not a doubt remained in Reb Hiyah's heart that Hananiah was the bridegroom for Miriam. The Lord wants to test me, he reflected, but I shall remain steadfast. And he said to his daughter:

"I congratulate you, my daughter! Tomorrow, by the will of God, your betrothal shall take place."

Miriam bent to kiss his hand. When she stood up, her father hardly recognized her, her face was so aglow with happiness.

"And you are not afraid, Miriam?"

"I place my trust in God!" she answered firmly. And her voice rang crystal clear.

But in his heart, Reb Hiyah was agitated. When his daughter left, he wrote letters to the headmaster of the Jerusalem Yeshiva and to the Nasi, or leader of the Babylonian Jews, in which he poured out all his grief:

"Tomorrow [he wrote] the betrothal of my beloved daughter Miriam is to take place. At times it seems to me that I am placing a golden crown upon her head; at others it seems that I am leading my only lamb to slaughter. . . . But I shall not go against the Lord and His will. I intend to have the wedding a month from now. In the meantime I shall follow your advice and suggestions. And I beg you to pray for me, for my daughter, and for the repentant Hananiah."

Reb Hiyah did not go back on his word.

The engagement took place the next day. Everyone was amazed. The students in the seminary were beside themselves: "Why does an ignorant sinner reap such honor?" But, out of respect for Reb Hiyah, they said nothing.

A month passed. There was no answer either from Jerusalem or from Babylon. Reb Hiyah believed this to be a bad omen. On the morning of the wedding, he called his daughter to him and said:

"Know, Miriam, that your bridegroom, Hananiah, is fated to die on the eighth day after the wedding." And, having told her about the serpents and about the two unanswered letters, he reminded her that she could still withdraw her promise.

"I am firm in my desire, and my heart is firm. And, knowing the decision of the Seat of Judgment, I also know how to nullify it!"

"You know how? On whose merits do you rely? Through what power will you achieve it?" asked Reb Hiyah, beside himself with astonishment.

And Miriam replied:

"Through the power of my faith. . . . Relying on the merits of my pious mother—peace unto her!—and on your merits, my father, on your service to the All-Highest!"

Reb Hiyah carried out her wishes.

The guests assembled. The bridegroom sat in his sackcloth, without uttering a word. Reb Hiyah made a speech, in his place, and Hananiah listened, filled to overflowing with joy and sadness.

The bridegroom was brought to the bride. She was dressed in a robe of coarse linen, and, instead of a wedding veil, her face was covered by an ordinary handkerchief.

When the handkerchief was lifted, it revealed a face that shone like the sun; her eyes were clear, filled with faith, gently and profoundly happy.

All the townspeople of Safed had come to the wedding—and seen a bridegroom clad in sackcloth, a bride in a robe of coarse linen, and a bride's father firm but tearful. Reb Hiyah began to read the text of the marriage ceremony; the bridegroom asked its meaning, and Reb Hiyah translated each word for him. The guests could not conceal their amazement. But, they thought, Reb Hiyah must know what he is about.

They were astonished further at the bridegroom's failure to utter a single word of learning. Even at the wedding feast, he kept silent. No gifts were presented to the newlyweds, as is usual after the bridegroom's speech.

The seven nuptial benedictions were recited in the garden: separate tables for men and women were set up in the broad center path. The bride sat like a beggar woman among the rich matrons; the bridegroom sat like a deaf mute among the town's elite and the learned rabbis. Reb Hiyah had to sustain the conversation of his guests all by himself. But even he was ill at ease, frequently fixing his gaze on the ground. Was he, perhaps, repenting his action? No! His eyes were seeking the serpent. And suddenly he saw it, crawling nearby and never taking its eyes off Hananiah.

On the eve of the eighth day, Reb Hiyah called his daughter to him and told her in a voice that was not his own:

"Tomorrow, daughter, is the Day of Judgment! You must have courage!"

"I am in good spirits!" answered the bride. "I have been blessed by the Lord. And," she added with firm hope, "perhaps I may yet save him from death!".

"May the Lord help you!" said her father, his eyes filled with tears.

"But remember, father," said Miriam, "that the miracle must take place tomorrow morning! His staff has to burst forth into blossom and his soul must follow. He will have to deliver a sermon before you. Come to us then, father, as early as you can. Do not oversleep."

"Will I sleep at all?" he wondered. But all he said was: " 'Tis well."

When he arrived early next morning, Reb Hiyah found Miriam already dressed; Hananiah, however, was still in bed.

"Forgive me, Master," Hananiah said, "I am not well." And he closed his eyes.

Reb Hiyah glanced at the withered stick that stood at the head of Hananiah's bed. He could not believe his eyes: tender green bark was gradually enveloping it; here and there the bark was swelling and buds were bursting out. . . . He wanted to step closer to make certain of the miracle, but he noticed a change coming over Hananiah's face; it was suffused with a rosy glow. Hananiah opened his eyes: they were clear and there was no longer a curse in them. Reb Yiyah watched in amazement. His eyes sought Miriam to see if she were witnessing this miracle, but she was not in the room.

In the meantime, Hananiah had begun his sermon. As he listened, Reb Hiyah forgot everything: the miracle of the staff, his daughter, the serpent that had been sent as a messenger of death. Pearls poured from Hananiah's lips; the Highest Wisdom was speaking with his tongue. Hananiah was opening up before him the gates of a new world of learning, a magnificent garden, an Eden with the Tree of Knowledge, the Tree of Life, and every conceivable kind of fruit tree. The light of the first seven days of Creation flooded the garden with a golden sheen. The trees were breaking into blossom, birds sang, everything was growing and flowering. Hananiah was speaking, and it seemed to Reb Hiyah that the soul of the Universe spoke through his lips! Was it a dream? Before his eyes there were broad vistas; his ears took in wondrous sounds, and a holy joy spread through his whole body. . . .

Reb Hiyah was delighted beyond all description. The mysteries of the Torah as revealed by Hananiah can be found in the book bearing his name and issued by Reb Hiyah.

No sooner had Miriam seen that the staff was blossoming and that her father had eyes for nothing but this miracle, than she seized her husband's sackcloth and left the room. The rugs muffled her steps completely as she ran through all the rooms to the one near the entry. She met no one on her way, for she had issued orders the evening before that no one was to appear until she called. Looking about her to be absolutely sure that no one was around, she disrobed.

"Lord," she whispered, "for the sake of saving his soul, forgive me the sin of putting on a man's clothing!"—and she donned her husband's sackcloth. Then she opened the door into the garden and sat down on the threshold. She sat in silence and watched the path stretching away into the distance from the door, losing itself among the oleanders.

As a serpent appeared and began crawling up the path, Miriam buried her face in her hands and, assuming a pose like that of her husband, offered a prayer begging the Creator of the Universe to accept her sacrifice.

Through her fingers, she saw that the snake was slithering along, drawing closer and closer. It was moving slowly, calmly, and with assurance, knowing that its victim would not run away. It looked at Hananiah and thought: "The victim is sitting quietly; his soul forewarns him of evil—he must be praying or making a confession. . . ." It had already thrust out its sting—its weapon was ready!

Miriam saw all this. The serpent, she noticed, was moving rapidly now: its desire to kill was growing stronger! By this time,

Miriam could hear its belly scraping the sand. She could hear its breathing. But when the serpent came close enough that its markings were clearly visible, she closed her eyes, clenched her teeth and, barely breathing, prayed: "Sovereign in Heaven, accept Thou my sacrifice!" She prayed softly, wordlessly, without even moving her lips. Before she had finished her prayer, she felt the sting.

"Sovereign in Heaven!" she called out, as she fell on the threshold. "Forgive me for the unborn prodigy with which Thou were about to reward me! Let Hananiah live in his stead."

And with that her body began to writhe and she was seized with paroxysms. The pain was intense as her soul departed her young body.

But God is the Lord of Justice!

When Miriam's soul ascended to heaven, it was expected—or, more correctly, the soul of Hananiah was expected. The righteous ones in paradise came forth to meet it.

And when it came before the Seat of Judgment it was questioned merely as a formality, for they knew everything about Hananiah beforehand:

"Wert thou fair in thy dealings with other men, O Soul?"

"I was never in trade," Miriam pointed out.

"Didst thou study the Word of God?"

The soul of Miriam smiled endearingly: "Why, has the Sovereign of Heaven willed it so that the daughters of Israel should take up learning?"

"Who art thou?" a confusion sprang up in heaven. "Who art thou?"

"I am Miriam," she answered, "daughter of Reb Hiyah and the righteous Sarah, and wife of Hananiah."

The commotion increased. They found out that she had sacrificed herself for her husband's sake and that the serpent had made a mistake. An innocent soul had been called up to heaven. And they commanded the soul: "Hurry back; return to thy body, before they bury it!"

But Miriam refused! No one was obligated to experience the agonies of death more than once, she told them! Unless, she added, this first death of hers would serve in place of Hananiah's, and he were to remain among the living. . . .

And the voices rang forth before the Seat of Judgment, for they were afraid that the soul would return too late.

"We consent! We consent!"

In an instant, Miriam's soul returned to her body; she rose up from the spot actually healed of the sting, as though nothing had happened. As soon as she had changed back into her own clothes she ran joyfully into the room where her father and her husband were and told them what had occurred. At the same moment two messengers arrived bearing letters: one from the headmaster of the Jerusalem Yeshiva, the other from the Nasi of Babylon.

Both letters consisted of only one word: "Congratulations!"

If Heaven is willing, we shall tell of the great prodigy born from the union of Hananiah and Miriam and the joys Reb Hiyah derived in his old age from his grandson at some other time.

For the present, we can only add that the serpent which allowed itself to be hoodwinked was removed from its post and no longer shows itself anywhere. . . .

Buntcheh the Silent

IN THIS WORLD, the death of Buntcheh the Silent passed utterly unnoticed. Just try to ask whether anybody knew precisely *who* Buntcheh was, *how* he lived, *why* he died: because his heart had burst, because his strength was exhausted, or because perhaps his back had broken under his inordinate burden?

If a horse pulling a street-car had dropped dead, it would have attracted more attention. The horse's death would have been written up in the newspapers; people would have come running by the hundreds to have a look at the unfortunate animal and at the spot where the accident had happened. Of course, horses *do* have the advantage of not being as numerous as human beings.

Quietly did Buntcheh live out his time; he passed quietly through this world—our world.

There was no wine at Buntcheh's circumcision rite, no clinking of the goblets. He did not deliver a militant speech at his confirmation. . . . He lived like an imperceptible grain of sand on the seashore, among countless numbers of others like itself. And when the wind lifted this grain of sand into the air and carried it over to the other shore, no one noticed.

When he was among the living, he left no footprints even on wet ground, and after his death the wind blew down the small board that had been placed as a marker over his grave. The wife of the cemetery-keeper found this small board and used it as firewood to boil a pot of potatoes. Only three days had passed, but already the cemetery-keeper could not for the life of him recall where Buntcheh was buried.

If there had been a monument over his grave, then perhaps a hundred years later some archaeologist might have found it and the name of Buntcheh the Silent would have sounded once more in this world.

He passed by like a shadow. His face left no impression in the mind or heart of a single person. Not even a trace of him was left.

He lived alone and died alone.

If it weren't for the tumult in which people lived, someone would probably have heard Buntcheh's back creaking under his heavy burden. If people weren't so frightfully busy, someone might have noticed that the fire in Buntcheh's eyes had been extinguished while he was still among the living and that his cheeks were horribly sunken; someone might have noticed that, even when Buntcheh was not crushed under a load, he plodded along with his head down, as though he were seeking a grave for himself while he was still among the living. If there were as few human beings as there are horses pulling coaches, one or another might have asked: "Whatever has become of Buntcheh?"

When Buntcheh was carried off to the hospital, the corner which he had occupied in a cellar did not remain unrented; it had been coveted by a dozen people just like Buntcheh, and they cast lots for it. From his cot in the hospital, Buntcheh was carried to the morgue—and his cot was awaited by a dozen of the indigent sick. . . . When he was carried out of the morgue, they carried into it twenty corpses—bodies of people who had been killed when a house had caved in and buried them under its ruins. And who knows how long he will rest in his grave, who knows how many people are already waiting for this patch of ground?

He was born quietly, he lived quietly, he died quietly, and he was buried still more quietly.

Things were different in the *other* world, though. *There* the death of Buntcheh created a great impression!

A huge trumpet of the "Messianic times" made the news known to all seven of the celestial spheres: "Buntcheh is dead!"

The highest of angelic hierarchy, with wings of tremendous expanse, flew from place to place and informed one and all: "Buntcheh has been summoned to a session of the Heavenly Tribunal!" And in paradise was rejoicing and commotion: "It is Buntcheh the Silent! Just think of it—it is Buntcheh the Silent!"

Boy angels, with eyes like gems, tiny wings of gold filigree, and silver shoes, flew eagerly to meet Buntcheh. The swish of their wings and the gay laughter of their rosebud lips filled the heavens and wafted up to the throne of the Eternal, and the Eternal Himself knew by now that Buntcheh was on his way.

Father Abraham had taken his stand at the heavenly gates and was holding out his hand, ready to greet Buntcheh. A radiant smile lit his aged face.

What is that rumble in the sky? It is the sound of two angels rolling a gold easy chair into paradise—a chair for Buntcheh.

And what is all that glitter? Why, it is a crown of gold adorned with precious stones—for Buntcheh. "Why is all this going on before the Heavenly Tribunal has handed down its decision?" the saints of righteousness ask, astonished and somewhat envious.

"It is only a mere formality," the angels answered.

Even the Heavenly Prosecutor could not find a bad word against Buntcheh. Everyone in Heaven knew that the "trial" would last for no more than five minutes. Just think of it—this was Buntcheh the Silent!

When the boy angels caught him in midair and chanted a song in his honor, while Father Abraham was shaking his hand as if it were the hand of an old friend, and when he heard that an easy chair was waiting for him in paradise and that not a word would be said against him at the Seat of Judgment, Buntcheh *kept silent*, as he had always done in this world. His heart contracted with fear, and he felt certain that it was all a dream or a misunderstanding. He had become accustomed to that sort of thing. Many times during his lifetime he had dreamed that he was picking money up from a floor on which millions were strewn, and yet awoke poorer than when he had gone to sleep. Many times people had smiled at him in a friendly way, or had a kind word for him— and then, realizing that they had mistaken him for someone else, had turned away disgusted.

"Such is my fate," he thought, resigned.

And he was afraid to lift up his eyes, so that he would not frighten his dream away and awaken in a cave full of snakes and scorpions. He was afraid to open his mouth, afraid to move a muscle, in case he would be recognized and cast down to Sheol [Hell].

He trembled and did not hear the praises the angels were heaping on him. He did not observe their joy as they circled about him, nor did he hear the hearty "Peace be unto you!" of Father Abraham, who was leading him up to the Seat of Judgment. He stood there without bowing or offering a word of greeting.

60

The man was completely beside himself with fright.

And his fear grew even more intense when he glanced at the floor of the Heavenly Tribunal: it was of real alabaster, paved with diamonds! "And here I am, actually standing on it!" With that he lost his head entirely. "Who knows what rabbi, what rich man or scholar they have mistaken me for. The one they expect will come—and that will be the end of me!"

So great was his fear that he failed to hear the announcement of the presiding angel: "The case of Buntcheh the Silent!" The presiding angel then handed the brief to the Angel for the Defense and said: Read it but waste no time!"

Everyone's attention was concentrated on Buntcheh. His ears were ringing, and all he heard was the sweet voice of the Angel for the Defense, pouring forth like the music of a violin:

"His name fitted him like a suit made for a graceful figure by the hand of a master-tailor—"

"What is he saying?" Buntcheh asked himself, and suddenly heard an impatient voice:

"Could you possibly manage without any further analogies?"

And the Angel for the Defense went on:

"Not once did he speak out against anyone—neither against God nor men. Not once did there flare up in his eyes the flame of hatred—never did his gaze turn up to heaven with a complaint."

Buntcheh again failed to understand a word, while the harsh voice interrupted the speech anew:

"No oratory!"

"Job could not endure and spoke up, and yet *this one* was far more unfortunate—"

"Give us facts—just bare facts!" the Chairman called out still more impatiently.

"On the eighth day after his birth, the rite of circumcision was performed upon him—"

"If you could only manage without *realism!*"

"The ignorant *mohel* [one who performs circumcisions] failed to stop the flow of blood—"

"Get on with your speech!"

"But he still kept silent," the Defender continued. "He kept silent also when, at thirteen, he lost his mother and acquired a stepmother—the wickedest of stepmothers, a positive snake.

"Are they actually talking about me?" Buntcheh wondered.

"I must ask you to avoid insinuations concerning third parties," the Chairman fumed.

"She begrudged him every morsel, gave him stale, moldy bread and meat so stringy it was like unspun flax, while *she* drank coffee with cream—"

"Stick to the subject!" shouted the Chairman.

"But when it came to blows, she was not sparing, and his body was covered with bruises that show through the holes in the old, rotted rags he had to wear. On the bitterest days of winter, she made him chop wood in the yard, even though he was barefooted. His hands were still small and weak, the logs were thick, and the ax dull—often he injured his arm or got his feet frostbitten, but still he *kept silent,* not even telling his father—"

"His father who was a drunkard!" the Prosecutor interrupted with a laugh. Buntcheh's whole body turned to ice.

"He was always lonely," the Defender went on. "He did not know what a friend was; he knew nothing of Talmud or the Torah; he did not have a single garment that was free of holes, or a minute to himself—"

"Facts!" the Chairman cried out once more.

"And he never complained," the Defender went on.

"Buntcheh kept silent even when his father, crazed with drink, had seized him by the hair and threw him out of the house, into the dead of winter. He rose in silence from the snow-covered ground and walked away in silence. When he was on the road, he did not break his silence, and during the most agonizing hunger he begged only with his eyes.

"One foggy, raw night in early spring, he found himself in a big city, where, one would assume, he was like a drop in the ocean, yet he spent his very first night there in a police station. He kept silent; he did not even ask why he had been arrested. When he was released, he began looking for work of the hardest sort—and still, he kept silent.

"Bathed in a cold sweat, bowed under the heaviest burden, his empty stomach contracting with pain, he kept silent.

"He kept silent when he was spattered with mud by strangers, when some man he did not know spat on him, when, with a burden on his back, he was driven off the sidewalk into the cobbled roadway among the horses, carriages, and street-cars and was almost killed.

"He never even attempted to guess how many hundreds of pounds he had to carry for a single copper, how many times he fell under his burden, how many times he all but starved to death while waiting for his pay. He made no comparisons between *his* fate and that of others; he still kept silent.

"And when it came to asking for the money he had earned through his own labors he did not do so in a loud voice. Like a beggar, he would take his stand by the door, his eyes pleading like those of a starving dog. If he were told to return and come back later, he would quietly disappear, like a shadow, only to return and plead for payment even more quietly later on.

"He also kept silent when people kept back as much as they liked out of the money he had earned or when they palmed off a counterfeit coin on him."

"So it *is* me they are talking about!" Buntcheh realized.

After a sip of water, the Defender resumed:

"One day a change took place in his life. A rubber-tired carriage was careering through the street; the horses had run wild. The driver had long since been thrown on the cobblestones and split his skull. The bridles of the horses spattered flecks of foam; sparks flew from under their hoofs and their eyes blazed like torches. The man in the carriage did not know whether he was dead or alive. And Buntcheh brought those horses up short.

"The man whose life he saved proved to be generous and he did not forget Buntcheh's good deed.

"He handed over to Buntcheh the whip of the coachman who had been killed, and Buntcheh became his new coachman. More than that, he found a wife for Buntcheh, and what is more, bestowed a child upon him."

Yet Buntcheh still kept silent.

"It's *me* they're talking about, *me*," Buntcheh said to himself, but he still did not dare to look up at the judges. And he went on listening to the speech of the Defender:

"He also kept silent when his benefactor went bankrupt and paid him no wages.

"He kept silent when his wife left him, abandoning a baby that was still at the breast.

"He kept silent likewise fifteen years later, when the child had

63

grown up and become sufficiently strong to drive him, this Bunt-cheh, out of the house."

"It's me they're talking about—me!" Buntcheh rejoiced.

"He kept silent," the Defender went on in a melancholy voice, "even when his benefactor paid off everybody but did not give him a red cent, and when this same benefactor, riding in a new carriage drawn by blooded horses, ran over him, crushing him. . . . He kept silent. He would not tell the police the name of the man who had crippled him.

"He even kept silent in the hospital, where people are *permitted to scream*. . . .

"He kept silent when the doctor refused to come near him because he did not have a fifteen-kopeck piece for him; he kept silent when the orderly refused to change his linen because he did did not have a five-kopeck coin for *him*.

"He kept silent during his agony; he did his dying in silence.

"Not a word of protest against God; not a word against men.

"I have finished."

Buntcheh was trembling as if with fever. He knew that it was now the Prosecutor's turn to speak. Who knew what he might say! Buntcheh himself did not remember all the events of his life; always forgot immediately all the things that happened to him. The Defender, however, had remembered everything—and who knew what the Prosecutor might remember!

"Gentlemen," the Prosecutor began in a dry, caustic voice—and broke off short.

"Gentlemen," he repeated, but in a softer voice—and stopped again.

Finally he spoke in a gentle voice that came from the heart:

"Gentlemen! He kept silent—and I, too, shall keep silent!" And suddenly, amid the ensuing stillness, a new voice resounded, gentle and tremulous:

"Buntcheh, my son, Buntcheh," it reverberated like a harp. "My dear child!"

Sobs welled up in Buntcheh's heart. He tried to open his eyes, but the tears blinded him.

Never yet had he experienced such a tender and melancholy feeling . . . "My son." "My Buntcheh. . . ." He had not heard these words since his mother's death.

"My son," the Supreme Judge went on, "you endured and kept

silent all the time. There isn't an unblemished spot on your entire body—you are all wounds, all blood; there is not an inch within your soul where the blood is not oozing—yet you kept silent.

"That was something they did not understand. And you, yourself, perhaps, did not know that you could cry out and that your cry could make the halls of Jericho shake and tumble. You, yourself, did not know of the power sleeping within you.

"In *that* world, they did not reward you for your silence. For they on earth are false and unrighteous. But here, in the Kingdom of Justice, your due shall be rendered unto you.

"The judges will not judge you; they shall not proclaim any specific reward for you. Take whatever you wish. Everything here is yours!"

For the first time, Buntcheh lifted his eyes. He was struck by the dazzling splendor that flooded everything. Here, everything flamed and sparkled; torrents of light spurted from all directions—from the walls, from the angels, from the judges.

And he lowered his tired eyes and averted them.

"In all . . . seriousness?" he asked, at a loss.

"Naturally!" the Supreme Judge said. "I repeat: everything is yours—everything belongs to you. Choose all you desire, inasmuch as everything that shines and sparkles here is but the reflection of your hidden virtues, the reflection of your soul. You will be taking what is only yours!"

"Really?" asked Buntcheh, by now in a firmer tone.

"Naturally! Naturally!" he was answered from all sides.

"Well, in that case," Buntcheh announced with a smile, "I would like to have a hot roll with butter for breakfast every day!"

The judges and angels were stunned. The Heavenly Informer burst into laughter.

The Three Offerings

Weighed In Heaven—Once upon a time, many years and generations ago, in a certain place, a Jew came to the end of his days.

Well, what of it? So a Jew came to the end of his days—no one
can live forever. They performed the proper rites over him; they
gave him honorable burial. A little mound rose up over his grave;
his son pronounced the memorial prayer for him, and his soul
went winging upward to appear before the All-Highest.

And in front of the judgment seat hung a pair of scales ready
to weigh this soul's sins against its good deeds.

The dead man's Advocate appeared—his erstwhile Good Angel
—and took his stand, with a fair, snow-white sack in his hand, to
the right of the scales.

The dead man's Accuser appeared—his erstwhile Evil Demon,
his tempter—and took his stand, with a foul, grimy sack in his
hand, to the left of the scales.

In the white fair sack were the dead man's good deeds; in the
black one, his sins.

The Advocate poured the good deeds out of the snowy-white
sack onto the right scale—the good deeds gave off a delightful
fragrance and glowed like the stars in the sky.

The Accuser poured the dead man's sins out of the foul sack
onto the left scale: black like unto coal were they, and reeked of
pitch and brimstone.

The poor soul looked on and was astounded. Down there it had
never even dreamed that there was so much difference between
good and evil. Down there it had often failed to differentiate between the two, mistaking the one for the other.

The scales swung gently up and down. The arrow quivered
above them, moving now a hairbreadth to the right, now a hairbreadth to the left.

Only a hairbreadth—and hardly that!

Just a simple Jew's, that soul, without any evil intent—yet also without any capacity for sacrifices. Petty are its sins; just as small are its good deeds—specks of dust, both the sins and the good deeds, sometimes so minute the eye could hardly detect them.

Yet, whenever the arrow did move a hairbreadth toward the right, rejoicing and jubilation were heard in the upper regions. And whenever—God forbid!—it moved to the left, a grievous sigh swept by and was wafted to the Holy Throne.

Painstakingly, the two Angels kept pouring one mote of dust after another out of their respective sacks, like poor worshipers bidding copper coins for the honor of carrying the Scrolls of the Law.

However, even a well can run dry. The sacks were emptied at last.

"Are ye done?" asked a Court Attendant—he was an Angel, like all the others.

The Good Angel turned his sack inside out; even as the Evil Spirit did the same. There was nothing left in either. Thereupon the Court Attendant looked carefully at the arrow to see where it pointed—to the right or to the left.

And the Attending Angel stared and stared—his eyes beheld something that had never yet occurred since the creation of heaven and earth.

"What is taking thee so long?" asked the Presiding Judge.

"The balance is perfect!" murmured the Attending Angel.

The arrow was at dead center. The sins and the good deeds weighed precisely the same.

"Exactly?" came the next question from the Celestial Seat.

The Attendant looked again and answered:

"They do not differ by a hairbreadth!"

And so a council was held in the Court of Heaven, and long was that council held, and the verdict it handed down was:

"Inasmuch as the sins have not outweighed the good deeds, the soul may not be condemned to the torments of Hell. On the other hand, inasmuch as the good deeds do not outweigh the sins, the gates of Paradise shall not open before the said soul. Therefore, the said soul is sentenced to wander through Eternity. Let it fly, let it soar, half-way between Heaven and Hell, until such time as the Lord shall, in His compassion, recall it into His Presence."

Whereupon the Attending Angel took the soul and led it out of Heaven. And the soul grieved and bemoaned its fate.

"What moanest thou?" the Attending Angel asked. "The joys and solaces of Eden have passed thee by, but then the griefs and torments of Hell will likewise remain unknown to thee."

But the soul would not let itself be comforted:

"Better the greatest of torments," it wailed, "than nothingness! Nothingness is most dreadful of all!"

Then it was that the Heavenly Servitor took pity on it:

"Fly down, little soul," he counseled it, "and soar thou over the many-peopled earth. As for the heavens," he went on, "do not even look up to them. What canst thou see up there? Nought but the little stars! For even if those stars be creations of light, yet they are chill; they will not exert themselves in the slightest for thee, they will not put in the least word in thy behalf before the Lord. 'Tis only the Saints of Righteousness in Paradise who can try to do something for a poor soul. Now and then memories of their contemporaries haunt them; they become filled with pity for the souls that languish, and then they try to do something for them. And as for the Saints of Righteousness of thy generation, thou woeful one—well, 'tis of no avail trying to conceal the truth —they are not at all reluctant to accept gifts. This, then, is my counsel to thee. Fly low over the earth; keep a sharp lookout as to how people toil there. But shouldst thou see ought that is amazingly beautiful, seize thou upon it and bring it as an offering to the Saints of Righteousness in Paradise. Knock thou on the gate with an offering in thy hand, and tell the Keeper of the Gates who thou art—thou mayest mention my name. And when thou hast brought three offerings, be thou assured that the gates of the Heavenly Mansions will ope before thee."

And, gently and pityingly, the Angel thrust the soul out of Heaven.

The First Offering—And so the poor little soul flew low over the populous earth, searching for gifts which it could offer up to the Saints of Righteousness in Paradise. It flew over the dwellings of men. It flew under the blazing rays of the sun, in needle-sharp downpours. At summer's end it flew among the silvery threads of gossamer suspended in the air. In winter, it flew among the falling flakes. And it was constantly searching, ever watchful.

No sooner did it spot a Jew than it fluttered up to him and gazed deep into his eyes: was he, perhaps, about to sacrifice himself for the sake of the Holy Name?

At night, if a light glowed through some window, the soul would fly near and look in, to see if any precious little flowers of God, known as good deeds, grew in the quiet house.

Usually, however, it was forced to retreat, trembling with fear, from the eyes that gazed out of the windows.

Months passed, and years, and the soul fell into grave despair. By now towns had become graveyards, and the graveyards were plowed up for fields. Forests had come to full growth and been cut down. Boulders on the seashores had turned into sand, and rivers had changed their courses. Thousands upon thousands of stars had fallen from the heavens and millions of souls had ascended—yet the Lord had not once recalled the poor soul to His thoughts. And the soul had not once come upon a thing of beauty to offer up to the Saints of Righteousness.

"The world is so poor," thought the soul, "and its people are drab. Their good deeds are trifling. How is one to come upon anything extraordinary among them? It is ordained that I wander forever, miserable and forgotten."

But hardly had this thought occurred when its eyes perceived a red glow in the midst of the dark, dismal night. The soul looked about and saw that the glow was escaping through a high window.

Thieves with their faces masked had broken into the house of a certain rich man. One brandished a blazing torch which lit up the whole scene; another had put a glittering knife to the breast of the rich man and was saying over and over, ceaselessly: "If you move, Jew, this knife will plunge right through your breast!" The others were ransacking chests and drawers, seizing on anything they could find. The Jew looked on, motionless, not a hair quivering in the white beard that reached down to his loins.

He stood there as if it were not he at all whom they were robbing! " 'The Lord giveth, and the Lord taketh away,' " he seemed to be thinking. " 'Blessed be the Name of the Lord!' A man is not born with all this, and no man can take it with him into his grave," his wan lips whispered. He looked on calmly as the last drawer of the last bureau was pried open and bags of gold and silver and precious gems were removed from it, and he remained silent.

69

It may well have been that, in renouncing his goods so completely, he sought to absolve the robbers from their evildoing.

But suddenly, when the thieves came upon the very last repository and pulled out of it a tiny bag—the old man's most cherished possession—he was overcome. His eyes blazed up, he stretched out his hand to retrieve it, and his lips opened to cry out: "Touch it not!"

Instead of the words, however, came a stream of blood, spurting from his breast in a thick jet. The knife had done its work.

Heart-blood spattered on the tiny bag.

The old man fell. The robbers hastily opened the tiny bag, in which they thought to find the most precious possession of all.

But they had erred grievously; in vain had they shed blood. Neither gold nor silver, nor precious stones lay in that bag—it contained nothing which is considered of great value in this world.

There was only a handful of dust inside, dust from the Holy Land, to put under the head in its grave. This was what the rich man had wanted to save—it was for this that he paid with his own life.

Bearing one blood-soaked grain of the holy dust, the wandering soul ascended to the gates of Heaven.

And the soul's first offering was accepted.

The Second Offering—"Remember!" the Attending Angel called after the soul as he shut the heavenly gates behind it. "Two more offerings!"

"God will help me!" the soul voiced its hopes and plunged down into space.

It was not long, however, before its joy dimmed. As years and years passed, it found no extraordinary deeds.

And the soul despaired anew.

"As a living wellspring did the Universe spurt forth through the will of God, and as a torrent did it begin to course down the river bed of time. And the further it flows, the more turbid, the muddier it becomes. The pettier people become, the shallower their good deeds, the more unprepossessing their sins; anything out of the ordinary is scarce.

"Were the Lord to ordain further weighing of the good deeds, and the sins of the whole world," the soul kept on thinking, "why, the marker would hardly swing, would barely tremble. Like me, the world can neither fall nor rise. It wanders, as do I, between the radiant heavens and the gloomy nether regions. And Advocate and Accuser contend throughout all eternity as light and darkness, warmth and cold, life and death contend here throughout all eternity.

"The world is troubled and can neither soar aloft nor plummet down, and therefore will there be weddings and divorces, births and burials, celebrations and funeral feasts, and love and hatred, forever and forever!"

Suddenly the soul heard the sound of trumpets and kettledrums. Looking down it saw a medieval German town: gabled roofs, covered with tiles of many colors, surrounded the square where the Magistrates sat in assembly. The square buzzed with its motley throng; the windows were crowded with heads; people were perched on the rooftops, some actually astride the gables, and the balconies were overflowing.

In front of the Rathhaus was a table covered with a green cloth and fringed with gold tassels. Seated behind this table were the Councilmen in robes of velvet with clasps of gold; their caps were of sable fur, the white plumes fastened with diamond studs. In the place of honor sat the Presiding Rathsherr himself; a banner, surmounted by an eagle cast in bright metal, fluttered over his head.

Standing to one side was a Jewish maiden, bound with ropes, while not far off ten or so Landsknechts had all they could do to restrain a wild horse. The Presiding Rathsherr arose and, holding the parchment on which the verdict that condemned the Jewish maiden was inscribed, addressed the people:

"This Jewess, this Israelite maid, has committed a grievous offense—so very grievous that the Lord Himself, for all His great mercy, could not forgive her! She sneaked out of the ghetto and, on our last holy day, paraded through the fair streets of our town. She hath defiled with her shameless eyes our holy images, which we were carrying through the streets to the sounds of song and trumpets. Her accursed ears heard the chanting of our innocent, white-clad children and the rolling of the holy drums. And—who knows?—it may be that the Foul One, in the guise of a Hebrew maid, daughter of the accursed Rabbi, hath touched our sacred things and desecrated them!

"What was the Devil after in the guise of this beautiful maid?

71

For—this is past denial—beautiful she is; she captivates with all the charms of Hell! Look upon her eyes, shining boldly from under their lowered, sullen brows. Look ye upon that face of marble, which during her long stay in prison has become paler but not less beautiful! Look upon her fingers, her long, slender fingers—the sun is shining right through them!

"This is what the Devil was after: to draw some Christian away from the ecstasy of the solemn procession. And he has succeeded!

" 'See what a handsome maid that is!' a certain knight, scion of one of our noblest families, had cried out. This was too much. The halberdiers noticed her and seized her. The Devil did not even try to resist. Pure were those Christian soldiers just then, cleansed of their sins, and he had no power over them. This, then, is the punishment to which we have condemned the Devil in his guise of this Hebrew maid—" here the Presiding Rathsherr began reading from the parchment—" 'Let her be tied by the hair, to the tail of the wild horse. Let the said horse run and drag her along the streets which her feet have trod, contrary to our sacred law. Let her blood stain these stones she has defiled with her steps!' "

A wild shout of approval was heard. When the turbulent rejoicing subsided, they asked the girl who had thus been condemned to death what her last wish was.

"All I ask for," she answered in a calm voice, "is a few pins."

"She is out of her mind with fright!" the members of the Council decided.

"No!" she answered calmly and coolly. "That is my last wish—that, and no other."

And her last wish was carried out.

"Now," came the Presiding Rathsherr's command, "tie her to the horse!"

The halberdiers approached and with trembling hands tied the long, raven braids of the Rabbi's daughter to the tail of the wild horse, which they could hardly restrain.

"Clear a path!" the Presiding Rathsherr commanded the crowd.

There was great turmoil. The people cleared a path, hugging the walls of the houses. And all raised their hands—some with quirts, some with thorns, some with knotted handkerchiefs—and all were ready to urge on the wild horse: all held their breath; their faces flushed, their eyes glittering. And during the turmoil no one noticed how the condemned bent down quietly and pinned the hem of her dress to her leg, sinking the pins deep into her flesh—so that her body might not be exposed when the horse dragged her through the streets.

Only the wandering soul noticed this as it hovered over her.

"Let the horse loose!" commanded the Presiding Rathsherr.

The mercenaries leaped back from the horse, and it broke away instantly, as the shouts of the mob burst forth. Quirts, thorns, and handkerchiefs cut and swished through the air, while the horse dashed through the square, and left the town behind.

But the wandering soul had already taken a bloodstained pin out of the condemned girl's flesh, and with that offering it soared upward.

"Only one gift more!" the Angel proclaimed.

The Third Offering—And again the soul flew downward, in search of one more offering.

But again months passed, and years, and again dismal thoughts overcame the wandering soul. The Universe, it reflected, has grown still shallower. Even pettier have the people become, and still even their deeds, the good as well as the evil.

"What if the Lord," it pondered on one occasion, "blessed be His Name, were to conceive the idea of halting all Creation and judging it once and for all, just as it is, and all of it at once. . . . And what if the Advocate were to take his place on one side and start pouring out of his sack the grains of sand and motes of dust while, on the other side, the Accuser were to pour out of *his* sack his motes of dust and grains of sand—why, it would take a long, long time for both sacks to become empty, so many are the petty deeds—so very many!

"Yet when the sacks were finally empty—what then?" the soul asked itself.

"The arrow would probably stop dead center!

"With humanity's deeds so insignificant, so trifling, can there be any tipping of the scales either way: what is there to make the good deeds outweigh the sins, or the sins outweigh the good deeds?"

One more straw, one more bit of down, one more speck of dust, one more grain of sand. . . .

And what would the Lord say then? What verdict would He

73

pronounce? That the world be turned into chaos again? But the sins did not outweigh the good deeds.

That it be saved? But the good deeds did not outweigh the sins. Well, what then?

"Go thou on!" the Lord might say. "Fly thou on between Hell and Heaven, amid tears of sorrow and streaming blood, between the cradle and the grave. . . . On, on!"

However, redemption lay ahead for the wandering soul.

Its thoughts were interrupted by the roll of drums.

Where was it? In what period of time?

The soul could recognize neither the place nor the era. But it saw a square before a prison. Sunbeams were playing over the iron bars of the small windows; they glided down the bayonets stacked along the walls.

The soldiers were ranged in two long rows, face to face, with a narrow passage between them. Someone was going to run the gauntlet.

Who was that someone?

That someone was a Jew. A tattered shirt hung over his emaciated body, and a skullcap covered his half-shaven head.

He was led up.

Why had he been condemned to this punishment? Who knows? For robbery perhaps? Or perhaps because of false information lodged against him.

But many a soldier smiled and thought: "Why have they called so many of us together and lined us up here like this? Why, he'll fall down when he's gone only half-way!"

There, now, they have pushed him in between the rows. He walked on. He walked straight. Without stumbling, without even flinching. He took the blows and stood up under them.

The soldiers became enraged. "He's still going—still going!"

And the birch rods swished through the air, coiling about his body just like snakes. Blood spurted from the emaciated body.

A bestial grunt came from one of the soldiers—he had struck too high and knocked off the condemned man's skullcap. A few steps—and the Jew was aware of his loss. He stopped, thought a little, and turned back—he would not walk on with his head bared. He came back to the spot where the cap was lying, picked it up, turned around again and walked on once more—all crimsoned with blood but calm and wearing his skullcap. He walked on, until he fell.

But no sooner had he fallen than the wandering soul flew up to him, seized the skullcap which had cost so many blows, and soared up with it to the gates of Heaven.

And the third offering as well was accepted.

And the Saints of Righteousness interceded for the poor soul: the gates of Paradise opened before it.

And a Voice was heard, coming from the Celestial Palace:

These are truly beautiful offerings—magnificently beautiful. ... Though of no intrinsic worth, they are wondrous gifts."

If Not Higher . . .

D URING THE DAYS of *Sliches,* when the Jews pray for absolution, the Rabbi of Nemirov had a way of disappearing.

He could be found nowhere: neither in the synagogue, nor in the two chambers where the devout scholars studied the holy writings, nor at prayer with a *minyan,* nor, least of all, at home.

His door was always open, and people came and went freely. No one ever stole anything from the Rabbi. And there was not a soul about the house.

Where could the Rabbi be? *Where* should he be, save in heaven? Is a Rabbi not inundated with all manner of cares on the eve of the Solemn Days?

Jews—may they be spared the evil eye!—need a livelihood, peace, health, propitious matches for their daughters. Jews wish to be good and pious, but their sins are many, and Satan, with his thousand eyes, surveys the world from one end to the other, prying into everyone's life and accusing and informing against all. Who is there to redeem a sinner if not the Rabbi? That was clear to everybody.

But one day a Lithuanian Jew came into town—and he laughed at the whole business. You know how those Lithuanian Jews are; they care little about devotional books, but they cram themselves full of the Talmud and similar codes. The Litvak can present you with chapter and verse at a moment's notice and leave you stunned. Even the great Moses, he will have you know, could not ascend into heaven while he was alive—Moses had to halt ten degrees *below* heaven. Now, go argue logic with a fellow like that?

"And where do you think the Rabbi goes?" we would try to pin the Litvak down.

"It's no concern of mine," he would answer, shrugging his shoulders, but at the same time he seemed intent on solving the mystery.

I don't have to remind you that there are no lengths to which a Litvak won't go!

When the evening prayers were over, the Litvak slipped into the Rabbi's bedroom and stretched himself out under the bed, watching intently. He was determined to keep vigil all through the night in order to ascertain, once and for all, where the Rabbi went during the early hours of *Sliches*.

Anyone else would have dozed off. But not a Litvak—never! He managed to keep awake by reciting a copious Biblical tractate over and over in his head!

At daybreak he heard the sexton's traditional call, rousing the Jews to attend the *Sliches* prayers. The Rabbi needed no one to wake him: he had been lying in bed moaning for almost an hour. Anyone who ever heard the moans of the Rabbi of Nemirov knows that they expressed all the woes of his sorrow-laden people. His moans were enough to make you burst into tears. But the heart of a Litvak is hard and cold. So he lay there under the bed, listening, while the Rabbi—long may he live!—tossed in his bed.

Soon, the Litvak heard the beds creaking throughout the house —the people were getting up. He heard a muttered word, the splash of water, doors opening and banging shut. After they had set out for prayer, silence reigned again, and all was dark, except for a faint beam of moonlight creeping in through the crack in one of the shutters.

The Litvak admitted afterward that when he was left alone with the Rabbi, he was frightened out of his wits. His skin was covered with goose pimples and his hair stood on end.

To be left alone with the Rabbi, at dawn, just before the *Sliches* prayers—that's nothing to joke about. But a Litvak is too obstinate to listen to the dictates of reason, so he lay there, shaking like a jelly-fish, and kept his vigil.

At last the Rabbi—long may he live!—got up. First, he observed the usual ritual. Then he walked over to the clothes closet, pulled out a bundle containing peasant garments: coarse linen trousers, high boots, a smock, a forage cap, and a wide leather belt studded with brass nail-heads. And he decked himself out in this outfit.

The end of a stout rope dangled from one of the pockets of the smock. When the Rabbi stepped out of the room, the Litvak trailed after him like a shadow. On his way out, the Rabbi entered the kitchen, stopped to pick up a hatchet which he tucked into his belt, and left the house. The Litvak was trembling all over but he followed the old man nevertheless.

A feeling of anticipation, due to the approach of the High Holy Days, hovered over the dark streets. Here and there one could hear the voices of a *minyan* at prayer or the moans of some sick person issuing from an open window. The Rabbi was making his way in the shadows of the houses and huts—and the Litvak was in hot pursuit.

The Litvak was aware that his heart was pounding to the beat of the Rabbi's heavy footsteps. But he kept right on his heels, and at last they arrived at the outskirts of the town.

There was a forest here, and the Rabbi—may his life be prolonged—went right into it. After forty paces or so, the Rabbi stopped near a young tree. The Litvak was astonished to see the Rabbi pull the hatchet out of his belt and start chopping away at the tree. He watched the Rabbi hacking with even strokes. Soon the tree creaked, then snapped and crashed to the ground. The Rabbi proceeded to split it into logs and then into firewood. With his rope he tied the chips into a bundle, threw the bundle over his shoulder, tucked the hatchet back into his belt and started back to return to town.

On reaching a narrow road, he stopped at a ramshackle house and knocked at a window.

"Who's there?" a frightened voice came from within.

The Litvak recognized the voice of a sick Jewish woman.

"It's me!" the Rabbi answered, and he sounded for all the world like a peasant.

"And who may you be?" the woman wanted to know, her speech, too, like a peasant's.

"Vassilii," the Rabbi replied.

"Which Vassilii is that? What do you want?"

"I've got wood to sell, very cheap—I'm practically giving it away."

And, without waiting for an answer, he groped his way into the shack.

The Litvak sneaked in after him, and, in the gray light of dawn, he saw a poverty-stricken room. A sick Jewess was moaning, huddled under ragged bedclothes.

"Sell, did you say?" she gasped. "And what is a poor woman to buy anything with?"

"I'll trust you," explained the Rabbi. "It won't amount to more than six coppers."

"But how will I ever manage to repay you?" the ailing creature moaned.

"Foolish woman!" the Rabbi reprimanded her. "Look here: you're a sick, poor Jewish woman, and I am willing to trust you for this bundle of firewood. I haven't a doubt you'll pay me some day. Whereas you, who have such a great God in heaven, haven't even six coppers' worth of trust in Him!"

"And who'll light the stove for me?" the widow groaned. "Do I look as if I had the strength to get up? My son is away at work!"

"I'll do it for you," said the Rabbi.

And, stooping down to lay the wood in the stove, he muttered the first *Sliches* prayer. And when the fire was going and the flames shot up merrily, he said the second prayer. And then he said the third prayer, after which it was time to replace the lid on the stove.

And that's how the Litvak who had witnessed the whole thing came to be a devoted follower of the Rabbi.

After that, whenever some Hassid would tell how the Rabbi of Nemirov would rise early on the solemn *Sliches* days and ascend right to heaven, the Litvak no longer challenged the story but would add quietly:

"If not higher . . ."

Shtraimel

B Y TRADE I am a hatmaker, but my specialty is the *shtraimel*. I earn my living, however, by making short coats out of coarse cloth for the peasants and sheeplined jackets for the laborers. And, now and then, Leib the miller drops in for some alteration on his raccoon coat.

It's rare—very rare—that I get a chance to make a *shtraimel*. For who wears a *shtraimel* today? An occasional rabbi, perhaps, but the hat always outlasts its wearer. And even when I do get a chance to make one, I have to turn it out either at half price or practically for nothing. Even under the best circumstances, it doesn't pay. Nevertheless, the *shtraimel* is my specialty, because it is a labor of love.

Working on it makes me feel younger; I realize who I am and what my capacities are! For what other pleasures do I have in life? There was a time when I got pleasure from making a peasant's coat. And why not? The way I look at it, the humble peasant provides bread for us. During the summer, when he works to exhaustion, I can't protect him from the heat. But I can protect him from the cold during the winter. I used to sing a beautiful little song while I worked on coats for peasants. I was young then, and my voice rang like a bell as I plied the needle:

> So the peasant may keep warm,
> Stitch, my needle, and stitch straight
> Through tough leather. Ho, there, wife—
> Let us drink to celebrate!

There were several more verses, of course. I had made up this song for the sake of the refrain: "Let us drink. . . ." For the humble handmaiden of God, Miriam Dwosheh, who is my wife wasn't sanctimonious then. She didn't call me Berele the Sausage, the way she does now, but just plain Berele, and I called her Miriam-darling. And we loved each other fervidly, sinners that we were. No sooner would she hear the refrain of my song than she would bring me some cherry brandy. That brandy has a powerful effect on the blood, and I used to grab her right then and there, plant a burning kiss on her tiny lips, and then, doubly refreshed, would resume work on the peasant coat. But now—no more cherry brandy! I am Berele the Sausage and she is Miriam Dwosheh.

When I learned that there is far too little land to take care of many peasants, that the excess peasants have to go hungry, that it is impossible to make a living from even six acres of land, and that there's no rest for the peasant, even during wintertime—that's when hauling begins—I stopped getting pleasure from making peasants' coats. Day and night and night and day the peasant has to haul the wheat to Leib's mill. How could I get any pleasure out of it when the coat which is the product of my labor is getting soaked all winter long as it plods after the two crowbait nags that are hauling the grain to Leib the miller over a five-mile distance at the rate of thirteen *groschen* for each bag!

And do you think I get any great pleasure from the workingman's sheepskin jacket? All winter long that jacket is dragging the flour at Leib's mill, and all summer it is in hock at the inn for a few coppers. In the fall, when it comes to me for mending, I get tipsy, that's how it reeks of whiskey. And even when Leib's raccoon coat comes my way, in all its magnificence, do you think it affords me rapture? A raccoon coat is, after all, an important article, and a great deal of respect is paid to it in our town, but little good it does me. I have acquired a vile habit—no matter what I may see, I think deeply about it. And so, when Leib the miller's furlined overcoat falls into my hands, I fall to thinking:

"Sovereign of the Universe! Why hast Thou created so many kinds of coats? Why does one man have a raccoon coat, another a sheepskin jacket, a third a short coat of coarse cloth, while a fourth has no coat at all?"

And no sooner do I begin to think than I become entirely absorbed in my thoughts and the needle falls out of my hands. And Miriam Dwosheh throws at my head whatever comes to hand first. She wants Berele the Sausage to think less and work more. But what can I do when I *must* think? For, after all, I am aware that Leib the miller gets a new shell for his raccoon lining only when he can snatch a copper off every bag hauled by a peasant coat and a copper off every forty pounds lugged by a sheeplined jacket.

Is that what I'm supposed to rejoice over?

Oh, I almost forgot: one autumn, I was given a very strange order. Fraidel, who collects money for the poor, came to me wearing what looked like a pair of enormous mittens. I took another look and realized that the mittens were actually a pair of peasant boots. I thought I would split my sides laughing.

"Good morning!" said she in her sweet little voice. "Good morning, Berele!" She was a friend of my wife and, like everyone else, she usually called me Berele the Sausage—but that day she called me Berele! And so sweetly, yet—you could have made jam from her voice. I knew she wanted a favor. It occurred to me that she had stolen those boots from some peasant's cart (after all, that's no worse than taking money from the poor-box) and that she wanted to hide them in my place, so I asked her in a stern voice what she wanted.

"Right away he gets suspicious!" she answered sweetly; honey was all but dribbling out of that old woman's mouth. "Right away he comes out with 'What do you want?' And where's your 'Hello'?"

"All right, hello. Now please make it as short as you can!"

"What's your hurry, Berele?" she smiled still more charmingly. "I came to ask if you have a few pieces of fur—"

"Suppose I have?"

"I have something to suggest to you."

"Well? What is it? Speak up!"

"If you were kindhearted, Berele, you would line these boots with fur. Then I would have something to wear when I went to the morning services in the synagogue during the week before New Year's and, without any real effort, you would be doing a deed pleasing to God."

You understand—some deal! A "deed pleasing to God" for almost nothing!

"Come, you know that Berele Sausage doesn't go in for deeds pleasing to God—"

"Come now, would you take money from a poor Jewish woman?"

"No, I won't take money. I'll make a bargain with you—I will

82

trim the boots for you, but *you* will tell me about the transgressions of your youth—"

Naturally, she wouldn't agree to that, so I sent her to the bookbinder.

Trimming boots! Life was rapidly becoming unbearable for me. You think that's funny? You know, when I haven't got an order for a fur-trimmed *shtraimel* everything seems unbearable to me. Then, too, the question arises—what am I working for? To stuff my sinful gullet! And with what? Bread with potatoes, bread without potatoes, and often potatoes without any bread. Something worth while, I must say! Believe me, when a man works for fifty years and eats potatoes day after day, life is *bound* to become unbearable for him. The thought is bound to come to him to put an end either to himself or to Leib the miller! And if I can go on calmly eating my potatoes and working, it's only because of the *shtraimel!* Let me get a hat like that in my hands, and the blood spurts through my veins with new force. Then I know what I am living for!

As I sit working on a *shtraimel* I feel that I am holding a bird; see, I open my hand and the bird soars high, so high that the eye can barely make it out! Me, I stand there full of delight: "That bird is *mine! I* created it; *I* loosed it to the heavens!"

In my town, through the grace of God, I have no influence whatsoever. They don't invite me to any conferences, and as for pushing myself, well, let me tell you I'm no miserable little tailor. I hardly show my face out of the house. I have no regular seat in the synagogue, nor have I one in the House of Study, not even in a private House of Prayer. In short, I'm a nonentity. The house where we live is my blessed wife's kingdom. I can hardly open my mouth before she starts hurling curses at me. You see, she knows in advance anything that Berele the Sausage intends to say and what he thinks—and she's off! She's off, and she sounds like a boiling cauldron.

What am I? Nothing! But let a new *shtraimel* come from my hands—and the whole community kneels before me. I sit home and say nothing, but the hat I made is in a place of honor at a wedding or a circumcision, or at some other religious celebration. It towers over the crowd at the communal elections or at a session of the rabbinical court.

And whenever I think of these honors my heart overflows with joy!

There's a trimmings-maker living across the way from me. Really, I don't envy him! Let one of his epaulettes or gold stripes dare to pronounce a steer unclean to eat or another kosher! That's something I'd like to see. But if my *shtraimel* feels like it, it can pronounce four steers in a row unfit for food; the butcher is done for, his workers can starve to death, the Jews in the little town are in for nine days of abstinence from meat, and a hundred Cossacks get beef at six coppers a pound—and you write the thing off! Nobody will say a word.

Now, *that's* power for you!

Don't you think I remember? Last year there was a murrain among the sheep. It seems that a sheep would spin round and round and then throw its head back and drop dead. I didn't see it myself. But whether the sheep spun around or no, Yankel the butcher managed to get mutton cheap. The veterinary came and announced: "It's unfit to eat—*trafe!*" Nobody listened to him.

He brought along with him four kinds of epaulettes and two types of gold braid—well, the meat was stolen right from under their noses, and three days later our little town was eating cheap mutton for supper.

But my *shtraimel!* Until it says: "You may eat!" not one mouth will open in the town.

You're thinking, perhaps, that power lies in what is to be found *under* such a hat? By no means. You, likely as not, don't know what's under it, but I, glory be to God, do happen to know.

The person I have in mind was a *melamed*, an instructor in Hebrew in a place even smaller than ours, and my father, before he became convinced that I would never amount to anything, sent me to study under this teacher. The world has never yet seen such a medocrity. A downright country schoolmaster!

The townsmen, observing that he had no sense whatever when it came to money matters, immediately cut his pay in half, while they paid off the other half in effaced two-kopeck coins instead of three-kopeck ones, or in small counterfeit silver coins. His wife, realizing that she could do nothing with him, took to plucking his beard. And you couldn't blame her. In the first place, there wasn't enough to buy bread with; in the second, women like to indulge in such plucking, and thirdly that little beard of his simply begged to be plucked—it begged so hard that it was all we, his pupils, could do to restrain ourselves.

Can a creature like that have any significance at all? Are you thinking, perhaps, that he changed for the better with time? Guess again! Not the least change took place in him. His small eyes were still the same—eyes with the fire all out of them, suppurating, always wandering and frightened.

True enough, poverty had brought his first wife to her grave, but what of that? What difference did that make? *Another* wife was now yanking at his little beard.

You wish to know what happened? Well, I made a *shtraimel* for him! I must confess that the initiative in this case was not mine. It never entered my mind. The community ordered the hat, and I made it. But hardly had the community learned that the *shtraimel* they had ordered and which I, Berele the Sausage, had made, was coming to our town to teach, than the whole town hastened to the outskirts a mile away, parading and rejoicing. Young and old, they ran; the sick jumped out of their beds. They unharnessed the horses and all of them wanted, all at the same time, to harness themselves to the carriage and to pull *my shtraimel*. God knows what set-tos there might have been over this, what arguments and fights! But a wise head came to the fore and advised that an auction be held for the honor. And Leib the miller gave "eighteen times eighteen" zloty for the honor of harnessing himself as the *leading* horse!

Now what do you think of the power of my *shtraimel?*

My wife, in addition to calling me Berele the Sausage, calls me a sensualist, a brazen fellow, a foul-mouth, and everything else that comes to the tip of her tongue. Of course, that's how human nature is: I love a well-turned word, I love to needle Leib the miller to his face and behind his back. I also like—no use trying to hide it—to keep an eye on the little housemaids who get water out of the well across the way; after all, they aren't high priests before the ark, whom you mustn't watch during their rites of benediction.

But, believe me, it isn't any of *these* things which sustain my desire to live. There is but one thing that consoles me: at times a new idol comes out of my hands into the world of God, and all bow down before it, before this creation of my hands!

I know that when my meek-minded spouse throws the keys at me across the table she is doing so at the command of my *shtraimel*. She doesn't want even to listen to me, but she *has* to obey my *shtraimel*. If she comes back from the butcher's on the eve of the Sabbath without any meat and is cursing the butcher, I know that he is not in the least to blame: it is the *shtraimel* that won't allow her to make meat that day. If she takes a clay pot that is still perfectly good and throws it out into the gutter, I know that it is my *shtraimel* which has tossed out that pot. If she takes a lump of dough and tosses it into the fire, raising her hands and rolling her eyes up to the ceiling, I know that the ceiling doesn't know anything about it and that the lump of dough was consigned to the flames by my *shtraimel!*

At the same time, however, I know that my wife is not the only woman in the community, and that the community is not the only one that God has; there are many such orthodox wives in the community, while God has many, many such communities. And it is the *shtraimel* I made which holds power over these millions of millions of orthodox wives!

Millions of keys are thrown at husbands, millions of women don't prepare meat, millions of pots are smashed to smithereens against pavements, and you could feed whole regiments, legions of beggars with the lumps of dough that are thrown in the fire!

And what causes all this? My *shtraimel,* the creation of my hands!

Let's go back to the trimmings-maker. There he is, sitting at his window. His face is all shiny, as if it had been smeared with fat.

Why is he all aglow? Why are his darting eyes so sparkling? He has just braided a pair of gold stripes.

In the first place, we know very well what gold is and what tinsel is.

Secondly, I am aware that a pair of gold stripes has under its authority ten times more uniforms than Leib's raccoon coat has peasant coats and sheepskin jackets under *its* power. But just the same, let the most outstanding gold stripe issue the decree: "Slaughter ten steers—but cook half the flesh of but one!" Or:

"You may be starving, you may have four different kinds of crockery, but just the same when you eat cooked udders, eat them on an overturned plate!" Or: "Every bridegroom must show me his bride beforehand, and every bride her bridegroom!" In other words: "All things exist only with me; without me there is nothings!"

The most renowned general's epaulette would not even dare to dream anything of the kind. And even if it should decide on such a venture it would be necessary to inundate the whole country with soldiers; there would have to be at least two Cossacks at every bedside, so that they could watch each other and the two of them could watch the bed. And, with all this, how many deceptions there would be and thefts and how much contraband! Lord, if I could but have all the wealth involved! But my *shtraimel* does all this quietly and decently, without quirts, without Cossacks.

I stay at home calmly and know that without the dispensation of my *shtraimel* not a single Moishele will as much as touch any Hannele—he wouldn't as much as dare to glance at her, God forbid!

And, on the contrary, let my *shtraimel* impose on Moishele and Hannele God knows what absurdity, and you might as well lie down and die. They can't get rid of each other—unless death comes to the aid of either. But if you don't want to wait so long, you've got to go to that same *shtraimel,* and bow before it and implore it: "Save me, *Shtraimel! Shtraimel,* break my chains, release me from my dark dungeon!"

There's an inn at the end of my street.

Ever since my wife, having taken to "collecting for the poor," has stopped preparing cherry brandy for me, I drop in there from time to time to refresh myself, especially during fast days. *I,* at least, am not obligated to fast: for, after all, the *shtraimel* is *my* handiwork!

I've known the innkeeper a long time. Like me, he doesn't live according to God's word and by doing only good deeds. But that's not the point. This innkeeper had two daughters—they were twins, I swear! Why, you couldn't tell the one from the other. And they were a lovely little pair—you could almost pray before them. Their little faces were like the apples of paradise stuck on top of the children's flags during the Rejoicing for the Torah. They were as fragrant as vessels of sweet-smelling ointments, as stately as palm trees, while their eyes—God save and spare me!—a glance from either and you saw the fire of a gem. In an inn, you'd think, but still far removed from the inn. They could not have been brought up better within the Tabernacle of the Ark of the Covenant itself.

They had been born in an inn, yet they were true princesses. There wasn't a drunkard that dared utter an unseemly word in their presence—nor a single policeman or excise man. Even if a person of the utmost importance were to find himself in this inn, he would never have found the courage to pinch the cheek of either sister; he would never have dared give free play to his hands or his eyes or even his thoughts. I was ready to say that there dwelt in *them* more power than in my *shtraimel*. But that would have been a gross mistake. My *shtraimel* proved to be more powerful than they—a thousand times more powerful!

They were twins—one never showed herself without the other. If one of them had pain the other suffered with her. And still, how quickly their paths parted. . . .

They both went through the same thing, and yet, go figure it out:

Both of them changed all at once; somehow, their gay moods and their sad ones were not what they had once been. I can't explain to you what came over them. The words are at the tip of my tongue, yet I can't get them out. Where do I get off, ignoramus that I am. . . . They became more absorbed, somehow, they withdrew into themselves, and at the same time both were sadder and more bewitching than before.

And the reason for this was known: fingers were pointed at two Moisheles, thanks to whom both Hanneles had become still more lovable, more kind, more bewitching—and, in some way, more grown up.

Eh, I've begun talking in a different language, somehow, not at all suitable for a hatmaker! Shedding a tear, actually—not a small thing for a man of my years. My wife would again say: "You sensualist!"

However, I'm not going to drag the tale out.

Both sisters went through the same thing, event for event. They weren't twins for nothing. Each one acquired a Moishele. And both, in a short while, had to put gores in their skirts.

Nothing to be ashamed of: it's a natural thing. Such is God's will—where's the shame in it, then?

But, just the same, things ended differently for each of them!

One of the sisters did not hide her pregnancy from anyone: not from God or from the people or from the policemen, or from frequenters of the inn. And later on she took to a clean bed, in a quiet, warm room. Curtains were drawn over the windows; straw was put down over the cobblestones, the midwife came, a doctor was called in. . . . And then there was a celebration—a new little Moishele began growing up. . . . The thing proved to her liking, and she began producing little Moisheles, year by year. And she enjoys universal respect to this very day.

The other sister, however, concealed her pregnancy; she gave birth in some cellar or other. A black cat swaddled her child. . . . Her little Moishele has long since been buried, and she will never again have other Moisheles! And God alone knows where she herself has gone. She just vanished. They say that she is living somewhere far away as a servant, feeding on the leavings of others. Others say that she's no longer among the living.

She came to a bad end.

And the whole difference lies in this: that with the first sister the consummation took place in the courtyard of a synagogue, on an old heap of rubbish, under a piece of cloth, soiled but embroidered with letters of silver, *and next to* . . . a *shtraimel.* But with the other sister the thing happened somewhere in a murmuring forest, on the fresh grass, amid flowers in full sap, under *God's own* dark blue sky, strewn with *God's own* little stars—but—*without a shtraimel.*

Of no avail the murmuring forest, the fragrant flowers, God's own sky or His stars—no, not even God Himself.

The power lies in the *shtraimel.* Not in gold stripes, not in epaulettes, not in the most beautiful Hanneles in the world, but in *shtraimels* alone—*shtraimels* which are made by me, Berele the Sausage!

That's what makes me hang onto this stupid potato-eating life!

The Reincarnation of
a Melody

S O YOU WANT ME to sing the Melody of Talna?
It doesn't appear to be a difficult thing to do. However, it's
not as easy as it seems.

The Melody of Talna can be sung only in the company of other
people. You promise to chime in? No, my friends, the Melody of
Talna can't be sung by Polish *Hasidim*. You haven't the least notion of what singing is. I've had occasion to hear your musicians
and your cantors. The musicians just strum, and when it comes to
singing the cantors crow at the top of their lungs, just like roosters
on a fence. The most soulful melody sounds uncivilized coming
from your lips. Take, for instance, your festive melodies [*a frailachs*]—why, they're worse than the gestures and faces you make.
No, *our Hasidim* are an altogether different breed.

Where did we ever get your melodies from? Perhaps they've
been handed down to us—or else the locality itself is to blame.

In our Kiev region you won't find a house without a fiddle.
Every lad whose family is at all well off has a fiddle of his own; he
is bound to know how to play. All you have to do is glance at the
walls to find out how many men there are in the house: so many
fiddles hanging up, so many men living there. Everybody plays:
the grandfather plays, the father plays, the son plays too.

The only pity is that each generation has melodies of its own—
each man plays differently. The old grandfather plays softly; he
likes chanted prayers such as *Kol-Nidre, Shoshanas-Yakov, Gdi-
Kshur-Yadaim*. The father—a *Hasid* soul—goes in for trills or for
something touching in a Jewish soul. As for the son, he plays ex-
cerpts from grand opera—from printed notes!

As the generation is, so is its melody.

When there's no vodka, the *Hasidim* talk about vodka.

To sing alone, without the high spirits created by the presence of others, is out of the question—so let's *talk* a bit about singing. Singing, you know, is a great thing. The strength of Talna lies in the Sabbaths—for the most part in the end of Sabbath when Jews are bidding goodbye to the departing Princess of the Sabbath—and the heart of these goodbyes is in melodies. The whole point is in *who* does the singing and in *what* he sings. Out of the very same bricks you can build a temple, a palace, a jail, or a poorhouse. The very same alphabet is used to record Holy Writ as—to make the distinction—heresy. With the same sounds you can rise to the highest degree of inspiration and mingle with Divinity or fall to the bottomless pit of hell, plunge into a putrid bog, and squirm there like a worm!

A letter is as you read it; a song is as you sing it.

Take a festive melody: a song of joy in virtue and faith can be merry; a Talna melody—"goodbye to the Princess of the Sabbath" —is a Sabbath hymn, but a joyful melody can also come from the lips of a loose wench setting out to ply her trade!

A melody flames, its very substance interwoven with love, and it breathes forth love. But there are many kinds of love: love for the Lord, love for people, love for one's fellow-Jews; some even love only themselves or—God forbid!—another man's wife.

A melody complains, a melody sobs, but one man may weep about the serpent who barred Paradise to man, while another weeps for the lost Divine Presence, for the Exile, for the destruction of the Temple—"O Lord, consider and behold our reproach!" the melody laments. And then, too, a melody can also be made into the lament of a man whose kept woman has run off.

There are melodies which are filled with yearning. But the point is in what the melody is yearning for. Is the soul yearning for its primary source, or is it an old toothless hound grieving for the years of its puppyhood and for the passions that were?

Let us take as an example the little song that goes:

"Reb Duvidel used to live in Vassilkov, in Vassilkov;
But now he lives in Talna, in Talna—"

This melody is sung both by the Jews of Talna and the Jews of Vassilkov. When the Talna Jews sing it, it radiates joy and glows with merriment. But when the Vassilkov Jews sing it, the melody is drenched in tears and saturated with melancholy. So you see its mood depends on what is put into it!

Every melody, as you know, is a combination of sounds. These sounds are derived from nature. Inventing them is out of the question, but there is no lack of sounds in nature. Everything has sound—if not a complete melody. The wheels of the Holy Throne, as tradition proclaims, sing in a great voice; each day and each night has a song all its own. Men and birds sing praise; the wild beasts roar forth their glorification. Stone taps against stone; metal rings. Nor does water keep silent as it flows. And what of the forest? At the least breeze its melody resounds—soft, sweet, pensive. Take the iron horse! Doesn't that wild beast with its flaming red eyes deafen us with its chant? Even a fish, a mute creature, emits sounds at times; an ancient narrative I once read says that certain fish swim up to the shore from time to time to beat their tails against the sand and rocks and take delight in the sounds they produce.

Is there any lack of sounds? All that is needed is an ear capable of accepting them and absorbing them like a sponge.

But sounds alone do not make a song.

A pile of bricks is not a house.

Sounds are but the body of the melody. It needs a soul as well. And the soul of a melody is in what a man feels: in his love, his wrath, his yearning, his mercy, revenge, compassion, woe; everything that man feels—everything!—he can transmit through sounds; out of sounds the melody is created, and it takes on life.

For I believe, my friends, that everything which puts life into me must bear life within itself—it must live. If a melody gladdens me, if it animates me, then a living soul is bound to exist within it.

Take a melody and split it up. Sing it the other way around. Begin in the middle, and then tag on the beginning and the end. Will it be a melody then? All the sounds are there in their entirety; not one has been omitted—yet the soul has vanished. Cut the throat of a little white dove, and its soul will flee under the knife. What remains is the corpse, the skeleton of the melody.

In Talna no one has any doubt that a song is a living thing.

A melody lives, a melody dies; men forget a melody, as they forget one who has gone to his long rest.

Once the melody was young and fresh; the life of youth played within it. With the years it grew weaker, its forces passed. Then its last breath went up, dissipated like vapor; the melody suffocated, and it no longer exists.

But a melody can also be resurgent. It will be suddenly recalled; it will issue from someone's throat. Men put a new feeling into it, new soul, and the melody begins to live, almost as if it were new.

This is the reincarnation of a melody.

You don't understand completely? What's the use of talking about the light to a blind man! Here's what I'll do. You like stories —so I'll tell you a story about the reincarnation of a melody.

About three or four miles from Berditchev is a little town called Machnovka. Now, Machnovka once had a band that wasn't at all bad. A certain Hayim was the leader. He was a very capable musician, a pupil of the famous Pedotsour of Berditchev. Hayim did not know how to compose songs, but when it came to playing a melody, to animating it, making its meaning clear and infecting the hearer with the spirit of the music, he was a master.

He was tall, thin, not much to look at, but when he began to play he was transformed. His lowered brows went up little by little; a glow came into his deep, gentle eyes and lit up his pale face. It was clear to all that he was leaving this world; his hands went on playing but his soul was hovering somewhere above in the world of melodies. At times he forgot everything and everyone and began to sing in a voice that was as clear and sonorous as a clarinet.

If Reb Hayim hadn't been a pious, simple Jew he wouldn't have had to struggle so in Machnovka with a family of eight; he would have been playing or singing in some theater in London or Paris. However, queer situations of that kind are found in Berditchev to this very day.

So Hayim lived on in Machnovka, running up accounts in all the small stores for months at a time against some wedding in a well-to-do family, an event which was eventually bound to happen. At the time I'm speaking of, a rich wedding was actually in the offing in Machnovka: the daughter of Beryl Katzner, the town's richest man, was about to be married.

Beryl Katzner, he should have hiccups in the other world, was a usurer. And that is not all—such a skinflint as he was, he begrudged a piece of bread even to himself. At dinner he would scrape the

93

crumbs together—they would do for the chickens. He had a stone in his bosom instead of a heart. Just before he died, almost at the very last gasp, he called his oldest son to him, ordered his account book to be brought, and, pointing out with a finger that had already turned livid the names of those who had failed to make the payments on the due dates, said: "Watch out! Don't you dare grant any extensions—or else you won't get my blessing!" Then he called his wife and ordered her to take down and hide the copper utensils hanging on a wall: "I have only to close my eyes," said he, "to have them drag off everything!"

He left half a million roubles or so.

It was the widow who was marrying off the daughter, hurrying the wedding along; she herself was not averse to finding someone suitable for herself; life, at long last, had smiled upon her as well. She had shed a burden—and had actually grown younger!

To Hayim, this wedding was as manna from heaven; he, too, had a daughter who was withering on the vine. However, the widow had gotten it into her head to import Pedotsour himself from Berditchev; there would be guests from Kiev, now, people who knew what was what when it came to music—she didn't want to fall face down in the mud before them. Pedotsour would compose a new *El Moleh Rachmim*, a new requiem of some sort for her late husband. The wedding had cost so much, let it cost a little more, just so the guests from Kiev wouldn't laugh at her!

With this, all Hayim's hopes went crashing about him.

The town began to buzz with talk. Everybody felt sorry for Hayim—after all, they were fond of him. It was a pity—the man was so poor. They began reasoning with the widow, and at last it was decided that Hayim and his band were to play at the wedding, with the proviso that before it took place he was to go to Berditchev and get a new requiem from Pedotsour.

Hayim was given a few roubles for this purpose; the greater part of what he received he left for his family. He hired a man to drive him, and set out for Berditchev.

It is at this point that the story of the reincarnation begins.

A poor man's luck never deserts him! Hayim goes to Berditchev —and Pedotsour goes away from Berditchev. Of all times, the *Tsaddik* of Talna had taken it into his head just then to invite Pedotsour to his place for the Sabbath. The *Tsaddik* of Talna, I must tell you, held Pedotsour in very high esteem. Religious mysteries (he used to say) lurked in the melodies of Pedotsour. The only pity was that Pedotsour himself did not suspect their existence.

So Hayim dashed through the streets like a man half crazed, not knowing which way to turn. Go home without the requiem, he could not; to wait here for Pedotsour also did not make sense—he wouldn't have enough for his expenses. The widow Katzner had given him little enough as it was—and yet he had left the greater part of it at home. What to do?

Suddenly he saw a scene in the street (this was on a clear, sunlit weekday): a young woman was moving through the street, attired as if for a holiday. She had on a headdress with long, long ribbons —multicolored—and in her hand she carried a large silver tray. Musicians were trailing this woman and playing. The woman danced as she moved through the street. Every so often she would halt with the musicians before some house or shop and dance. People gathered to watch; doors and windows opened, and the crowd grew larger.

The music played, the woman danced, her colored ribbons fluttering, her tray gleaming and sparkling. The people shouted "Congratulations!" and tossed coins to her; still dancing, she caught them in their flight.

What was going on? Well, Berditchev is a Jewish town; it has Jewish customs all its own. This was a way of collecting contributions for the wedding of a poor girl.

Hayim knew of this custom. He also knew that in such cases the women went to Pedotsour, and that he would compose a chant to which they could dance: this was his small offering! They would come to him and tell him about the bride, about her parents, about the bridegroom and the poverty of both bride and groom. Pedotsour would listen to them without a word, from time to time hiding his face with his hands, and when the women were through telling their story, Pedotsour would start humming a *frailachs,* a festive melody. . . . Hayim knew about all this. Still, he stood there, gaping.

Never yet had he heard such a *frailachs:* this melody laughed, and at the same time it wept. One sensed in it grief and joy and heartache and happiness. All this was blended together. A real *frailachs* for the wedding of an orphan!

Hayim suddenly gave a little leap: he had his melody!

95

He and the driver set out for the return trip from Berditchev. The driver took on several more passengers, to which Hayim offered no objections. These passengers, all of whom were good judges of singing, said later on that Hayim had begun to sing as soon as they reached the forest. What he was singing was Pedotsour's melody but the result was something new. The melody, composed for the occasion of a poor couple's wedding, became reincarnated as a requiem. To the accompaniment of the murmuring trees there emerged a gentle sweet chant—a many-voiced yet subdued choir. Murmuring trees seemed to furnish a beautiful background for the melody. The melody wept gently, despairingly; it begged for mercy like a sick man praying for life. After a while it began to moan; it broke into abrupt outcries, as if someone were confessing his sins on the Day of Atonement or on his deathbed.

Still louder, yet at the same time more restrained, was the voice —gasping as if stifled by tears, wrenched by suffering. A number of deep sighs followed, then a harsh wail—and another, and a third— and suddenly the melody broke off and all was still—a soul had reached its end.

Then the melody awoke; it launched into ardent, searing lamentations; its moans soared, overtaking one another, blending, winging their way to the very heavens; it wept and sobbed as if it stood over a newly-dug grave. One could almost hear a child's high-pitched voice, saturated with tears, tremulous and frightened, saying a prayer in remembrance of the dead!

The melody grew pensive, fraught with reveries, dreams, thousands of thoughts spread slowly into delectable, soulful melodies; they consoled, they soothed with kind words, with such strong faith that peace returned to the confused soul, and once more wanted to live—wanted passionately to live, to believe; hopes sprang into new life!

Those who heard were moved to tears.

"What sort of melody is that?" they asked.

"It's a requiem to be sung at the wedding of Katzner's daughter."

"It's not right really, to waste a melody like that on a soul like Katzner's, but it will please those who attend the wedding; the guests from Kiev will be delighted!"

The guests from Kiev were, however, not at all delighted. This wedding was not being celebrated in keeping with the ancient ritual, and the requiem was out of place.

The guests from Kiev preferred dancing with their ladies. What need had they of dismal melodies, what use had they for melancholy? And whose soul had they gathered together to remember—what soul were they supposed to pray for? Surely not for the soul of an old miser? Were that miser alive right now the bride would not receive even half her dowry! Let old Katzner rise up from the dead right now and see the bride's dress of white satin, her wedding canopy, and the profusion of flowers, let him take a look at the wines, the cakes, the platters of fish and meat under which the tables were groaning—and he would die all over again, but this time death would not come as easily to him as it had the first time! And, anyway, why those old, foolish customs?

"Play something more lively!" shouted the guests from Kiev.

The band stopped. Hayim, greatly agitated, began his violin solo. Tears actually appeared in the eyes of those in the gathering who were of the simpler sort. But suddenly one of the guests from Kiev shouted:

"What's the meaning of this? Have we gathered to bury somebody, or what?"

Hayim made believe he had heard nothing and went on playing; the guest from Kiev began whistling—and he was a master when it came to that sort of thing. He had instantly caught the basic melody and was whistling in time to it. His whistle shrilled, brazen and savage. The orchestra remained silent; all one could hear was the contest between the pious violin and the shameless, brazen whistling. The bow could not keep up with it. And the whistling won out! The violin no longer wept; it was merely moaning; then, of itself, it began to yelp in laughter. Hayim was infuriated; he bit his lips; a wild light sprang up in his eyes; he passed to another string, playing faster, ever faster, trying to get ahead of the brazen scoundrel mocking him. However, you could no longer call this playing the violin. The instrument emitted snatches of sound, horrifying screams. They darted about, they swirled in a tempestuous dance. Everything around seemed to be dancing: the house, the band, the guests, the bride on her chair, Hayim himself together with his violin. No *frailachs* this, nor a requiem—it was not a melody at all, but a dance for madmen, the convulsive twistings of an epileptic in a fit. And thus it went on until one of the strings snapped.

"Bravo, Hayim! Bravo!" shouted the guests from Kiev.

Did a requiem of that sort bring about the redemption of the soul of the old miser? Well, hardly!

It was probably one of the guests from Kiev who introduced this melody of ours into the theater.

What is the theater? Some will say that the theater is better than any book of devotion; you, Polish Hasidim, will surely say that the theater is worse than any other abomination. Among us we say that it all depends on *what* you perform in the theater.

This affair took place in Warsaw. The theater was packed; there wasn't room for a pin to drop.

The orchestra struck up.

What sort of music was that? Confusion, cacophony, babel! It was Hayim's requiem, but the unassuming melody had been succeeded by unbridled chaos. The sounds darted about, pursuing one another; they lashed the ears, rumbling, hammering, whistling shrilly. No thunderclaps here nor the crash of buildings falling, but simply an incessant din. Was it demons soaring over an icy sea or wild hyenas in an onrush? The whole theater was quaking.

Suddenly the bass viol intruded. Its growling sounded angry, yet one felt that its anger was assumed. A strange hiss swept through the orchestra like lightning, followed by truly diabolic laughter, guffawing and sniggering: the laughter of the clarinet was grating and choppy, as if it were taunting someone in deliberate mockery.

At this point the sounds of three or four violins emerged. Their playing sounded amazingly sweet, as the passion of love, a demon tempting a saint. Each violin crept into the hearts of the listeners; it flowed into each heart like fragrant oil, it intoxicated like old wine.

The audience caught on flame; mouths gaped, eyes blazed. The curtain snaked upward and He and She, the Prince and the Princess, came on and launched into song.

There were words to their song, fiery words. The glow of hell flickered on the faces of the performers; like demons they hastened toward each other. And their embraces, their kisses, their song, their dancing grew faster, ever more intense with every moment.

And again, the audience was aflame—from the orchestra seats

98

to the galleries; the women were affected as well as the men; all faces seemed incandescent, perspiring; all eyes were aglow with a wild light. A torrent of passion swept tempestuously over all those present.

And the whole theater took up the melody!

A sea of flaming lust crashed in a tidal wave; hell itself was ablaze! The fiends were dancing; witches were swirling in a dance.

That's what the *frailachs* which Pedotsour had composed for a poor orphan had become after its transformation into a requiem at the hands of Hayim—and all because of one guest from Kiev.

However, there are no bounds to degradation.

The Jewish theatrical enterprise failed; the Princes participating in it became cobblers and tailors again; the Princesses went back to their kitchens. Some of the musical themes in their theatrical renditions had been popularized by hurdy-gurdies, but you could hardly recognize our melody by this time.

A tattered rug is spread out on the bare earth of a courtyard. Two men in tights are performing tricks. There's a thin pale little girl with them whom they had kidnapped somewhere. One of them balances a ladder in his teeth. The little girl flies like an arrow up the rungs to the very top, then jumps from there to the shoulders of the other man. The first man slaps her on the back; she leaps, turning somersaults, and bows to the spectators with her hand held out, asking for contributions.

This, too, is a theatrical performance, but one meant for the simple folk, for menials and servants. They were performing under the open sky, and therefore their show was cheap. Yet how agile the scrawny little girl was! Large beads of sweat trickled down her pale face with its mottlings of red. Torment smoldered in sunken eyes—but this the crowd did not see; the little girl's breath was labored—but the crowd did not hear! All the crowd saw were the beautiful tricks; all it heard were the sounds of the hurdy-gurdy.

And both the soul in the thin little body of the poor kidnapped child and the hoarse, tinny voice of the hurdy-gurdy moaned, wept, quavered; both were begging to be redeemed.

And it was decided on high that the Melody of Merrymaking for a Poor Bride was to attain its redemption.

From house to house, from town to town, the acrobats took the little girl about with them until such time as she became ill. This happened at Radziwill, near the border. They left the sick child under a fence, while they crossed the border. Half-naked, her body covered with bruises from the beatings they had given her, the little girl lay there in a fever. Compassionate people found her and took her to a hospital. The little girl came through the typhus alive, but when she left the hospital she was blind.

And now she was living on charity. She went from house to house, from door to door and begged for charity. She hardly ever said anything. She could not beg in words. She would stop at some door and wait; if no one noticed her she would start her little song to draw attention to herself—the only song she remembered, the song the hurdy-gurdy used to play.

What did the melody say by that time?

It asked for pity. It asked compassion for an unfortunate child: "Evil men [its tone proclaimed] stole me away from a kind father, from a mother whom I loved, taking me away from a home where I was well-fed and warm. They deprived me of all joy, they used me and cast me aside, just like the shell of a nut after it is eaten. Take pity on a child!

"It is cold, and I am naked [this prayer, too, sounded in the melody]; I hunger, and there is no place where a blind, lonely little orphan can lay her head. . . ."

Thus wept the melody. And this was the first step in its reincarnation.

The melody called upon men to be merciful.

There was a certain learned Jew living in Radziwill. He was not, true enough, opposed to Hasidism; perhaps he even sympathized with the movement, yet somehow or other he had never been able to find the time for a trip to see the *tsaddik* [the local sage]. He did not want to leave his Talmud; he begrudged himself even a moment away from it. Since he feared that in a synagogue his studies would be interfered with, he used to lock himself up in his house—his wife was away in her store from morning till night and his children were in school.

Occasionally the thought "Should I go, perhaps?" would steal into his head; it was probably the Angel of Good that prompted this thought. But the Angel of Evil, assuming a pious visage, would whisper: "Why not make the trip? However, there's always time for that. The thing to do, however, before you go, is to finish this section of the Talmud." And thus months—and years—went by.

Yet Heaven demanded that this learned man should present himself before Reb Duvidel.

And this is what happened. The man of learning was sitting over his books when he heard someone singing outside. The man of learning was angry; he was angry at himself. For when one is at the Talmud one should not hear what is going on out in the street or beyond the door; the world must vanish when faced with learning.

Nevertheless he heard the melody. He stuck his fingers in his ears; just the same the melody crept in at his ear around the fingers. He became even angrier and thrust the end of his long beard in his mouth, chewing on it as he studied, trying to force himself.

The song went on, louder, more provoking. Suddenly the scholar became aware that the voice was a woman's.

A woman's voice! Infuriated, he shouted at her through the window: "Away, you worthless creature!"

The melody retreated. But—what kind of visitation was this? There was no more singing, yet the melody sounded in his ears, sang in his soul. He forced himself to stare at the book; he wanted desperately to plunge into the course of its thought—but it was no good. The scholar's soul was filled with the melody.

He closed the book and prayed.

The thing was beyond him; he could neither study nor pray. It was as if little silver bells were tinkling in his head; The man was beside himself, perishing from his torment. A day passed, a second, and a third; he was all but overcome with melancholy. He lost all desire for food; he tried fasting—but that didn't help. Nor would the song let him sing.

This man had not sung in all his born days; he had never read a prayer aloud in assembly. Even on the Sabbath he simply read the prayers glorifying the Lord and, instead of singing the appropriate chants, devoted himself to studying the Talmud.

He surmised, at last, that all this was happening through design. "The Fiend has been up to mischief," he reflected, and self-doubt assailed him. Apparently there was nothing else left but to make the trip to the *tsaddik*.

But the evil Spirit would not leave him alone:
"It wouldn't do any harm to go!" the spirit urged.

"Yes, but where to? There are many saintly sages; which of them is the *true* one; which can set me on the right path?"

Deep thought engulfed the scholar. And he received a sign.

Precisely at that time it happened that Reb Duvidel had to flee from Talna. On his way he had to go through Radziwill. You surely must have heard the story of the information that was lodged against him. I must tell you that this was a punishment sent by God. The *Hasidim* of Talna should not have taken Reb Duvidel from the people of Vassilkov, enticing him over to Talna. They did a wrong to a whole community, devastated a whole town. All the hotels here closed down; all the inns were deserted. Many in Vassilkov had to go out begging. So they sent a letter containing false information and Talna was done for.

Reb Duvidel used to sit in a gilt armchair, with the inscription over it: "Long live David, King of Israel!" The informers assigned a political character to this inscription and sent secret information to St. Petersburg.

We know, of course, that this inscription is metaphorical, in the Talmudic sense of "He who is king, he is the teacher!"—but go and make that clear to a general in St. Petersburg!

In short, Reb Duvidel had to run. On his way he had to spend the Sabbath in Radziwill. That was the night our scholar went to see him.

The evil spirit, however, had not yet quieted down. The scholar entered and beheld a squat little Jew, sitting at the table in the place of honor. You couldn't see a thing but a tall fur-trimmed hat and the silver of his beard. He was surrounded by the guests. Absolute quiet. No praying was heard; there was not a word about the Torah. The scholar became confused.

"Is this all?" he wondered.

But by this time Reb Duvidel had noticed him and spoke: "Sit down."

The scholar came to himself. He caught the Rabbi's gaze upon him—his soul was seared!

You probably have heard about the eyes of Reb Duvidel. There was might in his gaze, and holiness, and power!

Reb Duvidel had merely to say "Sit down!" for a place to appear at the table. The scholar sat down and waited.

"Sing something!" Reb Duvidel commanded him.

The scholar actually trembled. *He* was to sing! But someone nudged him in the ribs. When Reb Duvidel bade you sing, you sang! And the scholar began to sing.

He began in a tremulous voice; the first sounds barely emerged. What could he sing? The melody of the little orphan, of course. He knew no other. He trembled, he stuttered, but he sang just the same. But by now the melody had become different. It had acquired the spirit of learning, the sanctity of the Sabbath, and it was permeated with the repentance of the learned man. The scholar sang with increasing ease and intensity.

Reb Duvidel, as was his way, began to join in; the assembly noticed this and took up the melody. The singing of the crowd warmed the scholar; he caught the flame and began really singing!

And the melody spread in a river of flame; its waves warmer and more flaming. The melody felt confined under the roof of a house; it spread through the street, a sea of sanctity.

Wonderstruck, amazed, the people in the street asked:

"Can this really be the melody of the orphan?"

The melody had attained its redemption. And so had the scholar.

Before he left, Reb Duvidel called him aside.

"You have wronged a daughter of the Jews," he said. "You paid no heed to her melody; you called her a worthless creature."

"Rabbi, I am subject to your censure!" cried the repentant scholar.

"No need of that," the Rabbi—may the Kingdom of Heaven be his!—assured him. "Instead of undergoing censure, you had better perform a good deed."

"What is it, Rabbi?"

"Arrange a marriage for this girl. That would be a good deed!"

Now listen to something else. After a few years, when the blind girl had been long married to a widowed scribe, they learned about her origin.

It turned out that she was the granddaughter of old Katzner!

His son-in-law had gone to the theater with his young wife one night, and while they were gone their only daughter had been kidnapped.

But before she could be restored to them, her mother died, and her father went to America.

103

The Pious Cat

THERE WERE three canaries in a certain house, and there was also a cat who ended their activities, one by one. This was no ordinary cat, but a most pious one, you may be sure. Its coat was white as snow, and its eyes were of heaven's own blue. It was the sort of cat that cleaned itself ten times a day and nibbled its food delicately in some dark corner.

All day long it sustained itself on dairy products, but at night it was not above relishing the ritually-clean flesh of a mouse. It did not pounce upon its prey as some uncouth greedy creatures do, and it did not wolf its food, but fed leisurely in high spirits. Let the poor little mouse linger on a little, let it hop about and squeak its last prayer: a truly devout cat is never in great haste.

When the first canary was taken into the house, the cat was overwhelmed with a feeling of compassion for it.

"Such a beautiful, tiny creature," thought the cat, "Yet destined never to enjoy the bliss of the hereafter. But, indeed, how could it merit heavenly bliss," the cat reasoned, "when, to begin with, it so uncouthly immerses its entire body in its bath. Secondly, the very fact that it is imprisoned in a cage means that it is a wicked bird; though it is still very young, and apparently gentle and winsome, it evidently must prefer brute force. And what about all the noise it makes? It trills and whistles quite brazenly! Then, too, there's the arrogance to break out of its cage and soar through the world, through the great outdoors. Have you ever seen a cat confined in a cage? Have you ever heard a virtuous cat daring to sing with such abandon? It's a great pity, indeed," the cat went on with bleeding heart and almost in tears, "for after all, it's a living creature, endowed with a spark from above. And all its woes are due to its sinful body being so alluring—so tantalizing to the earthy and carnal nature—for the voice of the tempter sounds within it. How can such a dainty, tiny bird hope to withstand so overwhelm-

104

ing a temptation? And the longer this songbird lives, the more numerous will its transgressions be and the greater the punishment of Providence that awaits it."

A sense of righteousness flamed up in the cat's heart. The next moment, it leaped upon the table where the cage with the canary rested—and the floor was strewn with feathers in no time.

The cat received a thrashing but it accepted the punishment meekly, and it pondered the cause of its punishment and resolved to be well behaved. It had been beaten soundly (it reasoned) because it had scattered feathers all over the room and because it had sullied the white embroidered tablecloth with blood stains. Things of this sort had to be carried out calmly, decorously, without leaving a single trace of blood or feathers.

Consequently, when the second canary arrived, the cat strangled it quietly and swallowed it feathers and all, without much ado. Nevertheless, the cat was again beaten. At last, the cat realized that it was not at all a question of feathers or blood stains, but had to do with the commandment of *Thou shalt not kill!* One must learn to love, to forgive. It is not through revenge that a world steeped in iniquity can be redeemed. Those who have fallen into error must be brought back to the path of righteousness; it is to their hearts that one must appeal.

A repentant canary could ascend to heights so exalted that they were beyond the reach of even the most pious cat. And the cat was in a rhapsody of delight. The old times were over and done with. No more bloodshed—pity and loving-kindness were to be the order of the day. And it was in a burst of generosity that it approached the third songbird!

"Have no fear," it accosted the canary in the most mellifluous tones that ever issued from a feline throat. "True, you are sinful and depraved, but I will not harm you—I pity you. I will not pry open your cage, nor even touch you. Why are you so silent? But that's good: it's better to keep quiet than to whistle and warble so impertinently. You are flinching? That's admirable! Be in fear and trembling—not for my sake, however, but for Almighty's! May you abide thus immaculate, and shaking!

"I shall see to it that you go on trembling. From the very depths of my pious soul I will breathe upon you and inspire you with serenity and piety. May my breath imbue your being with hallowed faith, and your heart with repentance and humility."

By this time, it had dawned on the cat how gratifying it was to forgive and how satisfying it was to instill another with true faith and the cardinal virtues. The munificent heart of the white and pious cat was exalted. The canary, however, could not breathe in the feline atmosphere, and the poor thing died from suffocation.

Reb Noah and the Rabbi
of Brest

SURELY, you must have heard about the Rabbi of Brest and Reb
Noah, the Tsaddik of Biala. It isn't generally known, however,
that earlier in his career Reb Noachke, the Saintly Sage of Biala,
had been a zealous disciple of the Rabbi of Brest. Then one day
he vanished into thin air and, after a period of self-imposed exile
and deprivation, finally turned up in Biala.

The reason he had left the Rabbi was this: they had been studying the Torah, but this Torah, the Tsaddik felt, was a *dry* Torah.
They might be studying some law having to do with women's
ritual or the dairy and meat diets or civil suits. Well and good.
But let Reuben and Simon appear for the settlement of a dispute
or a messenger arrive with a petition concerning religious law
or a woman come to ask about some point of ritual—then the
Torah would become imbued with a soul and come to life, and
gain mastery over life. Otherwise, the Tsaddik felt, the Torah was
but a husk, just so much dry matter that, in his eyes, did not con-
stitute *the teaching of life!* The Torah was meant to be alive!

At Brest, it was forbidden to study cabalistic lore. The Rabbi of
Brest was a *mishaggid* and was by nature as "vengeful and as
tenacious in remembering evil as a serpent." All you had to do was
to touch the *Zohar* or the *Pardes* and he would put you under the
curse. Once a certain man was caught poring over a cabalistic
tome, whereupon the Rabbi ordered his beard to be shaved at the
hands of a Gentile barber. And what do you think happened? The
fellow went mad; he sank into a deep melancholy and—this is the
amazing part of it—no miracle-worker was able to help him thereafter. It was no joke to tangle with the Rabbi of Brest! So how was
one to depart from the Rabbi's seminary?

It is understandable, then, that the Tsaddik hesitated for a long while.

But the day came when he had a vision. He dreamed that the Rabbi of Brest came to him and said: "Come, Noah, I shall lead you to the lower paradise." And he took him by the hand and led him off. They found themselves in a spacious chamber that had no windows and only one door, the one through which they had entered. It was light in the chamber, however; the walls seemed to be of crystal, and a vivid glare emanated from them.

They walked on and on, and there was no end in sight.

"Hold on to my *kaftan*," said the Rabbi. "The labyrinths here are innumerable, and if you fall behind me, you will have lost your way for all time."

The Tsaddik did as he was told and they continued walking. He did not see a bench or a stool or, for that matter, any furnishings at all—none whatsoever!

"People don't sit here," the Rabbi of Brest explained to him. "They just walk on and on."

So he followed the Rabbi. Each hall was larger and more beautiful than the last, and the walls glittered now with one hue, now with another, and sometimes with mingled hues. Yet the Rabbi and his disciple did not come upon a single living soul.

The Tsaddik grew tired. He was bathed in a cold sweat, and a chill began to spread through his entire body. Soon his eyes were smarting from the ever-present glitter.

As he was seized with longing, he felt drawn to Jews, to friends, to all Israel. It was no trivial matter—this business of not seeing a single Jew!

"Do not long for anybody," the Rabbi of Brest told him. "This chamber is only for me and for you. The time will come when you will succeed me as the Rabbi of Brest."

Thereupon the Tsaddik became frightened and put his hand against the wall in order not to fall. And the wall seared him—not as fire sears, however, but with the dry burn of ice.

"Rabbi!" his cry rang out. "The walls are not crystal but ice—plain ice!"

The Rabbi of Brest said nothing. But the Tsaddik kept on shouting: "Rabbi, let me out of here! I do not want to be alone with you! I want to be with all of Israel!"

And hardly had he uttered these words when the Rabbi of Brest

108

vanished and the Tsaddik was left alone in the chamber. He did not know the way. Chill horror spurted from the walls. The longing for a Jew, the desire to see any Jew at all—even if he were a cobbler, a tailor—was consuming him, and he burst into bitter tears.

"Creator of the Universe!" he prayed, "Lead me out of here! Better to be in hell with all Israel than to be all alone here!"

At that instant there arose before him a simple Jew girded with the broad red belt of a carter and carrying a whip. Without a word this Jew took him by the sleeve, led him out of the chamber, and vanished!

The Tsaddik awoke. It was long before daybreak, but by the time the morning sun was up, he realized the extraordinary nature of his dream. He dressed quickly and decided to hurry to the synagogue and ask the Talmudists the meaning of the dream. But, as he was crossing the marketplace, he noticed an enormous, old-fashioned cart, and he recognized the carter instantly. Girded with a red broad sash and carrying a long whip, the carter was in every detail exactly the same as the one who, in his dream, had led him out of the chamber!

The Tsaddik knew this to be an omen. Approaching, he asked the man:

"Where are you going?"

"I'm not going *your* way," the carter answered roughly.

"But, just the same," the Tsaddik persisted, "Can't I go with you?"

"Why can't a boy like you go on foot?" asked the carter, after reflecting a little. "Be on your way!"

"Yes, but where am I to go?"

"Wherever your eyes may lead you!" answered the carter, and turned away. "What's it to me?"

The Tsaddik understood and set out on his wanderings.

As I have already said, the Tsaddik showed up several years later in Biala. How he happened to come there I am not going to tell you, although it really is an astonishing story.

About a year after the Tsaddik had appeared, a certain townsman in Biala by the name of Jehiel took me on as a *melamed*, or religious instructor. To tell you the truth, I wasn't so eager to take on this job. Reb Jehiel, you must know, was a very rich man. He gave his daughters dowries of a thousand gold pieces each and married them off to eminent rabbis. His newest daughter-in-law was none other than the daughter of the Rabbi of Brest.

You can understand my reluctance: the Rabbi of Brest was a *mithnaggid,* and the other kin of Reb Jehiel were *mithnaggdim,* so Reb Jehiel himself was bound to be a *mithnaggid* [or anti-Hasid]. But it happen that I myself am a Biala Hasid. How, then, could I settle down in such a household? Just the same, though, I was drawn to Biala. To be in the same town with a Tsaddik—that is not something to take lightly! I thought the matter over thoroughly, pro and con, and in the end went there.

However, Reb Jehiel turned out to be a simple and truly pious Jew. I would even go so far as to say that in his heart he was awed by the Tsaddik. And since he was no man of learning, he understood nothing of what the Rabbi of Brest stood for. He did not forbid me to mingle with the Tsaddik of Biala, but he himself kept aloof from him. Whenever I mentioned the Tsaddik he made believe he was yawning, although I could see his ears were pricked up. As for his son, who was son-in-law to the Rabbi of Brest, he wrinkled his brow, regarding me with a malicious sneer, but did not enter into any controversies; he was not, by nature, a talkative sort.

And then the time came for Jehiel's daughter-in-law, the daughter of the Rabbi of Brest, to give birth. It is no novelty, this business of woman giving birth. But on this occasion, there was a certain combination of circumstances that made it seem so. Everybody knew that the Rabbi of Brest had been chastised by the *tsaddikei hador,* the Men of Righteousness, because he had shaved off—that is, had ordered to be shaved off—a certain Jew's beard and ritual sidelocks: both the Rabbi's sons died within a period of five or six years, and not one of his three daughters brought forth boys. In addition to that, their labors were cruelly difficult and brought each of them very close to the other world. But since it was desired up there, in heaven, that there should be internecine struggle between the Hasidim and the *mithnaggdim,* it followed that although everybody perceived and knew that all this was meant as a chastisement of the Rabbi of Brest by the gathering of the Men of Righteousness, he himself did not perceive this with his clear-seeing eyes. It may be that he actually did not want to perceive it. And he went on waging his war with an armed hand—with anathemas and martial zeal, in keeping with the worst of those times.

I felt sorry—dreadfully sorry—for Gittele (that's what they called the Rabbi's daughter). First of all, she was a Jewish soul and, seconly, a pious Jewish soul. Such a woman of righteousness, so good at heart, the world had never yet beheld. Not one poor bride got married without her aid. What a wonderful creature—and she had to suffer because of her father's vindictiveness! Consequently, as soon as I noticed that the midwife had arrived, I made every effort to have the Tsaddik of Biala called. Let them send him a note, without any offering—he had no great need of offerings. The Tsaddik of Biala, as a general rule, did not have a high opinion about them. But to whom was I to talk about this?

I began with the son-in-law of the Rabbi of Brest. I knew that his soul was truly bound up with the soul of his wife for, no matter how he tried to conceal it, the nearness of their hearts was obvious in their every move. But, after all, he was a son-in-law of the Rabbi of Brest, and so he spat and turned away, leaving me gaping.

When I turned to Jehiel himself, he merely replied: "She is the daughter of the Rabbi of Brest. I can't go against him, even if, God forbid, my life were in peril!" I went to his wife—a pious woman, yet simple—and she said: "Let my husband bid me, and I'll immediately send my precious jewels to the Tsaddik—and they cost a pile of money! But, without my husband, I won't give a thing."

"But what about a note to the Tsaddik? How could a note hurt you?"

"Not a thing without my husband's knowledge!" she replied, as a pious woman should, and turned away from me. And I saw that she wanted to hide her tears—a mother, she, and her heart was already apprehensive.

When I heard the first scream, however, I went running to the Tsaddik, without waiting for anybody.

"What am I to do, Shmaiah?" was his response. "I shall pray—"

"Rabbi," I implored him, "Give me something for the woman in labor—a talisman, a coin—give me something—"

"That, God forbid, can make matters still worse," he replied. "Such things, if there is no faith in them, can only cause harm."

This took place at the beginning of the Feast of Tabernacles. What was I to do? Her labors were difficult. I could not help in any way, and so I stayed on at the Tsaddik's. I was like one of his family. I thought if I kept looking at him all the time with imploring eyes, perhaps he would feel compassion at last.

News reached us that things were going badly. The labor pains were going on for the third day.

Everything that could be done had already been done. They kept running to the synagogue; they measured the graves*; they burned candles by the hundredweight in the houses of prayer and distributed a whole treasury in alms. There was no counting all the things that were done! All the clothes closets stood wide open, coins lay in mounds on the table, and the beggars came and helped themselves, each taking what he wanted and as much as he wanted.

My heart contracted.

"Reb Noah," I asked, "Is it not truly said, 'Charity delivereth from death'?"

But he answered me with a question of his own:

"Perhaps the Rabbi of Brest will come?"

And who should enter at that point but Reb Jehiel! He did not address the Tsaddik. It was as if he did not see him at all.

"Listen Shmaiah," he said, seizing the lapel of his coat, "There's a cart standing by the house. Go, get in it, and drive to the Rabbi of Brest—let him come here." And evidently he sensed who was the stumbling block here, for he added: "Let him see for himself what's going on here. Let him say what's to be done."

And his face—well, what can I tell you? I've seen a corpse look far better.

Well, off I went. If, I said to myself, the Tsaddik knew that the Rabbi of Brest would come, perhaps something or other might come of it. There might be a reconciliation, even—if not between the Rabbi of Brest and the Tsaddik, then perhaps between the contending factions. For, surely, if he did come, he was bound to see. After all, he had eyes in his head!

But it would seem matters were not decided in heaven as quickly as that—those up there entered into conflict with me. Hardly had I left Biala when a cloud darkened the sky—and what a cloud: ponderous and black as pitch! Almost at once a wind

* During a critical illness the grave of some Jew noted for his piety would be measured, and candles corresponding in total length to the length of such a grave would be donated to a synagogue—*Translator.*

sprang up, as if spirits had come swooping from all quarters. The *mouzhik* [peasant] driving—well, even he understood. He crossed himself, and said it would be hard going and pointed to the sky with his knout. Soon an even stronger wind began to blow, tearing the clouds the way one tears paper into bits and piling them one on top of another, just as if they were ice-floes at the flood of waters. There were, by this time, two and three tiers of clouds overhead. I did not feel at all frightened, to tell you the truth. It wouldn't be the first time I got soaked to the skin, and as for thunder, I'm not afraid of it: in the first place there is no thunder during the Feast of Tabernacles and in the second, the Tsaddik had blown on the ram's horn during the New Year festival and, as everybody knows, that makes all thunderbolts powerless. But when lightning struck right before my face—once, twice, three times—the blood congealed in my veins. I perceived clearly that heaven itself was lashing me, driving me back!

And the *mouzhik*, too, was begging me to turn back.

But then I remembered that, back there, a human life was in danger. I sat in that cart while the storm raged. The moans of the woman in labor came to my ears, as did the sound of the Rabbi's son-in-law cracking his fingers. I thought I saw before me the downcast face of Reb Jehiel, his eyes smoldering and sunken in.

"Go on," he implored me, "Go on!" And on we went.

The rain came down in sheets. Water spurted from under the wheels and from under the hoofs of the horses. The road was completely covered over with water, and foam scudded along on top. It looked as if the cart would be carried afloat at any moment.

To top it all off, we lost our way. But, just the same, I kept to my purpose.

When I returned to Biala with the Rabbi of Brest, it was Hoshana Rabbah—the seventh day of the Feast of Tabernacles! No sooner had the Rabbi of Brest taken his seat in the cart than everything became utterly calm. The clouds burst apart, the sun peeped out, and we arrived at Biala without any trouble, neat and dry. Even the *mouzhik* noticed this and muttered something in his own language about the Great Rabbi, the Mighty Rabbi.

But things really began happening when we entered the house.

All the women swooped down on the Rabbi like a cloud of locusts. They all but fell on their faces before him and wept. You couldn't hear the woman in labor in the next room at all for the weeping of the others—unless, God forbid, she no longer had the strength to moan.

Reb Jehiel did not even notice us; he had his forehead pressed against the windowpane, as if to cool his head. Nor did the Rabbi's son-in-law turn around. He was standing with his back to us, and his whole body was quivering as he beat his head against the wall.

I thought my legs would no longer support me: that's how shaken I was with fear and pity. A chill went through my body and I felt my soul grow cold.

Incidentally, did you ever know the Rabbi of Brest?

This was a man—a pillar of iron! Of great height—a whole head taller than all those around him—he inspired one with as much awe as did a tsar. His long, white beard and thick eyebrows cast a luminous shadow over half his face. But when he lifted his eyes —my God, the women shrank from him as if they had been stunned by a thunderbolt. For in his eyes razors, sharp razors, glittered.

"Away, you women!" he cried out—and his shout was like the roar of a lion. Then he asked, but this time softly and gently, where his daughter was, and they pointed out her room. He entered, while I stayed behind, completely beside myself: such eyes, such a gaze, such a voice! He was from another world. The eyes of the Tsaddik glowed so warmly, so gently that one's soul rejoiced, and when he looked at you it was as if he were showering you with gold. His voice—that sweet, velvety voice—Creator of the Universe, it subdued your heart, that's how gentle, how tender, it was! It wasn't awe that one felt before *him;* the soul melted from love. The soul fought to escape the body, to mingle with his soul. It was drawn, just like a moth, toward a blazing flame. But the Rabbi of Brest—before him one felt only awe and terror! A mighty man of learning he was, a *gaon* of the olden times! And it was he who went into the room of the woman in labor. I was panic-stricken with the thought that he would turn her into a heap of bones! And I dashed off to the Tsaddik. He met me at his door with a smile.

"Have you beheld," he asked, "the grandeur of the Torah? The true grandeur of the Torah?"

I calmed down. There, there, I reflected, if the Tsaddik is smiling, it means that everything is all right!

And things really did work out well. She gave birth on Shmini-

Atserith, the eighth day of the Feast of Tabernacles. And the following day, as he sat at the table, the Rabbi of Brest was already delivering a sermon to us. To tell you the truth, I would rather have sat at another table, but lacked the courage to do so. All the more so since without me there would not have been a full *minyan* [quorum of ten adult Jews] and it would have been impossible to recite the appropriate communal grace.

"Well, now, what else was I going to tell you? Oh yes, about how the Rabbi of Brest knew the Torah. If the Torah were an ocean, then he would be a leviathan in that ocean! At a single stroke he would swim the length of ten tracts; at a single stroke he could penetrate the whole Talmud with all its commentaries. He rumbled, surged, seethed, bubbled—indeed, he behaved just the way the ocean does. Watching him, I was becoming dizzy.

But . . . *the heart knoweth the woe of the soul.* My heart was, after all, bereft of the joys of the holiday. It was at this point that I recalled the Tsaddik's dream—and I became petrified. The sun was shining in at the windows; there was all the wine you wanted on the table; all those present, I saw, were bathed in perspiration —but I felt cold—unbearably cold! Over *there,* I knew, they were taken up with another Torah. *There* everything was light and warmth . . . each word was saturated with love and rapture. Angels were soaring through the room; one could actually hear the swish of their great white wings. Ah, Creator of the Universe! Yet I could not leave.

Suddenly the Rabbi of Brest broke off his sermon and asked: "Who's your Tsaddik here?"

"A certain Noah," they answered him. And I felt as if someone had slashed at my heart. *A certain Noah*—oh, the cowards, the cowards!

"A miracle worker?" he went on with his questioning.

"One doesn't hear much about that, somehow. The womenfolk, true enough, tell something of the sort—but whoever listens to them?"

"Does he take money *just like that,* without any miracles?"

But by now they had plucked up courage enough to tell the truth: "He takes little—and distributes a great deal."

The Rabbi of Brest grew thoughtful.

"And does he know the Torah?"

"He's a great scholar, they say."

115

"Where is he from, this Noah?"

Nobody knew, and it was up to me to answer. In this way a conversation sprang up between me and the Rabbi.

"Wasn't this Noah in Brest at one time?" asked he.

"Was the Tsaddik in Brest?" I murmured. "Yes, it would seem so."

"Aha!" said he. "This is his Hassid!" He looked at me the way one looks at a spider. At this point he turned to the others present: "I had a disciple once by the name of Noah. He had a splendid head, true enough, but he was constantly straying. I gave him one warning, then another, and was getting ready for the third when he up and vanished. Could *this* be *he?*"

"Who can tell?"

And so he began sketching him for us: a gaunt little fellow, with a small black beard, with coiling black sidelocks, a soft voice, pensive, and so on.

"It's possible he is the one," said the others. "Sounds very like him."

By he time we began grace I was thanking God. But after the grace something happened that I could not even have dreamed about. The Rabbi of Brest got up from his bench, called me aside, and said to me in a whisper:

"Lead me to *your* Tsaddik and *my* disciple. The only thing is— do you hear me?—no one must know of this."

I obeyed him, of course, but on the way I asked him:

"Rabbi of Brest, what is your purpose in going to him?"

His answer was very simple:

"During grace the thought occurred to me that up to now I had been judging the man sight unseen. I want to see—to see with my own eyes. And perhaps," he added later on, "God may help me to save a disciple of mine. Do you know, you godless fellow," he went on, "if your Tsaddik is the same Noah who studied under me, he will be a great man in Israel, a Rabbi in Brest!"

By this time I knew with certainty that my Tsaddik was the very man, and my heart began to flutter.

The two were about to come together. Only a miracle from heaven could save me now!

The Tsaddik of Biala—his memory be blessed!—used to send his Hasidim during Simchath-Torah [the Rejoicing of the Law]

116

to stroll beyond the limits of the town, while he himself sat on his tiny balcony and watched them and rejoiced over them.

Biala of that time wasn't what it is today. Then, it was only a very small place; all the houses were of wood, except the synagogue and the Tsaddik's House of Study. On the second story of the House of Study there was a tiny balcony from which everything could be seen, eastward to the Knolls and westward to the river. And the Tsaddik sat there and contemplated the scene. He would see several Hasidim walking along in silence and would hum the beginning of a melody; they would chime in and resume their stroll with song and genuine rejoicing. As for the Tsaddik, he sat there alone on his tiny balcony.

The Tsaddik had evidently heard the sound of our footsteps as we approached the House of Study, for he got up and came toward the Rabbi of Brest.

"*Sholom Aleichem,* Rabbi!" he said in greeting.

"*Aleichem Sholom,* Noah!" responded the Rabbi of Brest.

"Be seated, Rabbi!"

The Rabbi of Brest sat down, while the Tsaddik of Biala stood before him.

"Tell me, Noah," said the Rabbi, raising his eyebrows, "why did you run away from my seminary? What were you seeking?"

"What I sought, Rabbi," the Tsaddik answered calmly, "was air. I could not breathe there."

"What does that mean? What are you saying, Noah?"

"It was not I who needed air," the Tsaddik explained with a calm smile, "but my soul—"

"Why, Noah?"

"Your Torah, Rabbi, is but an arid Law. It is without benevolence, without a spark of graciousness, this Torah of yours! And therefore it is joyless, airless—nothing but directives of iron and brass. Your Torah is far too private—it is only for men of learning, only for the chosen ones—"

The Rabbi of Brest was silent, and the Tsaddik went on:

"Tell me, Rabbi—what can you offer *all* of Israel? What have you for the woodcutter, the butcher, the artisan, the common Jew —especially the sinning Jew? What can you give to those who have no learning?"

The Rabbi of Brest still said nothing, as though he did not

117

understand what the other was saying. But the Tsaddik of Biala stood before him and went on:

"Forgive me, Rabbi, but I must tell you the truth: harsh was your Torah, harsh and dry—it was but the *body* of the Torah, not its soul!"

"The soul?" echoed the Rabbi, and ran his hand over his high forehead.

"Of course! *Your* Torah, Rabbi, as I've already said, is only for the chosen ones, for the men of learning, but not for all of Israel. The real Torah must be for all of Israel, for it is the soul of all Israel."

"And what about *your* Torah, Noah?"

"Would you behold it, Rabbi?"

"Behold the Torah?" the Rabbi of Brest voiced his wonder.

"Come, Rabbi—I'll show it to you. I'll show you the radiance, the joy that pours out of it upon *all* of Israel."

The Rabbi of Brest did not move.

"Come, Rabbi, I beg of you. It isn't far."

He led the other out on the tiny balcony. I followed them quietly. The Tsaddik sensed what I was doing.

"You can come along," he said. "You, too, shall see it this day, Shmaiah. And so will the Rabbi of Brest. You shall see *the Rejoicing of the Torah*—the true rejoicing of the Torah!"

And I saw what I had seen during Simchath-Torah, but in a different way—as if a veil had been lifted from my eyes.

I saw an infinite, boundless sky, a vividly blue sky larded with clouds, little silvery clouds that floated in the blueness, and if one looked at them closely one could see that they were tremulous with joy, that they rejoiced over the Torah. The town was girded with a broad sash of greenery, living greenery so alive that life itself hovered among the grasses. Tiny flames of delight, intoxicated with life, spouted up, and I could see with my own eyes how flames leaped and danced between the blades of grass as though they were embracing and kissing them.

And strolling in knots on the meadows, where these tiny flames danced, were the Hasidim. Their satin *kaftans* gleamed like mirrors—even the tattered ones shone. And the little flames danced out of the grass and clutched at the holiday clothes, encircling each Hasid with rapture and love. All the Hasidim were looking upward with hungry eyes toward the tiny balcony of the Tsaddik.

These eyes, I could plainly see, were feasting on the light that emanated from the face of the Tsaddik—and they chanted the louder. . . .

Each group of Hasidim sang a melody of its own; all the melodies and voices blended, and when they reached the Tsaddik they were as *one* song, one hymn. Everything reverberated with song— the vaults of heaven sang, as did the earth below. The soul of all creation was in song!

Creator of Universe! It seemed to me I would dissolve in rapture. However, this was not to be my destiny.

"It is time to proceed with the evening prayer," the Rabbi of Brest announced, suddenly and brusquely. And everything vanished.

It was quiet. The veil fell over my eyes again. Overhead was an ordinary sky; below, an ordinary world with its ordinary Hasidim in torn robes. Ancient, incoherent snatches of melodies were silenced. The little flames expired. I looked at the Tsaddik, and his face was somber.

There was no reconciliation. The Rabbi of Brest remained the same *mithnaggid* he always was.

But the meeting did have a certain effect, however: the Rabbi of Brest no longer persecuted the Tsaddik of Biala.

The Orphan

A Rich Man Rises from the Dead—and a Melamed *Suddenly Dies*
—For twenty years Avigdor had been a *melamed* [teacher of He-
brew]; for twenty years he had been instructing the children of
the more well-to-do families in the town—and then he took sick.
His throat began to bleed, he lost his voice and became ever so
thin.

"It's a pity," everyone said. "A scholar and a good teacher besides."

Avigdor was as lonely as a mile-post. He had come to the town
from some far-off place when he was still a young man and had
settled down to teaching the children. He had no relatives or
close friends here. He was a widower, with a four-year-old son.
Whatever children he had were not long-lived, and his wife had
at last died in giving birth. Verily, the ways of the Lord are beyond knowing!

The Jewish community took care of Avigdor. It was decided in
the synagogue not to deprive him of his pupils—the man would
starve to death. True, they say that consumption is catching—
but then, what won't people say! For we know that life and death
are in the hands of God: unless He wills it the Angel of Death
can't get at you.

This was decided in the synagogue at morning prayer and con-
firmed at evening prayers. But just the same, his pupils deserted
him.

A *nouveau riche* Jew, a cousin of the local *mumcha* [second-
class physician], was responsible for the whole business; and others
soon followed his example.

But the community as a whole could not look on with indif-
ference while a Jew, especially one so well versed in the Talmud,
starved to death. Something had to be done! Both piety and justice demanded it. The only question was, *who* should act? The

whole congregation reiterated unanimously that the obligation to help the old man rested on the shoulders of those who had taken their children away from him. But these people said: "Jews are responsible for one another"—in other words, the whole community was obligated to support a Jew, especially one so versed in the Talmud. Naturally, they would do everything possible, but to take the whole burden upon themselves was something they couldn't do.

At this point another question arose: Where was the community to get the money from? The town had three directors of communal administrations, but the real headman was Reb Shmerl, a devout person with a gentle, sincere piety. And Reb Shmerl maintained that the means at the community's disposal was vastly insufficient; the community was like a sieve; it was impossible to make ends meet and he had to dig down into his own pocket. He had only two alternatives: either to divorce his wife, who was generally raging like a thunderstorm, or to refuse participation in all community affairs—and let someone else wear the yoke! The congregation, however, was not impressed by Shmerl's ultimatum: they could either choose another elder or seek new and untapped sources of revenue.

They might, for instance, impose another tax—on Sabbath candles or provisions—it made little difference. Perhaps a tax on cake yeast. Or else they might rent out the baths for another three years—or, best of all, they might accommodate a fourth ritual slaughterer. The three they had were taking in the money hand over fist, so why shouldn't still another Jew make a living at slaughtering, even though he didn't happen to be related to Reb Shmerl? And, by the way, a crumb or two would fall to the community's share. They would have to resort to a tax anyway: it was absolutely necessary to repair the women's bath-house. Also, the room for studying the Talmud and the Torah had been closed several years now; it was time—high time!—to reopen it.

And if the members of the community refused their consent to all of these measures, then let them take up a collection among themselves—but let it be a decent sum! There were plenty of young married men being maintained by their fathers-in-law—they had time to spare, and their legs were sound enough.

While these discussions were dragging along, Avigdor was put out of his rooms and he and his son were left with no roof other than the canopy of heaven.

They managed to get through the day somehow; they sat in the synagogue, they dropped in on friends. Everywhere they went, they were treated to something or other: a glass of vodka (the boy was given a cordial) or a piece of cake. But when it came to offering them lodging for the night, nobody came forward. After evening prayer Avigdor and his little son remained alone in the synagogue—even those who usually stayed on after prayers for a stint of reading made haste to leave.

After a while Avigdor began to feel cold in the huge, empty synagogue. The child had fallen asleep on a bench; the father did not bother to awaken him, and went by himself to a bakery where the men worked all through the night. They let him sit down and he settled down by the wall, close to the blazing oven. No one disturbed him, and Avigdor slept until late in the morning.

The next night he brought the boy along with him. He took the same place as before; the boy sat down close to him and put his head on his father's knees. The two of them slept the night through.

This went on for several days. Then, in some way, the police got wind of it and a great commotion began. The baker missed going to jail by the narrowest of margins; he had a hard time buying off the police with a few roubles and gave a promise in writing not to let Avigdor even cross the threshold of his bakery. After all, what does it matter to the police that Avigdor is a Jew of great learning? A few of the propertied men did address a request to the right quarters—but what does a Jew's request mean in our day and age?

Avigdor took to passing the night in the bath-house—and there was the same commotion all over again. Again the police interfered and threatened to close down the bath-house and the women's bath as well. To object would have been very risky; the building was actually on the verge of tumbling down at any moment; one peep out of anyone and they would seal the doors of the place and set everybody back a thousand roubles. No one knows to this day who lodged the information, but it could not have happened unless someone had done so: the police never interfere on their own initiative.

Now Avigdor and the boy had no comfortable shelter and were forced to stay in the unheated synagogue.

Pity for them waxed greater than ever. People could not ignore the fact that neither father nor son had a shirt to his back. The whole synagogue now admitted that it fell squarely upon the community to provide for Avigdor. But what could the community do in this case? They kept on discussing and discussing, and came to the conclusion that renting out the baths for another three years was out of the question; no one would pay a copper until they were put in repair.

To take in still another ritual slaughterer was dangerous and would probably lead to dissension—not long ago, during dissensions over a slaughterer, almost half the town had had to pay a fine for "breach of contract." Such is the lot of Jews!

Then it turned out that the trade in cake-yeast was for the most part carried on by non-Jews. The tradesmen would not submit to any tax on foodstuffs—and the tradesmen and the Pallbearers' Guild were banded together in this matter. On top of that, the Burial Society would butt in at once. The tax on poultry was opposed by the majority of the well-to-do. They said they would either stop eating it if the tax were imposed or would arrange to have it slaughtered beyond the town limits. When it came to a tax on fish, it was found that fish was priced out of reach as it was. Putting the matter off was also out of the question. Therefore, only one course of action remained: to take up a collection among the congregation. They had even reached the point of discussing who was to go soliciting with whom.

However, man proposes but God disposes.

On a weekday, about this time, the usual quiet in the marketplace was replaced by extraordinary animation. Ahreleh the driver was perched on the box of his *britchka*, harnessed with two horses that were like lions, and flying back and forth over the marketplace, paying no heed to the roadway with its ruts and ridges. The clatter of the vehicle was deafening. Seated in the *britchka* was Reb Gabriel, supported on the right by his second wife (or it may have been his third) and on his left by the *mumcha*. The wife and the *mumcha* took turns poking the driver's back, urging him on:

"Keep driving, keep driving! Faster, you bandit! Better that ten horses should perish than one human being!"

Reb Gabriel—may this never be said of you!—had appendicitis. They were saying that he had had mercury administered to him, and it was also rumored that he had already taken musk. He could be saved only by God and by Ahreleh and his racers. But things did not look promising for him! The old sexton of the Burial Society, who in his time had seen more dead men than living ones, was saying that if the gut did not straighten out after this gallop through the marketplace, there was nothing further to be hoped for. The need was for the strongest influence Up There; you could not do without the boundless compassion of the Lord. A full-fledged physician was brought in from somewhere, but he, too, admitted that Reb Gabriel was in the hands of God.

Talk of a collection for Avigdor came to an abrupt stop. Why? No one could find the gumption to come right out with the reason, yet everybody knew what it was. The ranking elder of the Burial Society began putting on airs; he took to addressing even the ancients in familiar terms, and by now wouldn't give a pinch of snuff to anybody; if somebody bowed to him he would barely nod acknowledgment. He knew that power was in his hands now!

As for the community and Reb Gabriel, there had been a settlement of debts long overdue, and now there would be money sufficient not only for Avigdor but for others. Reb Gabriel was a well-to-do man—he owned three houses, two stores, and when it came to cash it went without saying that he had plenty. At the same time, he was childless. And he never made donations: he wouldn't toss as much as a copper into any box for offerings; he would give nothing for the poor to buy matzoth with, nothing when the plate was passed around, he would put nothing into the box kept in every synagogue in the name of Meir Baal ha-Ness (the miracle worker), nor did he ever invite a poor man to his Sabbath supper. Since the time of his last marriage (and that had taken place twenty years ago) he had not even treated the congregation to a piece of cake and a noggin of vodka—no, not even once.

No one—God forbid!—wished him any ill. A Jew is a Jew for a' that, and no one would butt in on God with gratuitous advice, but what's true is true.

Ahreleh the coachman had already had one of his horses founder, and the elder of the Burial Society got up still more courage—he got over being scared of his wife, even!

Miracles actually do happen in our day, though rarely. Reb Gabriel contributed a few pounds of candles to the synagogue, and this had its due effect: he rose up from the dead.

But as for poor Reb Avigdor, he suddenly died.

The Funeral—It was an impressive funeral—everybody came, young and old.

But, just the same, it was—I can't find another word for it—it was a *dry* funeral. He had left no widow—and only one orphan.

The women had nothing to grab hold of. Not one of them fainted; and the tears wouldn't flow, somehow. The poor orphan had as yet no conception of such words as *the grave, dying;* his face was frightened rather than tearful. There was really nothing here to stir up one's pity. If one of the women did happen to think of her own bitter lot and started wailing, her voice would remain hanging in mid-air; no one would join her, no one would carry on, and the lonely wail would immediately congeal and die away in space.

Jonah Batz, the ranking elder of the Pallbearers' Guild, noticed this and shouted after them:

"You women! Go home, go home! A funeral without tears is the same as a wedding without music."

The women reviled Lanky Jonah from a distance but nevertheless dispersed.

The men dispersed too, little by little.

Shopkeepers, who are eternally busy, and the old men and those who weren't strong, accompanied the coffin only as far as the end of their block. Others escorted the dead man to the town limits and stopped there, and, having stopped, knocked at the first window they came to. The people inside already knew what this signified and brought out a jug of water. Those who had been escorting the body poured a little of the water on their finger tips, heaved a few sighs, uttered the appropriate prayer, and then each man went his way to take up the affairs that had been interrupted.

The young married men, who were still being supported by the parents of their brides and were occupied with the study of the Torah, and who on a time had been Avigdor's pupils or had carried on learned discussion with him—these escorted him beyond the town limits. But they, too, never reached the cemetery

125

itself. The day turned out to be beautiful and clear, and they turned off to the right, toward the river, to wash their hands there. Some of them felt like taking a stroll—it wasn't worth while going beyond the town for that, but since they were already there, why shouldn't they avail themselves of the opportunity? Some of them even got ready for a swim.

There were only a few teachers of Hebrew left to strew earth upon the grave and to prompt the words of the mourners' prayer to the orphan. But they, too, were in a hurry to get back to their classrooms: their pupils must by now have surely turned everything upside-down there.

It was Jonah Batz who planted the wooden marker with the inscription *"Here Rests"*—a temporary monument which most probably would never be replaced by another more permanent one, heaping as he did so all sorts of curses on the well-to-do people of the town—they had drained Avigdor of all his strength, had extracted the last drop out of him, and then thrown him aside, like a squeezed-out lemon.

The pallbearers locked up the cemetery.

It was miles back to town. The sun was already setting. They would be back in time for the evening prayers and, like as not, would manage to toss off a mug of vodka. It was too late for any more work that day, for that reason they walked slowly, without ceasing to upbraid the rich for their heartlessness.

It wasn't only the teachers of Hebrew who received such treatment. How did they act toward the poor in general, and the craftsmen in particular? The pallbearers had already forgotten about the dead man and they passed on to the tribulations of the living. Only the poor belonged to the Pallbearers' Guild; it was the rich, the members of the Burial Society, who lorded it over the pallbearers. The latter were working themselves to skin and bones, while the former took in the money. A poor man's voice carried no weight whatsoever. Who picked out the cantor? The rich! But, if you were to ask them, would they be able to tell a real trill from a rooster's crow? Did they know what was what when it came to real singing? And it was these gluttons who picked out the cantor! Who appointed the ritual slaughterers? Shmerl the elder—may his name be obliterated! There were three slaughterers in the town, and all three were relations of his. It was high time to protest against all this, but what could one do, when prices

126

were so high right now? Our Jonah Batz was about to buy things for the treat the Guild arranged every year—but the prices were such that you couldn't touch anything. And, during a time of high prices, the tradesmen had other things on his mind beside. From discussions of the anuual affair the talk shifted to the last election, and the one the year before—humbuggery and swindling were all prevalent, and so on and on.

The poor orphan plodded behind, forgotten by all, altogether bewildered. His eyes had a frightened look, his thin little face was streaked with tears that had rolled down his soiled cheeks. His lips were trembling—he had not quieted down yet. He did not even feel hungry, although he had eaten nothing since morning. However, children do not know how to be downcast for any length of time. His attention was attracted by the stones along the sides of the highway. Every few steps there was a stone, on top of a hummock overgrown with grass. From a distance the stone stared at him with its single huge eye; he drew nearer, and saw that it was a circle with a figure inscribed in its center. It was of no interest to him to know the purpose of this stone; he was intent only on leaping over it. He succeeded! He hurried on to the next stone, leaped over it still more nimbly, and hurried on, until he overtook all the men there.

"Take a look, do—take a look! That orphan!"

"He's barefooted, the poor little fellow," Jonah Batz remarked with a sigh.

"My little ones also go about barefoot," Heshel the hatter commented.

"But at least they're not orphans," said Jonah.

At this point Berel the confectioner emitted a whistle which was supposed to signify that parents were but of little help when they themselves didn't have a stitch to their backs.

The day was drawing to its close. A scudding cloud of swallows appeared in the sky. The air filled with their chirping and the swish of their little wings. There was incessant piping and din; they were in play. In one game several swallows would swoop, pursued by several others, all of them describing erratic zig-zags, as they swooped lower and lower. The little orphan halted, gaping in astonishment as he watched the tiny birds. A few moments later strange sounds of some sort issued from his throat—he had struck on the idea of imitating the swallows. He began to hop, as

127

if to rise toward them; he clapped his hands, gazing rapturously at the gay aerial assembly. Suddenly he picked up a pebble and flung it at the low-flying birds.

"He has just been praying for his departed father," Heshel the hatter commented angrily. "Is it worth while bringing them into the world and educating them?"

"What does a child understand?" Jonah Batz interceded.

"Even a newborn calf—even a calf starts lowing when they lead the cow away," said Heshel.

"But then, the cow is its mother, not the father," the confectioner put in. "And the boy is no calf."

"Come here, little scamp that you are!" Jonah Batz called the orphan over to him.

Although Jonah's voice was ever so gentle the boy began to tremble. The smile and delight fled from his face; dull fright emerged in their place. He approached unwillingly.

"Come, I'll take you home."

"But where does a dog have a home?" jested the confectioner.

Jonah Batz became thoughtful but did not let go of the orphan's little hand.

The members of the guild were quiet as they entered town. None of them noticed that the boy had injured his foot and was limping a little.

And he was so frightened that he did not sigh even once.

Jonah Batz and His Friends—They arrived in town. Just where it begins, at the parting of two narrow streets, one of which leads to the main synagogue and the other to the synagogue of the Pallbearers' Guild, Jonah halted his companions and asked them what was to be done with the little orphan.

"Marry him off," the confectioner jested after his wont.

"Bring him to the main synagogue," Heshel the hatter advised.

"And that's all?"

"Haven't you enough children of your own?" asked the confectioner. "Let the rich take care of him."

"Do you remember Crazy Hannah's son?" Jonah countered. "Where is he now?"

"In prison," the confectioner remarked apathetically.

"He's better off there than my children are in my own house," Heshel said with a sigh.

128

"Fellow Jews," Jonah spoke up soberly, "don't sin before God by uttering such words!"

"Well?"

"Listen to me," Jonah went on in a changed tone. "It was we the orphan followed. That wasn't just chance. It must have been decided Up There."

"You don't say!"

"No, don't talk like that! How is it he didn't follow any of the others but stayed with us?"

"We were the last to leave—"

"This is God's will! Heaven keeps an eye on orphans; we must not abandon him."

The others shrugged. Jonah was unusually serious and mild to-day, somehow. They looked at the child and were frightened: what they saw was a trembling, frightened little bird—it was enough to make your heart shrink!

"What do they call you, boy?" the confectioner asked gently.

"Dovidle," the child uttered, in a voice so low that one could hardly hear him.

"Well?" asked Jonah. The others remained silent. "Come, give us some advice," Jonah begged them.

By this time, however, his companions had shed their mood of pity and no longer wanted to look at the orphan.

"Take him home with you," said the two of them, without looking up.

"But what about my wife?"

To that they had nothing to say. They knew well enough that it was his wife who held the reins in his house, that on his way home Lanky Jonah would let his head sink, and that before he turned the doorknob he would try hard to find some matter or other that still had to be attended to. If nothing turned up, he would stoop over still more. When he was in his house, he walked bent over almost double. Jonah the chatterbox, Jonah the ring-leader, the life of every party, of each gathering, Jonah who was fond of a drop, or of making free with his fists—Jonah, who was the terror of the rabbi and the community—when Jonah was at home you wouldn't hear a peep out of him; the man was utterly unrecognizable.

"She'll poison the boy's life," he said. "She won't permit even her own children a sigh," he added sadly.

"Well, what in hell are *you* around for?"

"What can one do against a woman?"

Whereupon all of them fell silent. Really, what could one do against a woman? If he got fed up with some rich man who had grown too uppity, Jonah would not hesitate to beat him up; he would cut a rabbi short with words so harsh that the rabbi would hide himself and you wouldn't see him around for a long, long time. But a woman? Where can one find protection against a woman with her wails, her screams, and her pointed nails? There was no salvation.

"You know what, Heshel?" Jonah came to with a start, as if he had just awakened. "Take him along to your house."

"You're out of your mind! My business is doing so well now I haven't bread enough for my own children."

"You'll be paid."

"Who's going to pay me?"

"How much do you want a week?"

"A rouble, at least," answered Heshel. "But, when you come down to it, who's going to pay me?" he persisted.

Everybody knew that it wasn't Jonah who held the purse-strings, but his Sorele; that he never had enough for a noggin of vodka, even though he wasn't making out so badly—he was a good hand at tinkering a kettle or a pot, glory be!

"But suppose the community pays you?"

"Oh, sure, they've gotten bighearted all of a sudden!"

"They *must* pay!" Jonah stamped his foot.

"Jo-nah," drawled the confectioner, "restrain yourself! Don't go butting into community affairs! Is it so long ago that there was dissension in the comunity? Do you want to fan the flames?"

Heshel shared the other's opinion.

"Let me have the orphan," said he. "I'll bring him to the synagogue."

"I'll bring him there myself," Jonah announced harshly.

"Why are you pestering us, then?"

Berel and Heshel shrugged and walked off.

For several moments Jonah stood deep in thought, before calling after them:

"Remember, then, Heshel—a rouble a week."

"I'll remember, I'll remember," Heshel responded.

"Some sort of a devil has gotten into him today, the Lord forgive me!" said the confectioner.

"But really, it is a pity," answered the hatter.

"Of course it's a pity. But pity is a most expensive dish for a poor man."

They turned off and stopped at the first inn they came to.

Jonah was still standing in the middle of the street, holding the orphan by the hand. He had not yet arrived at any definite decision.

In the Synagogue—Before the Evening Prayer—"Why are you here?" they asked Jonah on seeing him in the synagogue.

Everything was quiet in the town, glory be to God. They had all calmed down, lit their pipes, and launched into the usual talk to pass the time. There was a great deal of good said about the late Avigdor—everything that could be said. They passed on to deals in grain, they touched on the military service, on politics. They did not yet know anything about emigration at that time.

They received the orphan with kindness. Who was there who did not notice him? Here and there someone would even pat his little head.

Suddenly they all became agitated and directed their eyes toward the center of the synagogue, where the ambo was situated. Jonah had sprung up there and put the boy up on the table. The child burst into tears: he wanted to get off the table, he wanted to sit down; it frightened him to look down at the crowd from a height. But Jonah would not let him go. He was holding the child fast by the collar and trying to calm him.

"Be still, little David—be still. It's you I'm trying to do something for!"

The boy kept on sniveling, but not so loudly by now.

"Standing in boots on the ambo!" one of the rich shouted from the eastern wall—where the best seats were. "Get away from there, you infidel!"

Jonah recognized the speaker and answered calmly but firmly:

"Don't get upset, Ruveleh—don't get upset, righteous one! The little orphan is standing barefooted—he hasn't had any boots for a long time now!" And, growing heated at his own words, he went on balefully: "He'll go on standing here until the rich concern themselves with his welfare."

The gathering, interested now, kept silent.

"It's hard for him to stand. He went barefooted to the cemetery, and injured his foot on the way. But stand here he must, members of the congregation! He must, because he is an orphan, and there is nobody to be concerned about his welfare."

"Take a good look at this benefactor!" someone in the back shouted.

"To prayer! To prayer!" someone else called out.

"Go to the altar, cantor!" the sexton commanded.

Jonah struck his fist on the table with such force that the sound reverberated through the synagogue. Those who were closest jumped aside in fright. Standing by the ambo was the *dayon*, Reb Kleinimus, a genius of learning. During the scene he had had time to finish reading his prayers and put his hands over his face, exhausted with concentration (and, perhaps, hunger). But at this point he took his hands away; a mute, profound sorrow glowed in his ancient, faded eyes.

"Jonah," he said timorously, "you cannot resort to force."

"I won't let you pray!" shouted Jonah, grabbing up a candlestick from the ambo.

The sexton sat down. The cantor stopped halfway to the altar.

"Rabbi," Jonah turned with rancor to the *dayon*, "do you think they want to pray? God forbid! They want to eat supper. Their wives are preparing supper. There's hot soup waiting for them, and crackling rolls, and a piece of fat meat with sharp horseradish. Carrots cooked in honey, too, maybe. But the orphan hasn't a crumb to eat."

"It's none of your business," someone shouted as he hid behind the backs of others. Reb Kleinimus again buried his face in his bony hands, while Jonah shouted in answer:

"It is so my business! You scampered off after the funeral like mice but left the little orphan to me. It is not your will that will be done, however, but God's! God knows what He is doing. He knows that a poor man has compassion, that he will not abandon a helpless orphan."

The boy begins to grasp that he is the one they were speaking of. He straightens up a little, places his small right hand on Jonah's shoulder and remains standing thus, holding his injured foot in his left hand. The only button on his torn little *kaftan* coat has come out of its buttonhole, the emaciated, soiled flesh peeps through his tattered shirt. A strange, pensive smile flits over his face. He is not afraid of the crowd. He feels that Jonah Batz is lording it over all of them, and that he is leaning on Jonah Batz.

"Look, you rich ones! Look, compassionate Jews!" Jonah says softly. "The little orphan is barefooted; he has injured his foot—"

"I'll find a pair of boots for him, old, but still all there."

The voice is familiar to Jonah:

"Fine," he says. "That is a gift from Reb Yosele—a good beginning! But the boy hasn't even a shirt to his back—"

Someone else announces that his wife will surely not be niggardly and will contribute several shirts.

"Fine," repeats Jonah. "I already know that your Hannele will not refuse. But what about some clothes?"

Somebody else promises that. Jonah accepts everything.

"But what about food?" he persists. "Who's going to feed him? Why is Reb Shmerl keeping silent? Why doesn't the head of the community speak up?"

Reb Shmerl, a corpulent Jew with a bloated face and beetle brows that completely hide his eyes, does not stir as he sits over the Mishna.

"This is no place to discuss worldly matters," he says quietly and staidly to those of the congregation who have gathered around him. These words instantly circulate throughout the synagogue: "Reb Shmerl says this is no place for such matters."

"A shrewd Jew," somebody remarks.

"A Bismarck!" declares another.

"A plain pickpocket," a third says under his breath.

"Jonah!" another voice rings out from near the eastern wall. "Listen to me, Jonah! Drop this! This is Thursday—it's already evening. Come, why must this be today, without fail? There is neither custom nor law about interfering with prayers on a Thursday. Go home now and come on Sabbath morning. At that time stop, if you like, the taking of the Torah out of the ark—"

"And on the Sabbath," Jonah cuts him short, "Reb Rachmiel will say his prayers at home, have a hearty meal, and lie down for a snooze. Am I right?"

Laughter springs up—he has a profound knowledge of the human heart, Jonah has.

"Well, just what do you want, Jonah?"

"I? I don't want anything for myself. All I want is to feed the

133

orphan. The orphan must be fed, members of the congregation—
the orphan must be fed!" he begins anew. Involuntarily he as-
sumes the tone of the Burial Society when, at the laying out of a
departed one, they proclaim: "Two zloty as a *mitzvah!* Two zloty
as a good deed!" The atmosphere in the synagogue becomes more
cheerful.

"I'm taking him home for supper!" a voice is heard.

"That, too, is fine," says Jonah. "That, too, is all to the good!
This great benevolence will be credited to Reb Jechiel both in
this world and the next. Do you hear, little orphan?" he turns to
the child. "A good beginning has already been made. You no
longer have to worry about tonight's supper. But what of tomorrow?" he turns to the man who has spoken. "What will happen
tomorrow?"

"Let him breakfast at my place as well," says the same voice.

"And what about dinner?"

"Infidel!" they shout at Jonah from all sides. "Why, tomorrow
is Friday!"

"And what's going to happen on the Sabbath?" Jonah keeps
right on.

"Let him come to me on the Sabbath as well."

"But what about Sunday, Monday, Tuesday—in short, all
through the week, and again on the Sabbath, and on the following
week—what will happen to him then?"

"Why are you picking on me. Am I the only one here?"

"God forbid—I am addressing all those here. If every man here
had such a Jewish heart as yours, the little orphan would long
since have gotten off the table!"

Silence ensues.

"To prayer!" the shouting and hubbub spring up again.

"Go fetch his wife, then he'll run away at once!" somebody suddenly volunteers the advice.

Jonah looks as if a ton of brick had fallen on him. Lanky, big
Jonah suddenly becomes ridiculous—he is utterly at a loss. The
jest has gone home to him, has scored as David's pebble scored
against Goliath.

"To prayer! To prayer!" the shouts grow louder.

Jonah is silent; he does not raise the hand still holding the
candlestick. Where has all his courage gone?

134

Unexpected Aid—Who knows what would have become of the orphan if aid had not come to him from an unexpected quarter.

A young man with a luxuriant growth of hair on his face, suddenly leaped up on the steps leading to the sacred ark. Perched on top of his head was a small skullcap, with the ritual locks fluttering out from under it; the ritual fringed vest could be seen under his unbuttoned long *kaftan;* eyes, burning and restless, sparkled under a broad brow.

The hubbub intensified.

"Look, Look! Hayim Shmuel is here!"

Instantly all eyes turn from the ambo toward the ark. Even Reb Shmerl, who up to now has been calmly poring over the Mishna, lifts up his head uneasily.

"Who? Who?" he asks in his mawkish, cloying voice, in which there was nevertheless a note of alarm.

"Hayim Shmuel! Hayim Shmuel!"

"Members of the congregation!" the young man calls out as he takes his stand by the ark. "Mark my words! In all of our sacred writings it is said that the Lord is the father of orphans. You must not turn away from an orphan lest, God forbid, you yourselves leave orphans in your turn!"

"Get away from the ambo, you impious one!"

"Don't shout! I want to impart a good word to you, a true word!"

Everybody likes to hear a good word.

"Be quieter, then! You Jews are 'the sons of benefactors.' The heart within each of you is a Jewish one. Why, then, do you keep silent? Your pockets are full of holes, you say?"

There is a burst of laughter.

"Don't laugh: I am not joking. You have no money. Poor community! *You* have no money; *Reb Shmerl* also has no money. What is left, then? I will give you the money!"

At these words Reb Shmerl begins to fidget uneasily in his place. Finally he shuts the Mishna, stands up, and also turns in the direction of the ark.

"Jonah," the young man calls out, "have you already decided with whom to place the orphan?"

"Well, yes," answers Jonah, who has managed to recover by now.

"What will it cost, then?"

135

"A rouble a week."

"Very well; listen to me—I am giving the money. I will pay a rouble a week."

"You? You?" resounds from all sides. Everybody knows the young man hasn't a copper to his name.

"It's not my money I'm going to give. Listen to me! The money will not be mine but that of my father-in-law, Isaacle."

A hubbub springs up. Now all have grasped what is happening. Isaacle had a permit for ritual slaughtering.

Reb Shmerl turns pale. His eyes are darting sparks and little by little he is making his way to the ark, but before he can elbow his way through, the young man manages to say:

"My father-in-law will give a written commitment that he will pay a rouble a week for the orphan's support right up to his confirmation—even up to his wedding—" And, catching sight of Reb Shmerl already on the first step, he hurriedly calls out: "The tax will be only on poultry—on poultry only! Everybody call out *Aye!*"

This ruse proves to the liking of the assembly; the shouted consent is practically unanimous.

By this time Reb Shmerl is already standing by the young man's side, clutching him by the lapel, and meaning to drag him down, but the shouted ayes stun him.

"Isaacle the slaughterer!" Hayim Shmuel called out for the last time and sprang off the steps on the right, having no wish to collide with Reb Shmerl.

Reb Shmerl recovers little by little and begins talking, addressing the *dayon:*

"Reb Kleinimus, Reb Kleinimus—how could you ever permit this—?"

But Hayim Shmuel has already put on his praying-shawl, taken his place at the ambo, and now raises his voice:

" '*Vehu rachum*—Yea, He is merciful. . . .' "

The worshipers, swaying, begin reciting the words of the prayer, and the voice of Reb Shmerl is drowned out in the general volume of voices.

Reb Kleinimus stands, as before, with his face buried in his hands.

Two Deathbeds

I

ONE DAY an attendant in paradise—an angel whose brightness reflected the radiant grace of the Holy Name—came out of his dwelling toward evening, greatly perturbed. He opened a little portal in heaven, thrust out his radiant head, and, addressing the setting sun, asked in a sad and tremulous voice:

"Do you know, by any chance, what happened at the house of Laibel from Konskivol?"

The sun made no reply. Apparently, it did not know.

The angel withdrew his radiant head, more worried than ever. Nor was his concern unfounded, since, for many, many years, twice daily, the seven heavens had resounded with the solemn chant of Laibel from Konskivol: *Shema Yisroel*—Hearken O Israel, our Lord God, the Lord is One! And his "One!" was vibrant; it hummed and beat the air like moths fluttering toward a flame, searing themselves against it with delight in the "torments of love."

This affirmation concerning the singleness of the Lord had last been heard at morning prayer.

The prayer of all creatures, the anthem of all worlds, had been silenced; an instrument in the orchestra had suddenly fallen silent, a string had snapped on the first violin and it had become mute. Had Laibel from Konskivol forgotten his evening prayer?

The sun kept sinking. Lurking shadows received permission to emerge from their secret dwelling places, and they crept out of the fissures in the crags at the shore, out of pits and caverns and deserts where no man dwells, from under trees, from between the boughs and leaves of the forests. They spread, these shadows, over the populated places and entwined themselves around all things.

137

And now the sun was down. Gently, silently, the moon and stars sprang aglow and started upon their night-long vigil over the universe, weaving a silvery net about the weary earth.

When the sun vanished, so did a beast that bore the inscription "Truth" upon its brow, and when the moon rose, a beast appeared bearing upon its brow a small crown of silver with the inscription of "Faith."

Soon the portals of heaven opened softly to admit thousands of souls, the souls of people who had fallen asleep and now presented themselves so that the incidents of their last day on earth might be entered in the sacred ledgers. And there was much scraping of quills, and swishing of multicolored wings: some (these were rare) snow white, but most were drab and torn to shreds, while a few were stained with blood. The seven heavens were filled with rumblings, prayers of repentance, longing, love, hope and fear. Then, suddenly, all was silent.

Slowly, a silvery cloud unrolled itself about the Holy Throne, becoming darker and darker as it unfurled. And from behind this cloud came a melancholy sound, like the cooing of a dove:

"Woe unto me, that have ruined my house—"

"Woe unto me, that have consumed my mansion with fire—"

"Woe unto me, that have driven out my son, my only son—"

A shudder of pity was felt in the seven heavens. Then, once more, silence reigned. All those present held their breath, awaiting a miracle. . . . But nothing happened.

A voice came floating from below—the first crow of the cock. The cloud retreated from the Holy Throne. The spell was broken, dissipated. The gates of heaven opened, and the souls reluctantly took flight for their return journey. Angels armed with gem-studded fans drove out the laggard souls, those that were seized with trembling or tears or fear. A moment later, tapping could be heard from below. People were being awakened for the morning prayer. The inscription of Faith upon the small silver crown of the night-beast became paler and a reddish border arose in the east.

The heavenly attendant awoke (apparently he had slept soundly), walked over to the small window, opened it again, thrust out his head and called out:

"You moon, and you stars, tell me before you vanish—does anyone among you know what happened to Laibel from Konskivol?"

A mite of a star, quite a way off, burst into a golden glow, floated up to the little window, and replied:

"I know, bright angel! I was floating past Konskivol and happened to look in through the window of Laibel's house. He's dying, this Laibel from Konskivol. He's along in years. His white beard shone over the covers as if it were silver, and his face is wrinkled and yellow. He was in agony, and I saw them putting a feather to his nostrils—but I did not see it move."

And the attendant of heaven, without asking for permission from any superior but acting strictly on his own, flew like an arrow toward earth to fetch the soul of Laibel from Konskivol.

"There'll be joy in heaven—" that was what he believed.

Angels are fleet of wing—in this respect black angels are not inferior to white. And, as the bright angel landed at the head of the dying man's bed, he found a black angel already there. Had the black angel started his flight earlier, or was the distance he had to cover shorter? Who knows?

"What are you doing here?" demanded the bright angel, frightened and astonished. "Why, this is Laibel from Konskivol!"

"What of it?" snickered the black angel, and two rows of white teeth flashed between his twisted lips.

"This is my soul! I am the angel of heaven!"

"Pleased to meet you!" the black angel retorted. "I am only a servant of hell. However, we shall see." And, scraping his foot under the sickbed, he drew out a sack, tied at the top. "What do you think is in this bag?"

"A prayer shawl and phylacteries," the angel of heaven ventured to guess.

"Hidden under the bed? It is usually the sins that are hidden away."

The angel of evil, stooping over the sack, untied it and gave it a kick. A thousand gold pieces poured out and rolled about the room.

"Stolen money!" cried out the black angel. "Money from simple souls, money from poor-boxes. These coins have been washed with tears; blood clings to them. Look how upset he is as soon as his gold is touched!"

The dying man was tossing in the bed, though his eyes were closed.

The white angel trembled in horror, covering his face with his wings. A ray of sunlight burst in through a chink in the shutters and fell upon the eyelids of the dying man: his lids quivered. For the last time, he opened his eyes.

"Who's there?" he asked, his yellowed lips covered with foam, rustling like rotten leaves.

"I!" answered the angel of evil. "I, who have come to fetch your soul. It is time to go!"

"Where?"

"To hell!"

The eyes of the dying man closed in fear.

"Pray to God—pray!" the angel of God appealed to him. "Repent! There is still time. Renounce your gold—"

"*Shema Yisroel*—" the dying man began.

"He won't renounce it!" said the angel of evil, covering the face on the pillow with a heavy black wing. The man and the voice expired under that wing.

The white angel, disillusioned and humiliated, started back to heaven.

II

One dark night, a harsh voice resounded through hell, rising above its din:

"Nachmankeh from Zborozh is nearing his end! When he clipped his nails he failed to follow the sequence prescribed by ritual and paid no heed as to where he threw the parings. Many's the time he forgot to say his evening prayers! Who's going to fetch his soul?"

"I am!" answered one of the servants of hell. "In the meantime start a cauldron of pitch boiling!" and with that he leaped upward and flew toward earth.

The flight of evil angels is rapid, but fortunately the good angels fly also, and, while they are further from us, their compassion helps them along. As the evil black angel arrived at the deathbed, he found the good angel already there. He was at the head of the bed, consoling the man:

"Don't be frightened by death, poor man. It's only a bridge, a narrow boundary between darkness and light . . . a stage in the journey from cares and worry to repose and happiness—"

But the man in the bed apparently did not hear him; he was preoccupied with something else and his burning eyes were riveted on the walls.

The black angel halted near the door in wonder:

"You haven't made a mistake, have you, colleague?" he asked the bright angel.

"No! There is no mistake. I was sent to fetch this soul—this pure, merciful soul. You have no power over it."

"He did not observe the ritual in cutting his nails—"

"I know!" the angel of good interrupted. "But on the other hand he did not live a moment for his own sake—only for the weak and ailing, for widows and orphans, for those living in darkness, for those exhausted by suffering, for those who were weary—"

"Our ledger shows how many times he failed to recite his evening prayers!"

"But he never failed when there was a chance of helping anybody. He never forgot to console people, to encourage and strengthen them when their spirits were low, when gall was about to flood the purest soul, when the last hope was disappearing. He built no house for himself; he did not repair the roof over his head, he never made a soft bed for himself, never sought the love of a woman, he placed no hope in having pleasure from offspring. Everything was for others—he considered all others to be better than himself."

Black clouds trailed one another across the sky. Lightning cut through them, and the clouds turned still darker, pressing closely on one another's heels. The lightning awakened the dying man for the last time.

"Who's there? Who is at the head of my bed?" he asked through fever-parched lips.

"It is I, an angel of light, one of the bright servants of His Holy Name. And in His Holy Name I have been sent to fetch your soul. Come with me!"

"Where to?" gasped the dying man.

"Up there, to heaven—to paradise!"

"Heaven . . . paradise . . ." echoed the dying man. "And what is life like up there in heaven?"

"Beautiful! All souls are lighted by the Grace of God, they bask in the glory of the Holy Throne, they wear crowns of gold—"

"Glory . . . gold . . . crowns—" murmured the dying man. "What would there be for me to do up there?"

"There's not a thing for you to do. There you will find eternal repose, eternal rejoicing, radiant happiness without end. Come with me!"

"But how would I keep busy there?" asked the dying man, making a last effort and turning to face the angel. "Is there anybody to help, is there any need of supporting those who are falling, of healing the sick, feeding the hungry, moistening the lips of those who thirst, finding the lost? That is where my happiness lies!"

"No, there's nothing of that sort!" answered the angel in a voice that was not at all assured. "Nobody up there will be in need of your help—"

"What is there for me to do then, angel? There where nobody has any need of either my soul or my heart, or of the pity of a tear, a consoling word, or my hand to help him out of a pit?"

The evil angel listened: his tongue lolled, and he was licking his lips, a mocking smile stretching from ear to ear and his dazzling white teeth flashing like lightning in the dark room.

The brilliant angel was at a loss, not knowing what answer to give the dying man.

"What is one to do then, angel—what is one to do?"

The good angel turned to the window and, looking up to heaven, awaited advice and instruction. But heaven was sealed up: not a word emerged nor a ray of light, nor as much as a spark. New clouds crawled across the sky, heavier than before. A shadow fell across the face of the radiant angel; heaven seemed wrathful and cruel, devoid of all pity. Never yet had the good angel seen in heaven such a mood. And he kept silent.

Whereupon the evil angel took advantage of the moment and drew near the bed of the dying man:

"Better come with me!" he whispered in his ear.

"Where to?"

"Where your soul is needed. To those who are unhappy, to those who hunger and thirst. You are needed there by those who are worn out and weary, by those who are lost, cursed, forgotten by God. You won't be able to help them, but as for suffering with them and commiseration—"

"I'm going, I'm going!" the dying man called out with an effort.

The good angel withdrew, empty-handed.

Miracles on the Sea

IN A RAMSHACKLE HUT on the seashore, somewhere in Holland, there lived a quiet soul, a Jewish fisherman called Sotye (probably after a great-grandfather by the name of Saadia). But he was hardly aware of this or, for that matter, of his Jewishness in general. Born of generations of fisherfolk, isolated with his family in a Gentile settlement, how was he to know anything about his faith and his people? Sotye's calling was that of a fisherman; his wife wove the nets and attended to household chores. Their children rolled about in the sand and hunted for ambergris. And whenever Sotye ran into a storm and his life was in danger, neither he nor his family knew how to supplicate the Lord in the simplest prayer, the *Shema Yisroel!* At those times, Sotye would stare at the overcast skies, his wife would clutch her head or glower at the wrathful clouds, and his children, throwing themselves flat on the sand, would scream: "Sancta Maria! Sancta Maria!" just as all the other youngsters did.

How were they to know any better? It was too far to walk to the Jewish community and, since he barely eked out a living, Sotye and his family could not afford to ride there. Furthermore, he could not escape easily from the clutches of the sea. Sotye's father, grandfather, and great-grandfather had perished at sea, yet the watery expanse seemed to cast such a spell over him that even though it was at times his deadliest enemy, he cherished it and was irresistibly drawn to it. And since there was no escaping it, he became reconciled to wresting a living from it and finding a violent death in its bosom.

There was, however, one Jewish custom—and the only one—to which the family clung: that of Yum Kippur, the Day of Atonement.

At dawn on the day preceding Yum Kippur, Sotye would choose the biggest fish in his catch, proceed to town, to present it to the

143

shohet (ritual slaughterer), and, at the end of the solemn fast, partake of it with his family. They spent the solemn day in the Dutch House of Worship, listening to the singing of the choir, the liturgical organ music, and the chanting of the cantor, even though they could not understand a word of the services. They merely stared at the holy ark and at the rabbi in his skull-cap. Whenever that skull-cap arose, they got to their feet, and when the skull-cap sank they settled back in their seats. And if the weary Sotye happened to doze off, the man next to him would nudge him awake.

That was Sotye's entire conception of Yum Kippur; he was unaware that on this Judgment Day the very fish tremble in the waters and that there is a great commotion in heaven. He did observe faithfully the custom of listening to the liturgical chants, without partaking of any food on this solemn day, and when the congregation had recited the *Ne'ilah* (he was mystified even by this term which signified the concluding service on the Day of Atonement), his family would take their meal at the ritual slaughterer's. However, in all likelihood, the *shohet*—at least in Holland —probably knew little more himself! After sipping some black coffee, Sotye and his family would exchange lengthy good-bys with their hosts and then start on their all night trek back to the sea. That's just the way they always put it: back to the *sea,* and not back *home.*

They were always adamant about leaving.

"Why, you've hardly seen the town!" their hosts would plead.

To which Sotye would merely retort with a wry face: "The town, indeed!"

Sotye was not much given to talk. The sea imbues one with silence. Besides, he had no great love for the town, its confinement, its patches of polluted sky that could be seen between one roof and another. But the sea was boundless, the out-of-doors infinite!

"But that sea is your enemy, your death," Sotye's friend would remind him.

"But a good death," the fisherman would counter. He wanted to meet his Maker as his father and grandfather had done, to be suddenly swallowed up by the sea, and thus be spared prolonged agony on his deathbed and burial in the hard ground. The very thought of such an end sent chills down his spine.

The wayfarers would trudge through the night, toward their

home, the sea. And when at dawn they made out the reflection of the sandy shore and the glittering mirror of the sea, they were elated and clapped their hands for joy.

A bridegroom and his bride could hardly have been any happier. Like the sea, life rolled on, year after year. One fisherman replaced another, and ritual slaughterer succeeded ritual slaughterer, though not as often, but the tradition persisted inviolate. And to Sotye, the custom still consisted of fasting, of choir and organ music, of the big fish eaten at the house of the slaughterer after the concluding prayer, and the mutual good-bys. This ritual was the only link between Sotye and his fellow-Jews.

One morning, the eastern horizon began to glow as the sea stirred languidly from its slumber. The breaking of the surf was so muffled that it was barely audible. Here and there, a pair of white wings fluttered, a cock would crow, and then solemn silence would reign once more. An iridescence shimmered over the rippling water; splotches of radiance glided upon the yellow sand. The fishermen's cabins dotting the coastline were quiet. One door creaked open, however—and Sotye stepped out.

It was the day preceding Yum Kippur. Sotye's face was somber, and there was a glow in his eyes. He was about to embark on a deed pleasing to God: that of catching a fish for the Day of Atonement.

He made his way to the boat and, as he loosened it from its moorings, the chain rattled.

"Don't go! Don't go!" his neighbors warned him as they peered through the tiny windows.

The great watery expanse lay calm and quiescent, blending with the horizon of the cheerful morning sky. The sea was hardly breathing and its ripples smiled like the wrinkled face of a jolly old man. It seemed to murmur, as if it were regaling the scattered water reeds and moss-covered rocks with a story, while caressing them gently.

The fishermen, however, knew the sea only too well, and warned Sotye:

"Don't go! Don't go!"

For the peaceful sea would go on a rampage and its radiant mirror would splinter; its geniality and muffled surge would become howling gusts and thundering crashes; its ripples would become

145

tidal waves capable of engulfing ships, as the Leviathan devours little fish.

"Don't go! Don't go!"

A barefooted old man, his gray hair wind-blown, his face wrinkled like the sea but without the sea's guileful smile, stepped out of his hut and, putting his hand on Sotye's shoulder, pointed to a dark spot in the sky, so small as to be perceptible only to a fisherman.

"That's a storm cloud gathering there!"

"I'll get back long before it gathers," Sotye replied. "It's just a single fish I'm after."

"You've got a wife and children, Sotye," the old man persisted with evident concern.

"And a God in Heaven," Sotye commented with assurance. He was about to carry out *His* behest, and the next moment he was off in his boat.

The tiny craft glided merrily, swaying on the waves, and the sea sang a tender song to it, showering it with its most precious pearls. But the old fisherman still stood, rooted to shore, murmuring, "Sancta Maria! Sancta Maria!"

The boat kept on its course and its net grew ever heavier: Sotye had to exert all his strength to pull it up. It yielded every kind of seaweed, but not a single fish.

By now, the old man could no longer see the boat. Sotye cast his net a third and a fourth time, but his hauls still consisted of nothing but seaweed.

The swell of the sea was increasing. The sun appeared at last, but it was misted over—a weeping sun. What had been a mere dark speck in the sky was now like a brown snake lurking behind the sun.

Half the day was gone, with Sotye still trying his luck.

"The Lord," he said to himself, "apparently does not want me to carry out the divine commandment this year. I must turn back." He grew despondent at the thought that the Lord did not wish to receive an offering from him on this occasion. But just as he took firm hold of the rudder in an effort to steer the boat toward the shore, he felt a splash on his face, and—wonder of wonders!—he beheld a huge golden fish darting among the waves and lashing them with its tail.

146

This fish must be caught, come what may! The Lord must have rewarded him with this fish—the Lord, who had witnessed his grief, his fervent wish to make an offering to Him. And he started in pursuit of the fish.

The sea was becoming angry; its waves swirling and surging around the boat. The sun was already half-eclipsed by a dark cloud, although a few rays still struggled through. The fish was riding the crest and Sotye's boat pursued it. Suddenly, a tidal wall of sea came between Sotye and his quarry, and he lost sight of the fish.

"It's leading me a wild chase, mocking me," Sotye thought, about to give up the chase and head for the shore. But the giant wave sank as suddenly as it had risen, and the fish swam by, close to the boat. Its huge eyes seemed to say: "Please take me in your net . . . let me help you fulfill the divine commandment."

Hardly had Sotye veered the boat around, however, when the fish submerged again! A second tidal wave sprang up in front of the fisherman, and the sea was once more in turmoil. It was not a gentle song that the sea sang now, and to ride its crests was perilous. Even the sun hid behind a cloud, as if awed by the watery monster. The wind had evidently been waiting for the sun's retreat, for immediately it lashed out in all its fury. It buffeted and thrashed the waves like a scourge, and the sea was its accompaniment, a cacophonous orchestra of a thousand bass viols and kettledrums, growling and thundering with rage.

"Go back—go home!" Sotye's heart warned him. And, gathering the nets into the boat, he mustered all his strength to steer the craft homeward. The veins on his hands swelled until they were near bursting; the waves played with his boat, hurling it up and down like a hollow nutshell. The sky was shrouded in darkness, the riotous sea had turned to brown, but Sotye still strained to make shore.

Suddenly, he caught sight of someone drowning. The waves were tossing a woman toward him, a woman with hair black as his wife's. Her white hands reminded him of his wife's hands, and when her cries for help reached his ears, her voice was the voice of his wife. She must have followed him in another boat, and now she was drowning and screaming to him for help.

He altered course, attempting to reach her, but the angry sea would not allow it. But through the raving gale, he still heard her crying: "Help! Help me, Sotye!"

He redoubled his efforts to get to her: he could no longer see her hair—only her white dress, as it bobbed in the water, barely an oar's length away . . . But a heavy swell hurled the boat in one direction and the floating body in another.

"It's a mirage!" he thought, and then he recalled the vision of the golden-hued fish. Scanning the shore, he noticed lights in the fishermen's cabins.

"Yum Kippur!" It dawned on him suddenly, and the oars fell limply from his hands.

"Good Lord," he cried out, "I am at Thy mercy—I will not row on Yum Kippur!"

The gale continued unabated, playing havoc with the boat. But, having relinquished the oars, Sotye sat stolidly, staring calmly at the overcast heaven and at the seething, foaming sea.

"Thy will be done, Lord! May Thy judgment prevail!"

Suddenly a liturgical melody flashed through his mind, and he began to hum it. He had resorted to the only medium at his command of communicating with God: this liturgical melody. The sky turned darker and more dismal, the waves rose higher, and the gale grew more threatening. The boat was tossing up and down like a bit of driftwood, about to be devoured by a gaping sea. The tempest raged on, yet Sotye still intoned the melody of *mi yonuach umi yonua* ("Who shall be at ease and who shall wander about") as he had heard it sung by the choir and played by the organ.

Waves buffeted the boat mercilessly and Sotye was still chanting —at this point the boat capsized. However, he was not yet destined to yield up his ghost.

Two white figures from out of the mist came walking barefoot over the surface of the waters, linked arm-in-arm, with hair fluttering and their eyes aglow. And, as Sotye struggled with his boat, they drew near and helped him get to his feet, after which they thrust their arms through his and led him across the waves. He stared at them, eager to speak, to question them, but they silenced him:

"Sing, Sotye! Your chant will triumph over the wrath of the sea."

And as he advanced between the two figures, Sotye heard his

boat trailing behind him. He turned around—and there was his boat, with the golden-hued fish enmeshed in his net!

When he reached shore, he was released by his ghostly companions, and he went to his cabin. There he found the ritual slaughterer and the slaughterer's wife.

The town had been swept by flames, and they had come to spend Yum Kippur with the fisherman.

The fish was prepared for the repast at sundown—and the custom was followed as always.

A Conversation on a Hilltop

Two Jewish women were walking along, outside the town limits. One had malicious eyes: she was tall, full-bosomed, heavy of step; the other was thin and pale, her head cast down.

"Where are you taking me, Hannah?" asked the thin woman.

"Be patient, Grunnah. It is only a few more steps—you can see the spot over there, on that little hill."

"Why are you doing this?" Grunnah persisted in a trembling voice, as if frightened of something.

"You'll find out. Come on."

They reached the knoll.

"Sit down," said Hannah. Grunnah sat down submissively, with Hannah close beside her.

And in the stillness of the summer day, far from the hustle and bustle of the town, their conversation began.

"Grunnah, you know who your husband was—he should rest in peace—?"

A shadow fell over Grunnah's pale face.

"I know," she answered, biting her lips.

"He was a scribe, Grunnah: a pious scribe of holy scrolls and phylacteries."

"I know," said Grunnah impatiently.

"Before writing down a single letter, he would perform an ablution—"

"Nonsense! It's true, he did go to the ritual baths a couple of times a week—"

"He was a real Jew."

"That's true."

"May he intercede for us!"

Grunnah made no answer.

"You have nothing to say?" Hannah asked.

"What does it matter!"

"But, it does matter! Let him intercede for us, do you hear me?"

"I hear you!"

"What have you to say to that?"

"What am I to say? All I know is that he did not intercede for us—"

There was a pause. The two women understood one another: the pious scribe died, leaving his widow with three little orphan girls. Grunnah did not remarry because she did not want her children to have a stepfather. She supported herself and them through her own labors, yet had no luck in anything. *He* had not interceded for them!

"And do you know why?" Hannah broke the silence.

"No—"

"Because you are sinful—"

"I?" Grunnah jumped up. "I am sinful?"

"Listen, Grunnah, every human being is sinful and you are all the more so—"

"I all the more so?"

"Grunnah, it wasn't just by chance that I brought you here, to the river, out into the open—although it isn't the fresh air we need, glory be to God. You see, Grunnah, a mother—and especially if she is the widow of a pious scribe—must be—"

"Must be what?"

"Must be more God-fearing than others. She must look after her daughters better than other mothers, and more closely—"

The pale Grunnah turned white! Her eyes blazed up, her nostrils flared, her parched lips began to quiver.

"Hannah!" she cried out.

"You must know, Grunnah, that I am your friend, but I must tell you the truth or else I'll have to answer to God. I'm not going to gossip; it won't be because of me that your name will be on every tongue. What we say here will remain between us—only God in heaven will hear."

"Stop tugging at my soul!"

"Listen, then! To make a long story short—last night, I was on my way home and I saw your Myrel on the knoll—"

"Alone?"

"No!"

"Whom with?"

"How do I know? He wore a hat of some kind—it may have been

an opera hat! He was kissing her on her throat and neck. She was smiling and eating candy—"

"I know all about it!" Grunnah answered dismally. "That's not the first time—"

"You know it? What is he, engaged to her?"

"No."

"No? And you say nothing?"

"Yes."

"Grunnah!"

By now Grunnah was calm:

"Now, you keep still and listen to me," she said, seizing Hannah by the sleeve and forcing her to sit down again. "Listen," she went on, "I'll tell you everything, and only God in heaven will hear us. When my husband died—" Grunnah began.

"Is that the way to say it, Grunnah?"

"Well, how shall I say it?"

"Without 'he should rest in peace'? And you should say de-parted—"

"It's all the same—they buried him, didn't they?"

"He returned to his ancestors—"

"So be it. All I know is that he left me with three little girls."

"Poor man, he left no one to say the memorial prayer for him."

"Three daughters, of whom the oldest—"

"Genandel—"

"—was fifteen."

"In the hands of another mother, she would be already a bride."

"We had no bread! We had other things on our minds besides matchmakers!"

"The way you're saying things today, Grunnah!"

"It isn't me saying them but the ache in my heart. Genandel, as you know, was the most beautiful girl in the town."

"And is, even now—may she be spared the evil eye!"

"Now she is a dried-out lemon; she's gray already! But at that time, she glowed like the sun. And I was the widow of a pious scribe: I guarded her carefully, from stray playboys, musicians, tailors, and old bachelors. That's what a mother is for, isn't it? A girl of marriageable age must be as spotless as a mirror. And I got my way: there wasn't a speck on her. I protected her, I watched her, I never took my eyes off her. I wouldn't let her out of the house alone for even a second, and I was forever lecturing her, drilling morality into her: don't look there, don't peek here, don't stand on that spot, don't go to that place—don't even watch the little birds flying by—"

"Then you did right—"

"Remarkably well!" Grunnah said with bitterness. "Come to my house and see what she looks like! Yes, she is truly an honest girl—but a girl of thirty-six! She's so thin you can count her bones; her skin is as wrinkled as the parchment that's used for phylacteries; the fire has died out of her eyes; her face is sour, with never a smile; her lips are always drawn tight. A flame does spring up in her eyes often enough—but it is hatred that burns there, and rancor, as if she were in hell. And do you know against whom that rancor is directed? Do you know whom she hates—whom she curses in a whisper?"

"Whom?"

"Me! Me—her own mother!"

"Whatever are you saying? What does she curse you for?"

"Perhaps even she doesn't know why, but I know. I stood between her and the world—between her and the sun. I would not allow any warmth or light to reach her body. I have spent whole nights going over and over it all, until finally I understood. She is forced to hate me—every bone in her body hates me!"

"What are you talking about?"

"Just what you hear. She also hates her sisters. They are younger and better looking than she!"

Grunnah found it hard to catch her breath; Hannah was having difficulty recovering from the shock. She had heard something horrible, something worse than disease or death—worse, even than *death under the wedding canopy:* which is the greatest calamity that can befall a Jew. And still . . . Lord of the Universe, it must be so!

"The youngest, Leah, I no longer kept at home. I let her go to work as a servant," Grunnah went on, her voice hoarser and more broken.

"I was quite indignant at that," Hannah recalled. "The daughter of a scribe working as a servant!"

"I wanted her, at least, to get married; I wanted her, at least, to have some kind of dowry, however small—I couldn't provide a dowry for her by trading in onions. And I looked after her, too. More than one employer watched her with desire in his eyes; more

than one employer's son wanted to make her a plaything of his—
but then I am a mother! And a devoted mother! My legs would
not carry me, yet I would run ten times a day to see her in her
kitchen. I wept, I fainted, I preached morality to her, I gave her
pious lectures. I passed whole nights without sleep, reading the
Kav Hayoshor and other books of devotion, and in the morning
I would dash over to see her, to tell her in my own words what
I had read—and sometimes a thing or two of my own! And she
was a meek, honest daughter; she let herself be guided. Except
for her eyes, she is the very image of her father; pale, without a
drop of blood, and what kind, sympathetic eyes—but then she
used to be better looking—"

"You speak of her as though she were dead, God forbid!"

"Well, do you think she is alive? I tell you she isn't! She provided her own dowry—but it was I who got her a husband! She
cried, poor little thing; she didn't want to marry him—he was
too coarse, too common for her. But then, a man of learning
wouldn't marry a servant girl—especially one with all of thirty
roubles as a dowry! I thanked God for him; even though he was
a tailor. He lived with her for a year, deprived her of her money,
her health, her last bit of strength, and then ran away from her.
He left her without a rag or a pair of shoes—but with consumption. She coughs up blood! She's a shadow now, not a human
being. She nestles up to me like a little baby; she lies down close
to me like a ewe lamb . . . and all through the night—night after
night—she weeps. And do you know against whom her tears are
directed?"

"Against her husband—may the very memory of him be erased!"

"No, Hannah. It's against me her tears are directed—against me!
Her tears fall on my heart like molten lead; they are like poison
to me, these tears. . . ."

She again fell silent, hardly able to catch her breath.

"And so?"

"And so? Why, I've already told you. Let my third daughter
live at least—let her live as she wants to. She works in a factory
for twelve hours a day; she earns barely enough for a dry crust of
bread. If she wants hard candy, let her eat it! If she wants to laugh,
to fool around, to kiss—let her! Do you hear, Hannah—let her! I
can't provide her with sweets—and I surely can't provide a husband
for her. To make a dried-out lemon out of her—I'd rather not;

154

to give her consumption—never, never! Let my daughter not hate me—let her not direct her tears against me!"

"But, Grunnah," Hannah cried out in fright. "What will people say?"

"Let people have compassion for poor orphans first of all; let people not mistreat them, as if they were beasts of burden, with absolute impunity. Let people have human hearts, and let them not squeeze all the juice out of them, as if they were no more than lemons—"

"But what of God—may His name be blessed?"

At this point, Grunnah stood up and cried out as though she wanted God in heaven to hear her:

"God must first of all take care of those who are among the oldest daughters—"

A heavy silence ensued. The two, breathing hard, stood facing each other, their eyes afire.

"Grunnah!" Hannah cried out at least. "God—God will mete out punishment!"

"Not to me, not to my daughters! God is just: He will punish someone else. . . . Someone else!"

Ne'ilah

A LAME *mouzhik* entered the synagogue and lit the fresh candles in the candelabra and in the lusters on the reading stands.

The worshipers within the hall, all of them garbed in white, resumed their sighing; those who had been having a respite outside re-entered the synagogue; all were now rising up from their pews.

"*Yisgadel, v'iskadash—*" the cantor's hoarse and high-pitched voice droned the behest to magnify and sanctify the Lord's name. The male worshipers drew the prayer shawls over their heads; those in the women's section burst into sudden wailing. This resulted in much tapping of the pew ledges to make the women quiet down. They would not desist, however, and there was comic indignation upon the tear-stained and wan faces of the men.

"*Shmai rabbo!*" the Name of the Lord escaped the cantor in a gasp. The wailing abated a little. The men swayed and their woeful voices chimed in with the singing of the choir.

It is the *Ne'ilah*—the concluding prayer at evening services on the Day of Atonement.

The heavens were going to open, and then the Gates of Mercy would close and lock again. Hence the rush on the part of the worshipers. Each felt that if he did not do so immediately, he would never have such an opportunity of turning to Heaven. True, the seventh day of the Feast of Tabernacles still lay ahead, but trouble was surely in store for those whose sentence was put off to the last minute. It was best to act now—right now!

The women's section influenced the men's. The concluding prayers were drowned in ardent, scalding tears. The winds had begun to blow, the rivers were stirred up, primordial forests were noisy; all these noises blended into the mourning and agitation in the synagogue.

156

"Now therefore, O Lord our God, impose awe upon all Thy works and Thy dread over all that Thou hast created . . ." wept the worshipers, failing to keep in unison or to convey the true significance of the words. And truly, was it of much concern to the proprietor of the Tsehanovka baths before whom Pahrol the bath attendant stood in awe? Or, for that matter, what concern was it of Shloimeh Zetz, the well-to-do householder who kept running his hand through his white beard even during so solemn a prayer as the Eighteen Benedictions?

"After all, are there so many of these people of other blood in Tsehanovka? Perhaps it is even better that the judge and the town clerk aren't Jews. God save us from having a Jew for an administrator—he'd flay seven skins off each one of us. There are, true enough, many Christians in the settlement, living in their small neat houses with curtains and flower pots on their windows —but then, they are merely *mouzhiks*. Let them stay in their ignorance! But, Sovereign of Heaven—put the dread of Thee in my daughter-in-law, so that she may not demand a divorce from my son, who is an epileptic. It's no great matter—she'll get used to it! Dread and fear." Shloimeh put a great deal of feeling into the last three words; then it occurred to him that it was unfortunate that there had been such a sudden drop in the price of wheat. "Great God," he reflected, "may they all band together and set a single price. . . ."

" 'Thou hast chosen us!' " Bendet the tailor lifted up his voice and repeated: "Thou hast chosen us!" It was now the second year that his wife was ailing and coughing up blood, yet they had only one room, and not a customer wanted to cross their threshold. "Our ever-loving Father—Thou hast chosen us! Why, Thou didst join us in marriage! And Thou didst come to love us. Tell me, did I treat her badly? 'And Thou didst wish—' Was it this I wished, was it this I hoped for? And Thou didst draw us near Thee, Our King, to serve Thee. What's the good of all my work?" When he came to the words: "There is no remission to the victims of our debts—" at which point his sobs drowned out his voice: his debts were past all counting.

The congregation had at last finished praying. It was now time for the cantor to read. They were waiting only for Hayim Behr to finish. The sexton was eager enough to thump on a lectern but Hayim Behr's kinsman, Yonah Wolf, who leased an orchard and was the most influential man in the synagogue, would not allow this signal to the cantor. Let Hayim Behr bewail his woes to the end. Hayim Behr was the father of eight children, yet couldn't earn enough for a crust of bread.

"And Thou hast no wish for their death," Hayim Behr still gulped his tears, "the death from starvation of my poor little ones, of my Rachel. And why should you die, children of Israel? Why, for what reason? Wherein have they sinned? Death from torments, from evil afflictions. They are all ailing—with scarlet fever, measles, intestinal worms, bad teeth—Sovereign of Heaven!"

The cantor began his recitative. The worshipers in the pews leaned on the reading ledges, seconding the cantor in muted tones. Some (Hayim Behr among them) remained standing, pressing their fevered brows against the chill wall and sobbing softly from time to time.

It was *Ne'ilah*. The gates would soon close; every minute, every second was precious. Tears flowed without end.

Yet was it so long ago that Hayim Behr had been young and full of hopes? Only nine or ten years ago he had chanted the prayer *Take pity upon Thy creations and rejoice over Thy creations* with a light heart and a gay tone. He recalled how on that occasion he had begun to chant in a deliberately loud voice, so that Rachel might hear him in the women's section. The recollection sent an uncomfortable flush all through him. He sang and kept gazing at the curtain of the opening at which she was standing, and it seemed to him that her small round face had flitted by behind the grating. Her eyes had probably been seeking him.

At that time, he had been an altogether different man on the Day of Atonement. He had been young and in full bloom, in a brand new prayer shawl embroidered with silver, his belt and skull cap gleaming with silver and gold! Black curly hair, a little black beard, warm socks. He had felt carefree and at his ease then, and ever so light at heart; as for his sins, he had believed but little in them at that time—he knew he would be forgiven. Yonah Wolf had once slapped his cheek before all the people during the Great Sabbath—and right in the synagogue, during the very sermon—yet he had forgiven him; he had forgiven him this slap. How, then, could God fail to forgive him his own sins? Besides, what did his sins amount to? The Day of Atonement would blot out a great deal; a great deal would also be covered by his fasting—the rest, with God's help, would also be erased.

There had been a certain smugness about his chanting. When he had felt too hot, he would walk out into the entry for a recess; whenever his stomach reminded him that it wanted food, he haughtily chided it: "Quiet, you glutton. Hasn't Rachel prepared plenty of chicken?"

But now he did not leave the synagogue even for a moment, from the evening of Yum Kipper till its conclusion—twenty-four hours later. And all that time he remained on his feet, never sitting down; nor did he chant but lamented and prayed. By now he believed in his sins. For sins he surely must have—great sins, frightful sins, even though he did not know just what they were. Otherwise misfortune would never dog him like this!

"And therefore instill Thy fear?" the cantor launched into his prolonged high notes. The congregation relaxed; only rarely did any sound interfere with the chanting. The singer was reciting the prayer, but Hayim Behr still kept standing with his head pressed against the wall. He seemed to be praying, yet his mind was a jumble of thoughts that were not at all in keeping with the direct sense of the words of the prayer.

"And Thou shalt destroy the kingdom of evil upon earth," the cantor announced with feeling. Of course, Hayim Behr would not have been at all averse if the judge and the scribe were to become kinder of heart. The bailiff, now—he wasn't so bad: you could get along with him; a large bottle of vodka and you could make him see reason. But as for the town clerk: all you heard him talk about was arrears in taxes. How come, and for what? True enough, Hayim Behr paid hardly any attention to him of late. It was several years since there had been a pillow in the house or any crockery; the little house itself was sold long ago. Let him cry "Arrears!" for the next hundred years, even. Let him collect them, if he could! Taxes were being collected on the basis of Tsehanovka having been a town once upon a time, with a governing body, a police force, and other such civic arms. Was Hayim Behr bound to pay old debts now, when Tsehanovka was simply a neglected dot on the map and he was perishing from starvation? Of course, if Hayim Behr had redeemed the pillows he had pawned, it would behoove him to beware; he would be praying together with the cantor that the kingdom of evil might be destroyed. But now he didn't give a snap of his fingers for the judge and would thumb his nose at the clerk!

With his head pressed against the wall he swayed slightly and his lips whispered after the cantor:

"May the memory of us and the memory of our fathers go up and appear before Thee. . . ."

He recalled that his father had been a devout Jew, that his father-in-law had been a transcriber of Holy Writ, and he decided that it behooved them to put in a good word for him before the Throne of the All Highest. That was why, when it came to the words "And the memory of the Messiah, the son of thy servant David, and the memory of Jerusalem, Thy holy city," he recited them without any feeling.

You must not think that Hayim Behr was opposed to the national idea, that he had read too much cosmopolitan literature and was therefore disinterested, or that he was a heretic and did not believe in the coming—the speedy coming—of Messiah. Not at all: Hayim Behr, even though he was an intelligent man who knew what was what, was nevertheless a simple Jew and, like all the others, simpleheartedly believed—the Messiah could come on the morrow, for all of him! To cross over into the Holy Land over a bridge of cobwebs he considered a mere trifle. He would go there without a second thought; it wouldn't be a bad thing at all to live in Jerusalem. Besides that, it was nigh time for the Messiah to come; the surest sign of his coming—"the disappearance of the last copper from one's pocket"—had manifested itself long ago. But Hayim Behr also knew that until the war between Gog and Magog was fought, until the Turk conquered the seventy nations, until the coming of Elijah the Prophet and the Messiah, and until the son of Joseph succumbed in the struggle against evil, he, Hayim Behr,would have his fill of going hungry, and so would Rachel and their eight children, the healthy as well as the ailing, Lord God, where is Thy mercy?

He realized, however, that he, himself, was first and foremost at fault—and, after that, perhaps the Lord was to blame as well. Couldn't he have gone in for trading or opened a shop or an inn, or have become a broker, like other Jews? No, he had to be an inventor. His intelligence had ruined him. In his childhood, he had been a master at molding lead tops and making lanterns; he had been a good swimmer, had skated astonishingly well—he had evinced all sorts of talents and had wanted to know everything in order to be able to do all things. He had invented a new way of making twisted candles by winding them around a stick and, by way of reward, used to get the thickest candles from the sexton to study by on winter nights; candles like that were now turned out in abundance; at that time, however, no one had known the secret and these candles had been named after him. He had been a skilled builder; out of a few boards and almost no tools he would construct a most excellent booth for the Feast of Tabernacles.

But his intelligence had ruined him. To become a trader right after his marriage, as other Jews did, was something he had not wanted to do. He preferred turning out some product through a secret process. He began by purchasing from some fly-by-night peddler a formula for cleaning fluid. The peddler had wangled a hundred roubles out of him, and Hayim Behr had set out into the world to sell this cleaner. His wife had wept; she did not wish to be separated from her husband right after the wedding; fur- thermore, she had no faith in the ultimate success of this enter- prise. She did not consider this cleaning fluid as real merchandise: who needed cleaner? Let it be green soap, say—that was used for washing the heads of little children, or ordinary soap, the kind you wash linen with; but a cleaning fluid for clothing? Women's garments were easily laundered, and little attention was paid to men's clothing; as soon as a man married he stopped thinking of tidiness. But Hayim Behr knew what was going on in the great world beyond Tsehanovka; he knew that Tsehanovka was no cri- terion, that stained clothing wasn't a universally accepted thing. He promised her that as soon as he had accumulated two thou- sand roubles he would come back, buy a small house, and that would be the end—he'd never stir from Tsehanovka again. He would open an inn or a shop and start a peaceful life. His wife yielded to him, and he wandered around for half a year without a copper in his pocket. The cleaning fluid did not even repay his expenses, and he had come home in rags.

Poor Rachel had burst into a flood of scalding tears and sent her husband off to seek advice from a certain rabbi.

He undertook the trip. At his departure he told her:

"You know, Rachel, you have deprived me of a part of the Kingdom of Heaven. I thought I would come home and you would start screaming, scolding, cursing—that you would even pull my hair or try to pluck my beard out. But you didn't do anything! Just cried a little. Would you believe it, this irks me exceedingly—"

Rachel had smiled through her tears. She had hopes that the Lord and the rabbi would put him right.

He sent her a letter after he left. In the first place (he informed her) he was in good health, and he hoped to hear the same news about her. Secondly, he was not on his way to the rabbi, as he had planned, but was once more about to tackle the great world; he had had a stroke of luck and bought a new secret formula for the preparation of china cement. This (he wrote) was merchandise in universal demand: every Jew had two sets of dishes—and a family that went in for breaking them. He therefore hoped that, with God's aid, etc., etc.

Once more Rachel wept for half a year and once more Hayim Behr came back home empty-handed. This time, however, he brought back with him a formula for homemade cider. For this formula he paid out his last copper and struggled with the venture for several years. During the first year there had been a fine crop of fruit; all the fruit trees in Tsehanovka and its environs had been so thick with apples, pears, and plums that it was necessary to prop up their branches. Hayim Behr took a new lease on life. He began totaling up his future profits for Rachel: the main ingredient for the cider would come cheap—fruit could be bought for a song. But, poor fellow, he had miscalculated badly. Since fruit was so cheap, people bought it and had no need of his cider.

Every year it was the same: the yield was good. On holidays he did a little business, but on ordinary days did not take in a copper. Then winter would come and put an end to his sales.

"Sovereign of Heaven!" Hayim Behr prayed in his heart, "let the crop of fruit fail but once; let the wind tear the blossoms off the trees, let there be a plague of worms, oh God, Most Beneficent!"

His thoughts were interrupted by the cantor's chant: "Open the gates unto us—"

The concluding prayer was said by Hayim's kinsman, Yonah Wolf.

He, too, spent the whole day of Yum Kippur on his feet and prayed fervently with all his heart; he, too, prayed in a rumbling bass, bawling at the top of his voice and pounding the wall with his fist—but, the while Hayim Behr wept and prayed as an ailing child prays to its father for a crust of bread, Yonah Wolf for the most part sang the glory of the Creator, expressing his gratitude for the benefits bestowed upon him. It was the sixth year that he was leasing an orchard, and year by year his affairs were getting better. True enough, he had to heave a sigh when it came to the passage: "Remember us, and inscribe our names in the Book of the Living." Health—it was the most important thing in the world! And, as he thanked the Lord for his own health and the health of his wife, he also asked health for his little ones. One of them was an unfortunate creature: very often the boy had sores on his head, there was always a reddened area under his nose, and from time to time, lumps appeared on his neck. When the child was cutting his teeth, everybody felt certain all these things were due to that. Then, they tried to find the cause in intestinal worms, and the lad was fed medicated cookies, which did not help at all; a letter, enclosing a monetary contribution, was sent to a wonder-working rabbi to have him pray for the child; even brought the boy himself to the rabbi. At first the child seemed better, but soon the sores and lumps reappeared.

A local *feldsher* [male nurse who performed medical duties] said that the boy had scrofula; he advised salt baths or taking him to some mineral springs. There wasn't money enough for a trip of that sort, even if Yonah Wolf were to pawn all the family's possessions down to his wife's earrings.

There was no room in the house for a bathtub; in the orchard, where the family lived during the summer, there wasn't water enough for drinking, and water for cooking had to be hauled a mile and a half.

The boy was growing—and so was the mangy spot on his head. The redness under his nose would not go away, and the glands on his neck swelled and puffed more and more. And yet the lad had potential; during the winter he studied at the Hebrew school, and the teacher hardly stopped singing his praises.

That is why Yonah Wolf wailed: "Inscribe our names in the Book of the Living—my boy, my clever boy, my consolation!"

Toward the other prayers Yonah Wolf remained indifferent, as though they did not concern him at all. All day long he had been praising and glorifying the All Highest, but because of his poor

163

learning he confused the texts and often shed tears or went into raptures in the wrong places. And, truth to tell, if Yonah Wolf weren't a trifle uncertain in his book-learning, not one of the good men in the synagogue would have been able to sit in the same pew with him. Whenever he came upon a familiar prayer, he let out the throttle and let his gullet go; he bellowed without sparing himself; he drowned out both the cantor and the choir, and if the walls of the synagogue hadn't been made of stone, they would have trembled and probably collapsed. But, fortunately, he encountered unfamiliar prayers more frequently and would quiet down.

During these involuntary recesses, he resorted to guile, puckering up his forehead, closing his eyes, swathing his head in the prayer shawl, so that people might think he was in deep meditation about the salvation of his soul.

He deafened even himself with his shouting; in the quiet, under the prayer shawl, he thanked the Creator and praised Him in words that were his own words that no one had prompted him to utter. He was getting along not too badly. Riches were still a long way off, but poverty had long since been left behind; he had managed to buy his wife a bit of jewelry; there were silver candlesticks in his home now; a little something had been put away for a rainy day. True, there was his child, the poor little lad—but what could one do? The Lord would help; Yonah Wolf himself had been afflicted with a mangy scalp at one time, and now his baldness was like a halo around his whole head—but still, what did it matter!

He recalled how his classmates in the Hebrew school used to make fun of him—all of them, with the exception of Hayim Behr. The latter always protected him, first by right of kinship and second as an innately good-natured lad. However, it was precisely because of Hayim Behr that he had had to endure so much. Hayim Behr knew his lessons by heart; Yonah Wolf just couldn't memorize them. Hayim Behr was good looking and neat; Yonah Wolf's face was nothing to speak of and he was always slovenly. Hayim Behr was a master at all things; Yonah Wolf was neither fish nor fowl nor good red herring. The teacher used to beat him to the refrain of "You might learn from Hayim Behr!" His mother beat him until there wasn't an area of body that wasn't sore—and then she would hold Hayim Behr up to him as an example. His father made his life miserable with beatings and scoldings without ever ceasing to sing the praises of Hayim Behr. And, even though Hayim Behr was on his side and had saved him more than once from the clutches of his classmates, Yonah Wolf hated him passionately just the same. Why? For what reason? Out of envy! Yonah Wolf was deeply repentant about this now. He no longer felt envy; there was no more rancor in him, and he prayed that Hayim Behr's years might be many.

Actually, he had great love for Hayim Behr now and pitied him quite sincerely; three-quarters of the sighs he emitted during his praying had been evoked by the miserable lot of Hayim Behr.

"May the All Highest take pity upon him, the poor fellow. He'll drag through the winter somehow—good or ill, he'll live through it. But let the summer at least smile upon him. If he were to do well in business, if he only had two coins to rub together he would perk up a bit—"

As the cantor launched into "Many are the needs of Thy people," Yonah Wolf became silent. It was the beginning of a bad stretch, a road all bumps and holes. He lowered his eyes to the prayer book before him and fell into deep reflection:

"Sovereign of Heaven, if I, or my wife, or my children have found favor in Thine eyes, or if the prayers of my ancestors and intercessors have reached Thine ears—may my child be made whole and may my apples grow in profusion, juicy, sun-kissed delicious apples that melt in your mouth. Sovereign of Heaven, let Thy people rejoice in my apples, let them find delight in juicy fruits! Also, Lord, forget not Hayim Behr in Thy beneficence— let him, too, make a good thing out of his ciders—"

At this point he came to with a start: the words "Recall the covenant of Abraham and the attempted sacrifice of Isaac—" caught his ear. The way was smooth here, it was thoroughly familiar. True, even here one came upon occasional small depressions, pebbles, shallow broken spots, but things weren't so bad that one couldn't mumble and sneak past them under cover of the chanting. And the further he went the easier things became: by now he was bellowing, chanting, booming just as if there were not another soul in the synagogue.

As he was leaving he met Hayim Behr:

"May God send you what you have prayed for!"

"The same to you!" Hayim Behr responded.

165

"May He fulfill all your desires!"

"And yours also, Yonah Wolf. Lord, send us both a good year—"

"—and good business to both of us!"

Each was sincerely wishing the other well but, having parted, each lifted his eyes once more to heaven:

"May there be a great yield of apples, juicy and golden!" prayed Yonah Wolf.

"May the apples rot on the trees!" prayed Hayim Behr.

In the evening Yonah Wolf sent Hayim Behr a huge fattened capon, while Hayim Behr sent Yonah Wolf three bottles of cider. And both were full of hope as they fell asleep.

Yonah Wolf was full of hope that there would be an unprecedented yield of apples, and Hayim Behr, that the fruit would rot and that he would be doing a brisk business in cider.

Their wives, however, could not sleep. Hayim Behr's wife was pondering how she could accumulate enough to buy bread for the holidays, while Yonah Wolf's wife pondered how she could accumulate enough, by the time the holidays came around, for half a dozen silver spoons.

Domestic Idyll

H AYIM was a porter.
When he trudged through the street, doubled over under some huge crate, he was dwarfed by his burden, and the crate seemed to be propelling itself on two legs, except that Hayim's rhythmic panting was clearly audible.

When he had delivered his load and pocketed his coppers, he would straighten up, catch his breath, adjust his hemp rope over his coat, mop the sweat off his brow, amble over to the well, help himself to a drink of water, and then rush to the courtyard of the house where he lived. Hugging the wall and raising his huge head so that the tip of his beard, the end of his nose, and the visor of his cap were all on the same horizontal plane, he would call out:

"Hannah!"

A woman's head in a white cap would appear at a small window near the roof and ask:

"Hayim?"

Then, the two would eye each other affectionately; the neighbors called it billing and cooing. Hayim would roll up the scanty coppers in a scrap of paper and toss it up for his wife to catch—it wasn't the first time they had gone through this performance.

"A plucky girl!" Hayim murmurs, apparently reluctant to resume his work.

"On your way, Hayim," she urges him with a smile. "I can't leave the sick child alone. I moved the cradle close to the fire, so that I can skim the soup and rock her at the same time."

"How is the poor little thing?"

"Better."

"Praised be the Lord! And Havah?"

"She's at the dressmaker's."

"And Yossel?"

"He's in *cheder*."

167

Hayim walks off, and his wife's eyes follow him until he is out of sight.

On Thursdays and Fridays, their conversation is somewhat more extensive.

"How much have you got in the paper?" Hannah would ask.

"Twenty-two *groshen*."

"I'm afraid that's not enough."

"What do you need, Hannah?"

"Six groshen's worth of ointment for the little one; a few more for candles. A white loaf for the Sabbath—well, I already have it; the same goes for the meat—I have a pound and a half. But we ought to get a little wine for the *kiddush*. Then we need some firewood—"

"About firewood I'm not worried at all; I can pick up enough in the marketplace."

"And come to think of it, I also need—" And she would go on enumerating the items she lacked for the Sabbath. It would finally be decided that the benediction could just as well be pronounced over the white loaf instead of wine and that, with the exception of the Sabbath candles and the ointment, they could do without some of the other things.

However, if through God's grace the children were all well, the brass candlesticks were not pawned, and a *kugel* were available, the whole family would be overjoyed. Hannah was exceedingly skilled in the preparation of *kugel*. Invariably, one of the ingredients—flour, eggs, fat—was lacking but, just the same, the dish turned out savory and delicious enough to gladden anybody's heart.

"An angel must have prepared it!" Hannah would remark, beaming with joy.

"An angel, indeed!" Hayim would comment with a laugh. "You are little short of angel, yourself, to be able to put up with me and the children. What a pest and a nuisance you must find them at times! I know they make me lose my temper every now and then. Yet do you ever raise your voice at me, the way other women do at their husbands? There's very little pleasure I can give you—both you and the children go about in rags. What good am I? A real nobody—I can't even chant the Sabbath service properly—even—"

"All the same, you're a good father and a fine husband," Hannah replies. "I and all of Israel could not wish for a better. May the Lord grant us a long life together."

The pair look into each other's eyes lovingly and with such devotion that one would think they had just stepped from under the wedding canopy. Their happiness increases as the meal progresses.

Following his Sabbath nap, Hayim repairs to a small House of Study, to listen to a lecture on the Torah. A *melamed* [religious instructor] holds forth there on the *Alshish* commentary on Holy Writ before a congregation of simple people. The day is warm: some of the faces are still heavy with sleep. Here and there a man is napping or yawning; when the lecture touches on the Hereafter and the Gehennum, where the *reshoim* [the wicked] are beaten with rods of iron, or with tales of the Garden of Eden where the *tsaddikim* [men of righteousness] walk about in golden crowns and dedicate themselves to the study of Holy Writ, the assembly suddenly becomes wide awake; their mouths gape and their faces flush as they listen with bated breath to what will befall them in the World to Come.

Hayim usually posted himself just by the stove. Almost in tears and trembling all over, he felt himself in the other world. He shared the doom of the wicked; he floated in boiling pitch, was catapulted into the infernal pit, had to pick fagots in primeval forests. He entered into the spirit of the thing to such an extent that he was drenched in perspiration. Then the scene shifted, and he trod enchanted ground along with the righteous; sharing with them the radiant Garden of Eden, the Heavenly Host, the Leviathan, the Behemoth, and all the other heavenly rewards. He visualized all this so intensely that when the speaker had finished and closed his folio, kissing it, Hayim would return with a start from the other world.

"Lord of the Universe," he would mutter after relaxing from his tension, "If Thou wouldst but grant me the least particle, a mere moiety of *olem haboh* [the World to Come] to me, to my wife, and to my children!" But here his spirits would droop. "By what right do I merit all this—through what good deed?"

After one of these discourses he asked the *melamed* in a quavering voice: "Rebbe, would you be good enough to advise me what I must do in order to be found worthy of the World to Come?"

169

"Devote yourself to the study of the Torah, my son," the other counseled him.

"But I don't know how!"

"Then study the commentaries, the religious legends, or, at least, the Ethics of the Fathers."

"I don't know how to do even that."

"Recite the Psalms, in that case."

"I can't spare the time to do so."

"Pray with fervor and ardor, then."

"But I don't understand the words of the prayers!"

The *melamed* regarded him with loving kindness and asked: "What is your trade? What do you do for a living?"

"I'm a porter."

"In that case, you can be of service to the Talmudic scholars."

"How?"

"Well, for one thing, you could carry a few pails of water to the House of Worship every afternoon for the scholars to drink."

Hayim beamed with joy:

"But what about my wife, Rebbe?" he persisted.

"If the husband finds a seat in the Garden of Eden, his wife becomes his footstool."

When Hayim came back home to chant the *Havdalah* benediction, and found his wife reciting the prayer "God of Abraham," he was stirred to the depths.

"Hannah, I won't stand for your being my footstool!" he blurted out as he embraced her. "I shall raise you up and seat you alongside of me. We will sit together, like equals, as we do now. It is so good to have you near me—do you hear, Hannah? You must sit right alongside of me. The Lord of the Universe will simply *have* to sanction it!"

The Cabalists

I N BAD TIMES, there is depreciation even in the best of wares which is the Torah.

Out of the entire *yeshiva* in Lashchev there remained only Reb Yekel, the *rosh-yeshiva* (head of the seminary), and his only scholar, Lemech.

The head of the seminary was a gaunt, aged Jew with a long, tangled beard and old, dull eyes. His beloved scholar, a young man, was also gaunt; he was tall and pale, with black ritual locks, dark eyes with dark circles underneath them, parched lips and a prominent Adam's apple. Since they had no shirts, and they walked about in rags, their breasts were bared to the elements. The head of the seminary could barely drag along in his heavy peasant boots, and the scholar's shoes kept slipping off his sockless feet.

That is what was left of the famous seminary! The impoverished little place sent less and less of provender as time went on, it provided fewer and fewer of the days when its pupils could eat at the tables of the town's Jews, and the scholars had drifted off to other towns. But Reb Yekel wanted to die there, and his Lemech remained to put the shards over his eyes when they closed in their last sleep.

They went hungry most of the time. From lack of food came lack of sleep and the sleepless nights and hungry days led to a great yearning after the Cabala! And, actually, if they *had* to keep vigil night after night and go hungry day after day, they might at least derive some benefit from it: let these circumstances be extenuating, at least, and let the gates of the world of mysteries, of the dwelling-places of the spirits, fly open!

And come to think of it, they had been engrossed with the Cabala for quite a long time.

There they were, the two of them, sitting at a long table. Everyone else in the town had long since finished his dinner—these two

171

had not yet had their breakfast. But they were used to it. The rosh-yeshiva began to speak while, his eyes uplifted, the scholar sat with his head propped on his fist and listened.

"There are many motifs to be found in the Cabala," said the head of the seminary. "One man may know a part of the melody, another knows half of it, while a third knows all of it. Our Rabbi, blessed be his memory, knew the whole melody—and even the refrain. I was found barely worthy of a bit as small as this," he added despondently, measuring off the tip of his last finger.

"There is the melody which needs words. That's the lowest degree. There is a higher degree: the melody which is sung without words—pure melody. But that melody still needs a voice and it needs lips from which the voice can issue. And lips, you understand, are only flesh. While it is true that the voice itself is noble, it is nevertheless of the flesh, earthy. Let us admit that the voice stands on the boundary between the carnal and the spiritual! But, still, the melody which is brought forth by the voice and depends upon lips is not completely pure—it is not completely spiritual! True melody is voiceless; it is expressed within the heart, in the secret places of one's being.

"This is the hidden meaning of King David's words in the thirty-fifth Psalm: 'All my bones shall say: Lord who is like to Thee?' The song must sound in the very marrow of the bones; it is there that the melody must resound the highest praise to the All-Benevolent. A song by a man of flesh and blood cannot achieve that easily, for it is not a *contrived* combination of sounds: it is a part of the melody through which God created the universe, and a portion of the soul which He implanted in the universe. It is the melody sung by the Celestial Spheres! Our rabbi—may his memory be blessed—sang that melody!"

Reb Yekel's lecture was interrupted by an urchin who wore a rope around his waist. He had entered the house of prayer and placed on the table in front of the old man a bowl of steaming buckwheat hominy and a slice of bread, saying in a gruff voice: "Reb Tevel sends dinner to the rosh-yeshiva." He then turned around and added, as he was about to leave: "I'll come for the bowl later."

Distracted, the head of the seminary got up slowly and, dragging his enormous boots, went toward the washbasin. As he walked, he continued to speak, but with less animation. Lemech followed him with enraptured eyes.

"But," Reb Yekel continued in his melancholy voice, "I was not found worthy to attain that degree, although," he added with a smile, "I do know the necessary incantations. I know them all, and perhaps I will reveal them to you this very evening."

The eyes of the scholar were all but popping out of his head. He sat there, his mouth agape, hanging on every word. But Reb Yekel spoke no more. He washed and dried his hands, recited the grace, went to the table, and with tremulous lips, pronounced the benediction over bread. His bony hands lifted the bowl. The steam cast a light haze over his emaciated face. He set the bowl down, took the spoon in his right hand, warming his left against the bowl, and took his first bite of the salt-sprinkled bread. Having warmed his face and hands, he frowned and pursued his lips, blowing on the porridge.

All this time, Lemech had not taken his eyes off him. And when the master brought the first spoonful up to his lips, something clutched at the student's heart; he buried his face in his hands and his whole body seemed to shrink.

A few minutes later, another boy entered with bread and a bowl of buckwheat porridge:

"Reb Joseph sends dinner to the scholar!"

The scholar, however, did not take his hands away from his face.

The rosh-yeshiva put down his spoon and approached Lemech. For a moment he looked at him with proud affection; then he wrapped his hand in the skirt of his robe and tapped him on the shoulder:

"They have brought your dinner," he said kindly. The scholar took his hands away from his face. His face was paler and his sunken eyes blazed wildly:

"I know, Rabbi," he answered, "but I am not going to eat today."

"Fasting for the fourth day?" asked the wonder-struck rosh-yeshivah. "And without me?" he added reproachfully.

"This is another fast," said Lemech. "This is a fast of penitence."

"What are you saying? You—a fast of penitence?"

"Yes, Rabbi—a fast of penitence. Just a moment ago, when you

173

began to eat, the temptation came to me . . . to transgress the commandment *Thou shalt not covet!*"

Late that night, the scholar awakened his master. The two were sleeping on opposite benches in the synagogue.

"Rabbi! Rabbi!" he called out in a faint voice.

"What is it?" Reb Yekel awoke in fright.

"Just now I had reached the highest step—"

"How did it happen?" asked the sage, not yet fully awake.

"The singing was *within* me!"

Reb Yekel sat up abruptly.

"Tell me exactly how it happened."

"I don't know myself, Rabbi," Lemech answered. "I couldn't sleep, pondering the meaning of your words. I wanted to learn this melody and, because of my grief at my not being able to reach it, I began to weep. Everything within me wept before the Creator of the Universe. At that point, I resorted to the incantations which you had taught me. And, strangely, I did not do so with my lips but somehow inwardly—it somehow came by itself. Suddenly a light shone over me; I kept my eyes closed, yet there was light, intensely bright light."

"That's it, that's it!" whispered Reb Yekel.

"Then, because of this light, I felt buoyant . . . it seemed to me that I had become weightless and could fly—"

"That's it, that's it!"

"Then a feeling of great joy and well-being came over me; my face did not move nor did my lips, but I was laughing—and my laughter was good!"

"That's it, that's it! That was because of your joy—"

"Then something began to sing within me."

The *rosh-yeshiva* jumped off his bed and with one leap was at Lemech's side: "Well, go on!"

"Then I heard the melody beginning within me!"

"What did you feel? What was it like? What was it like? Tell me!"

"I felt that all my external senses were stopped up, while within me something was singing—without words, just singing—"

"How? How?"

"No, I'm unable to convey it . . . but up to now the knowledge

was mine. Then this singing resolved into it . . . resolved into—"
"Into what—to what?"

"Something that was like music, as if a violin were singing within me. . . . Or as if Jonah the musician were sitting within me and playing songs at a feast, at the table of a saintly sage. But the playing was even better, more tender, more inspired—and without any voice it was completely spiritual—"

"You are blessed! Blessed!"

"Now it has vanished!" said the disciple sadly. "Now my external senses have been restored and I am tired, so . . . tired—" the last word was a sigh. "Rabbi!" he cried out abruptly, clutching at his breast. "Let us read the prayer for the departing! They have come for me. They are short a singer in the Celestial regions. . . . It's an angel with white wings. . . . Rabbi, Rabbi! Shema Yisroel—Hearken, O Israel . . .

Everybody in the town, to a man, wished a similar death for himself. But for Reb Yekel, even that was not enough: "Another fast," he sighed, "and he would have died from the Kiss itself . . . the Kiss of the All-Highest!"

The Messenger

H E PLODDED on and the wind fluttered his long beard and the skirts of his gabardine.

Every minute or two he clutched at his left side, each time he felt the stabbing pain. But he refused to admit this, even to himself; he convinced himself that he was merely checking the contents of his breast pocket.

"It'll never do to lose the contract and the money!" That is the only thing he was apprehensive about. "And suppose I do feel a stitch—what of it? It's all nonsense! I'm strong enough to go a distance like this, glory be! Another man at my age wouldn't have covered a mile, even, whereas I, thanks to the Lord, have no need of any man's help and am earning my own crust of bread.

"Praise the All-Highest, people trust me with money. If all that other men entrust me with belonged to me, I wouldn't be a messenger at seventy. But if that's the way God wants it, then all is well!"

The falling snow had turned to large, cottony flakes. The old man had to wipe his face frequently.

"I have half a mile more to go," he thought. "What a long stretch! Nonsense, it's far shorter than the distance I've already covered."

He turned around. By now he could no longer see the tower of the town hall or the Roman Catholic church or the barracks.

"Well, Shmeryl, stir your stumps!"

And Shmeryl plodded on through the wet snow. His old feet sank into it, but he kept on going.

"Thank God, the wind isn't high."

To hear him talk, it would take a storm to qualify as a high wind. It was blowing directly in his face, hard enough to make him gasp constantly. Tears came to his eyes and pricked him as if with needles. But then, he had always had trouble with his eyes.

"With the first money I get," he promised himself, "I will buy goggles for the road—big round goggles that will protect my eyes. God's willing, I'll get them. If I could have just one commission a day, and the further away the better." He still had strength to walk, thanks to God, and could scrimp and save and scrape together a little something, enough to pay for the goggles.

He also needed some sort of fur-lined jacket; perhaps he wouldn't have such stabbing pains in his chest then. However, he did have a warm cloak for the time being. If only it weren't splitting apart at the seams, everything would be fine. At this point Shmeryl smirked a little. This wasn't one of the cloaks you got nowadays, just basted together out of thin, sleazy material; its garment was made of sturdy goods that would, no doubt, outlast its wearer. It was also a good thing that it had no slit in the back; the skirts didn't go flying every which way, and in front they overlapped by almost a yard. Things would be easier, of course, if he had a fur-lined garment—they were so much warmer. But still, the goggles ought to come first. A fur-lined jacket was useful only in winter, whereas goggles you needed all the year round. Come to think of it, in the summer, when the wind tossed sand right in your eyes, things were even worse.

And so it was all decided: first the goggles, and then, perhaps a fur-lined jacket. If, with God's help, he were to get through with the incoming shipments of wheat, he would surely receive four gold pieces.

Shmeryl plodded on. The wet, icy snow glued his eyelids together, the wind was rising and the pains in his side were intensifying.

"If only the wind would shift! However, it's best so; on the way back I'll be still more tired, and the wind will then be blowing at my back. Oh, I'll be moving at quite a different speed then!"

He had to stop for a moment to catch his breath. This disturbed him.

"What's come over me? Haven't I gone through enough blizzards and frosts when I was being trained as a soldier?"

He recalled his military service, the time when he had been a soldier for Nicholas the First. Twenty-five years of service, not counting his childhood, which he had spent in a military canton—a soldier's son doomed to military servitude. He had done a good bit of hiking during his lifetime, marching over hill and dale through blizzards and all kinds of storms. Trees split, birds fell dead to the ground, but the soldiers marched briskly on, singing as they went and often dancing a *kamarinsky* or a *trepak* at the end of the march.

The thought that he had gone through the thirty years' of service with its painful trials, that he had endured so many blizzards and storms, so many deprivations and so much hunger and thirst, and had come home in good health—all these things evoked a sense of pride. He straightened his back, raised his head proudly and strode on with renewed vigor.

"What's a little snow like that mean to me?" he laughed. "Back in Russia, now—*there* things were altogether different."

He kept going. The wind had died down a little. It grew darker; night was coming on.

"What a day! It's over before you have a chance to look around—" and he quickened his steps, apprehensive that night would overtake him halfway to his destination. He studied the Torah in the synagogue during Sabbaths and knew very well that *one must leave and return in good time.*

Hunger welled up in him, and whenever he felt hungry he somehow had an excess of good spirits. He knew that appetite is a good thing: the merchants for whom he ran errands were constantly complaining that they never felt hungry. He always had an appetite, thank God, except, perhaps, when he didn't feel quite himself—like last night, for example. The bread had tasted sour.

Nonsense! The very idea that the bread they bake for soldiers can be sour! That may have been true in days gone by, but now the Gentiles baked bread that put the Jewish bakers to shame. As for that loaf yesterday, it was brought hot from the oven. Just slicing it had been sheer pleasure. But, true enough he hadn't been well; shivers had kept running through his body. That kind of thing, however, happened to him rarely—glory to Him Whose Name he was not worthy of uttering!

Now his appetite was back; he had even brought some bread and cheese along on his journey. The cheese had been provided by a merchant's wife, God send her health. She was a real philanthropist and had a truly Jewish heart. If only she didn't scold so, she would be a really splendid person. And he recalled his wife, now dead.

"Every bit like my Shprintzeh! She, too, had a kind heart—and

178

the habit of scolding over every little thing. No matter which one of the children I sent out into the world she would weep, despite the fact that at home she swore at them constantly. And it's no use telling what went on when one of them died. For days on end, she'd writhe on the floor like a snake and beat her head with her fists. Once, she even reached such a point where she wanted to throw a stone at the heavens! Think of it! As though God would really pay any attention to a foolish woman. And she refused to let them carry the bier out of the house. She struck out at the women, and as for the pallbearers—she yanked their beards out! What hidden strength was in that Shprintzeh! She was a tiny person, but what strength she had—what strength! Yet, she was a kind-hearted woman. She didn't bear any enmity even to me—although it was a pity that she could never find a kind word for me. She was forever demanding a divorce and threatening to run away. But divorce was really the furthest thing from her mind.

At this point he recalled a certain event and he smiled.

It had happened many years ago, at the time when a man had to buy his freedom. He was a watchman at that time, making the rounds of a warehouse all night and night after night, armed with a length of iron. He knew his business thoroughly; he had been through a good school—his instructors in the army had been excellent!

It was winter, just before daybreak. He had been relieved by the day watchman, Hayim Yonah—may the Kingdom of heaven be his! —and Shmeryl, thoroughly chilled, his arms and legs blocks of ice, had come home. He had knocked on the door and his wife had shouted at him from the bed:

"May you fall through the ground! I thought it wouldn't be you returning but your ghost!"

Oho! She had been angry at him ever since yesterday. He actually couldn't remember what had happened yesterday, but there *must* have been something.

"Shut your mouth and open the door!" he had shouted.

"I'll split your skull!" she retorted.

"Let me in!"

"May you fall through the ground!" she repeated.

He thought the matter over and set out for the synagogue, where he deposited himself behind the stove and went to sleep. As ill luck would have it, however, the stove was faulty: he was all but asphyxiated and was carried out half dead.

You simply couldn't describe how Shprintzeh carried on. He could hear clearly what was going on around him. He heard them telling her that he wasn't in any real danger; he merely breathed in some coal fumes. But no, nothing would do but they must fetch a doctor. She would faint—she would throw herself in the river! And she kept yelling at the top of her voice: "My husband! My husband! My precious!"

Gathering his strength, he sat up and asked her calmly:

"Well, now, Shprintzeh—do you still want a divorce?"

"May you fall through—" but she never finished her curse and broke into deafening sobs:

"What do you think, Shmeyel? Will God punish me for my curses, for my vile temper?"

But no sooner had he recovered than she became the same old Shprintzeh: her tongue knew no restraint, but she was as strong as the devil and could claw like a cat.

He felt sorry for her; she hadn't lived long enough to have any joy from her children. They must be getting along well there, in a foreign land—artisans they were, every one of them. With a trade, one can't starve to death anywhere; they're strong, thank God— they took after their father in that. And as for their not writing to him—well, what of it? They didn't know how to write themselves, and as for asking others to write for them—well, what flavor would there be to a letter like that? It would be like gefülte fish without pepper! Besides, you had to take their years into consideration— they were mere children, young and forgetful. They must be living well, indeed.

The only thing was, Shprintzeh was in the cold ground, poor thing. A great pity about Shprintzeh.

"When the time of buying yourself free was over, she changed so that you couldn't recognize her. Then, too, it must be said that until I got used to my present calling of messenger, before I learned to address a Polish landowner as Serene and Lordly Pan instead of by the Russian 'Your Honor,' and they began trusting me with money and documents, I had to starve for rather a long while. Well, now, I'm a man, a soldier from my childhood—I could go without eating for a day or two. But she, the poor little thing—

180

she had to pay with her life for such privations. The foolish woman —the least little thing and she lost her strength; toward the end she couldn't even scold. Weep—that's about all she could do.

"That poisoned my life. I don't know why, but she suddenly began to be afraid of me. And when she became afraid, I'd pluck up my courage; I'd yell and scold. 'Why don't you go and stuff yourself?' I would shout at her. At times she'd make me furious, she'd bring me to such a pitch it was all I could do to keep my hands off her. But how can you beat a weeping woman when she just sits there with her hands folded and won't budge? As soon as I'd spit on my hands and go for her, she'd up and tell me: 'You eat first, and I'll eat later.' And I was forced to eat the bread first and to let her have the leavings.

"Sometimes, just to pull the wool over my eyes, she'd send me out of the house: "Go, I'll eat without you; maybe you'll manage to earn something,' and she'd try to smile and would even snuggle up to me now and then. But when I'd get back, I'd find the bread almost untouched. She used to try and convince me that she couldn't eat the dry bread—she had to have buckwheat grits."

His head sank, as if a heavy load had been piled on him, and sad thoughts raced through his head.

"And what a row she raised when I wanted to pawn my Sabbath cloak—the one I'm wearing now! It was just too horrible, the way she carried on, and ran as fast as she could to pawn her brass Sabbath candlesticks. And up to her very death she said the Prayer over the Tapers with the candles stuck in potatoes. Before she died she confessed to me that she never wanted a divorce and that she talked that way only to spite me.

"'My tongue—my tongue!' she wailed. 'Merciful God, forgive me my tongue!' And she died actually afraid that she would be hanged in the other world because of her tongue. 'God,' said she, 'will not be merciful to me, for I have sinned far too much. The only thing is, when you get there—oh, not soon, God forbid, but in a hundred and twenty years—take me off the gallows as quickly as you can. Tell the All Highest that you've forgiven me.'

"She had all but lost consciousness when she suddenly began calling the children. It seemed to her that they were right there, close to her, and she began imploring them for forgiveness. Foolish woman, as if there were anybody who wouldn't have forgiven her.

"How old was she, after all? Fifty! She died so young. It's not a trivial thing when a human being takes things so to heart. When anything went out of the house it seemed to her that part of her own body, half her health, was being taken away. She became yellower, greener with each day. She dried up altogether, somehow and actually shrank. She knew that she was dying.

"How she loved the house, with everything that was in it! No matter what was taken away—a chair, an iron skillet, no matter what it was—she watered it with her tears, her bitter tears. She parted with every object the way a mother does with her child; what more do you want—she'd clasp these things to her and all but kiss them! 'Oh' she used to say, 'I'll die and you won't be in the house any more!'

"No use talking—a woman will always remain a fool. She might be a Cossack in a petticoat, but let the least thing happen and she turns into a baby. Just think of it, isn't it all the same if you die with a chair with or without it!

"My!" he cut himself short. "The things that pop into my head. Because of all this I've slowed down. Well, you old soldier, step lively!"

He looked about him. There was nothing but snow. Far above, the sky was gray, spottily patched with black.

"It's as patched as my undershirt!" he thought. "Can it be, Great God, that you have no credit at the store either?"

In the meantime the snowfall had thickened. His beard and mustache had become icicles. He was breathing more easily but his face felt flushed; beads of sweat had come out on his forehead, and with every step his legs grew more tired and chilled. He wanted to sit down, but was too ashamed to do so. For the first time he felt the necessity of resting during such a short journey—a mere two miles. He did not want to admit that he was past seventy and that it was high time he retired for good.

But no; he must go on. Go on without stopping. As long as one walked the legs carried on, but all you had was to yield to the temptation and sit down for a little while—and you were no longer good for anything.

"You can actually catch a cold that way," he cautioned himself, making every attempt to overcome the strong desire to rest. "The village isn't far off now; I'll manage to rest there just as well. I absolutely will have to rest up. I won't go directly to the landowner—you have to wait a whole hour for him in his yard; I'll drop

182

in on some Jew first. It's a good thing, too," he assured himself, "that I'm not afraid of the landowner's dogs' but at night, when they unchain Brownie things get dangerous just the same. At least I have my supper with me, and Brownie likes cheese, but just the same it would be better to rest my bones first. Yes, I'll drop in at some Jew's, warm myself a little, wash my hands, have a bite of something—"

At this point his mouth watered; he hadn't eaten a thing since morning. But that was nothing. He wasn't worried because he was hungry—it actually gave him pleasure, for if a man was hungry it was a sign he was alive. But his legs!

There were only two-thirds of a mile left to go. Through the mist he could make out the big sheds of the landowner. His legs, however—*they* could see nothing and demanded a rest, come what may.

"On the other hand," he reflected, "what of it if I should take a little rest? For just a minute—even half a minute! Maybe I really should take a rest? Let's try it. My legs have obeyed me so long— let me obey *them* this once."

And Shmeryl sat down on a snowdrift by the side of the road. Only now did he hear how hard his heart was beating, and feel how keenly the pain was stabbing at his side. His forehead had broken out in a cold sweat and he was filled with fear. Was he taking sick, by any chance? He was carrying money belonging to others! He might yet, God forbid, lose consciousness!

"Glory be," he consoled himself, "There's no one in sight! And even if someone should pass by, it will never as much as occur to him that I have any money on me. It's enough to make a cat laugh —the idea of anybody entrusting money to anybody like *me!*"

Sit just a little while, and then resume the journey. . . . But his eyelids stuck together.

"There, Shmeryl, get up—get up!" he commanded. He could still command, but it was not so easy to carry out the command. He was not in any condition even to move. Yet it seemed to him that he was going on, moving faster and faster. He saw the little village huts ahead: Antek lived here and, over there, Vassili; he knew them all, had hired drays from all of them. He still had far to go to reach the house of a Jewish friend, but it was best to stop there first. . . . sometimes one came upon a *m'zumen* there, three adult Jews who could say grace together. And it seemed to him

183

that he was walking toward the little house of a Jew—but the house was moving further and further away. Probably that's the way things had to be. There must be a cheery fire going in the stove: there was a reddish, cheery glow in the little window. Probably the stout Mirl was cooking a big pot of potatoes—she always served him with potatoes: hot, crumbling potatoes! And he (so it seemed to him) was forging ahead.

The cold had lessened a little and snow was beginning to fall in big downy flakes. And it seemed to Shmeryl that he was already in the house of his Jewish friend. Mirl was pouring off the water from the potatoes: the old messenger could hear the water gurgling. The water was trickling down his cloak of lasting as well. Jonah, his friend, was pacing up and down the room, humming softly. That's a habit of his: humming after the last evening prayer, because that's the time he's hungry, and he kept urging his wife "Come on, Mirl!" But Mirl took her time: the work went more pleasantly if one was leisurely about it.

"Am I sleeping and is all this a dream?" This thought was abruptly replaced by a pleasant feeling of surprise: it seemed to him that the door opened and his oldest son had entered. Honoh, Honoh—oh, he recognized him! But how did he happen to be here? Honoh did not recognize his father and pretended utter ignorance. A fine thing, to be sure. He told Jonah that he was on his way to see his father; he questioned Jonah about him. He hadn't forgotten his father! But Jonah was being sly and wouldn't tell him that his father was sitting right in this very room on the bench! Mirl was busy: she was mashing the potatoes with a big wooden spoon and was all smiles.

"Oh, Honoh must have gotten rich—very rich! Everything on him is brand new. And a watch chain, too! Perhaps it's pinchbeck? No, it must surely be of pure gold: Honoh would never wear a pinchbeck chain, God forbid!"

Shmeryl broke into laughter and cast a glance on the ledge on top of the oven. He laughed again; he was all but splitting his sides from laughter. Yekel, Beryl, Zachariah. All three had hidden themselves up on that ledge—the scalawags. And he laughed again. It was a pity about Shprintzeh though—a pity! It would have been fine if she, too, had lived long enough to rejoice at this homecoming. Meanwhile Honoh had ordered two geese for supper.

"Honoh, Honoh—don't you recognize me? Why, it's me!"

184

And it seemed to the old messenger that he was kissing his son. "Do you hear, Honoh—it's a pity about your mother, it's a pity she can't see you. Yekel, Beryl, Zachariah—get down off that ledge! Why, I recognized you right off! Get off there, now; I knew you would come. Here's positive proof of it: I've brought you some cheese—real sheep milk cheese! Just take a look at that, children— if I remember correctly, you were fond of soldier's bread—isn't that so, now? Yes, it's a pity about your mother!"

And it seemed to him that all his four sons had surrounded him, that they were kissing him, clasping him hard in their arms.

"Go easy, dear children—easy, now. Don't hug me so hard! I'm no longer a young man—I'm headed into my eighties. Go easy! You're strangling me; go easy, my children. My bones are old. Careful! There's money in that pocket: they entrust me with money. Enough, children—enough!"

Enough. He froze to death, his hand pressed against his breast pocket.

A Marred Holiday

THE EVE of the Sabbath. Near the threshold is a little pile of rubbish, waiting to be swept out. The noodles, boiled and drained, are in their bowl—all that remains to be done is to pour a spoonful of chicken soup over them to prevent their sticking together. The table is set with vodka for the *kiddush*, and with two white loaves covered by a small damask napkin.

Zorech, the young master of the house, has already washed up. He is squeezing the water out of his ritual sidelocks between the thumb and index finger of each hand. Miriam, the young housewife, is standing near him and cleaning his Sabbath kaftan.

"Oh, you . . . careless fellow!" she says, smiling. "It's only a year and a half after the wedding, and yet, see what the kaftan looks like! See—there's a spot of candle-grease on the lapel!" She scrapes the spot off with a fingernail and then runs a brush over that segment of cloth.

"That's enough!" Zorech pleads with her. "Your hands will get tired from that. You've already exhausted your strength; drop it!"

"No great matter! I'd rather have my hands ache a little than have them saying in the synagogue that your wife is so lazy and careless that she won't even clean your Sabbath clothes."

She notices another tiny spot, bends over the garment and goes on with her cleaning. Her small pale face has flushed, her eyes are glittering, and she is breathing hard. But she has gained her end: Zorech kisses her head.

"What do you like about it so much? The way I have tied my headkerchief?" Then she adds softly: "You ought to be ashamed before my mother, at least."

Her kerchief (which covers her whole head), and the stern vigilance of her mother, who has now turned her back to the two, making believe she is looking for her prayerbook in the closet— these are the two things which haunt and crush Miriam.

186

Before her wedding Miriam had had two long, thick braids; all the girls had envied her flaxen-fair silky hair. When she had gone down the street people had said to themselves "There goes Temptation itself!" Zorech, when he had become her fiance, used to be aquiver with joy whenever he had touched her head. But did he continue to make that gesture often? They had been betrothed half a year, and had seen each other only a few times. One evening, on the holiday of Rejoicing over the Torah, they had managed to slip out before the ceremony of the procession with the Holy Scrolls, and on one other occasion they had met during Passover, while strolling beyond the town limits. That was the time they had been caught redhanded! What rumors sprang up after that, and what gossip! The rabbi, having summoned the parents, informed them that though he hadn't the least doubt of the innocence of the young people, *his* advice would be, just the same, to schedule the wedding right away now.

Long Serel, Miriam's mother, actually hadn't had time to get all the featherbeds and pillows ready; Zorech's father, who made his living by making ropes, had not yet collected all the dowry; but the wedding was held then just the same. And, before the wedding ceremony, Miriam's silky, flaxen-fair tresses had been shorn!

Miriam had wept bitterly while this was being done. At the same time, Zorech had been sitting amid a crowd of young people, but as he told the story afterward, he had sensed the moment when the scissors had touched her hair. It was just as if something sharp had slashed across his heart. At the wedding supper both of them had looked as if they had lost God knows what.

Oh, that headkerchief of hers!

Her hair would have grown to its former length, except that the religious laws made it compulsory for a married woman to keep it cropped. Zorech, it's true, maintained that there were certain towns where Jewish women wore the ritual wigs prescribed for married women and at the same time kept their natural hair, but then everybody knew that Zorech was a bit of a freethinker.

"If God would help me, and I should win a lottery," he used to say (to get rich at his trade would really be too great a miracle), "I'd leave my mother-in-law a couple of thousand, while Miriam and I myself would move to a big city to live!"

But Miriam would not hear a word of all this. She would implore Zorech not to say such things, kissing and hugging him to make him keep still.

In the first place, in whose care were they to leave her mother? True, her mother would actually have money then, but she was no longer young. What if she should fall ill, God forbid? There wouldn't be anybody to give her a sip of water, even then. Secondly, Miriam herself was afraid of committing a sin. True enough, such towns did exist, Zorech knew what he was talking about. But God knows what sort of towns they were! After all, there had been such places as Sodom and Gomorrah, spoken of in the Old Testament; there had been still others, where the ways of the inhabitants were still worse! Iron bedsteads which strangers had to be made to fit (Miriam must have had Procrustes in mind), children smeared with honey so the ants would eat them. "And who knows, perhaps the Lord will look down, hold counsel with the angels and then, no later than tomorrow, will decide to run the Sodoms and Gomorrahs of today off the face of the earth?"

Miriam knew, however, that God, may His name be blessed, was forbearing. He must surely be patiently waiting now to see if the people would repent.

"Well, now," Zorech had told her, "does that mean that one must renounce life altogether?"

"No, Zorech," she had answered. "Only I don't want to do such things. If you are told you mustn't do something, it means you mustn't."

She had to endure still more from her mother. Long Serel loved her daughter with greater capacity than any ten mothers could. She would never say a harsh word to Miriam, but ever since that time when Miriam had been caught actually walking alone with her fiance, on the outskirts of the town, her mother was constantly suspecting her of something and was safeguarding her.

"Your soul," she would say to Miriam, "is pure, but your heart is yielding, whereas to withstand the Tempter one must have a will of iron. A human being must fight like a lion, for the Tempter is more dangerous than a serpent."

And she had taken to admonishing her kindhearted but weak-willed daughter, this pure yet unstable soul, in order to teach her how to resist the demon Tempter. But after each such lesson Miriam felt out of sorts: her chest ached; she was suffocated by nightmares. No sooner did Zoreh leave the house than Miriam's mother would launch into her admonitions. Serel herself was a well-informed person; she could read the jargon fluently and had gone through the whole Pentateuch with its sundry commentaries as well as through several other holy books. Hell was something she knew all about—she was as familiar with it as with her own house. She knew just where the sinners were boiled in pitch, where they were seared with the Black Fire, and where the devils roasted them on spits, like so many spring chickens. She knew all the interior arrangements of the other worlds—for what sins they hanged you up by your tongue, for which you were cast into the void between heaven and earth, where the eagles and the ravens plucked out pieces of your sinful flesh. She knew the transgressions for which you had to go scurrying through forests where the wild beasts nipped at your heels; she knew too, for what transgressions your skin would be flayed and you would be enveloped in thorns, on top of which you'd have to dip up water with a pitcher that had no bottom. The only salvation lay in the fulness of God's mercy—all He asked was repentance.

Miriam would listen to all this with a face as white as chalk, her heart pounding and her lips trembling.

She was filled with fear; she knew that sin was lying in wait for mortals everywhere. Things were still worse during those certain days of the month when woman is beset by evil spirits, when the effluvia of hell dance about her . . . when she must not even look into a mirror, lest it become spotted with tarnish. Woman's breath was filled with impurities then, and her clothes were strewn with the devils and monsters of hell. How afraid of Zorech Miriam was at such times!

But the mother's fears began even before the coming of this period each month. She would ask her daughter almost every minute:

"Little daughter, perhaps it is already time? Are you concealing the matter—do you want to ruin your young life by such a heavy sin? Look, maybe it has happened already? Perhaps you weren't observant enough before?"

"Mamma dear," Miriam asked her once, "why does Zorech regard this matter so lightly? He actually laughs when I toss him the keys!" *

* During menstruation women are even forbidden to hand anything directly to their husbands, according to the orthodox Jewish religious rules.—*Translator.*

189

"That's not right, child; it's a great sin," the mother had assured
her. "But that's how men are by nature. Come, do they know? And
what has man to fear? He'll skim through a chapter of the Mishna,
and at once six pages of his sins are cancelled. And when are they
ever called to account, these men? Once a year, on the Day of
Atonement! But woman—the poor thing—what does she signify? A
pitiful creature, no more than a turkey-hen, the Lord forgive us!
But when it comes to pregnancy, to child birth—why, her life then
actually hangs by a hair. That's when the Days of Atonement come
upon her. And what do we poor things have for the salvation of
our souls? Only the Pentateuch. And really, a fine fellow Zorech
is—he won't even wear the ritual fringed vest. After all, there are
just three rites left for us women to perform: the Benediction of
Dough, the observance of certain purificatory periods, and the
Benediction of Candles. The Benediction of Dough—well, it's not
so very fearsome; one can always attend to it; that also goes for the
Benediction of Candles—all one has to do is get everything ready
for the Sabbath on Friday, by noon. But when it comes to . . . you
know . . . how can one guard oneself? If your glance," said the
mother, "should fall on . . . the spot where his glance fell, if your
breath should mingle with his, you're done for! Lilith snatches up
that glance, she blows that breath up on high, straight to the very
Throne of the All-Highest, and fans the matter into a real judicial
storm . . . and right off women in childbirth and little children
start dying off . . ."

Miriam realized that she had sinned more than once on both
these things her mother had mentioned. And each time, after sinning thus anew, she had been unable to fall asleep because of her
dread that her soul would go up on high and, on its own initiative,
make an entry of the new transgression.

It had once so happened that a temporary session of the circuit
court had been held in the little town. The whole populace had
come running to look on, as if at a miracle. Miriam had also gone
to see the trial. This had happened shortly after her wedding,
when one is attracted by all sorts of novelties. She had beheld three
judges, the prosecutor, the court clerk, and the man on trial. She
had not understood just what was being said, but she had seen the
defendant keel over as if he had been struck by lightning, when a
sentence to hard labor has been pronounced. From then on she
had dreaded the judgment of Heaven. On this spot the Prosecutor

would be delivering his speech, stammering a little, while over there Satan himself would appear on the scene. Satan would be spewing black fire, and boiling pitch would be pouring out of his mouth. Come, what did a sentence to hard labor amount to! In the other world the stentorian decision would be *kaph-hakal!* * She would be sentenced to roasting, to burning!

"How the soul will swoon then!" Miriam pondered. She was seized by tremors while the pain in her chest turned to pricking needles.

Zorech did not as much as suspect all this. In his presence Miriam's mother kept silent. But Miriam, whenever he was around, was an altogether different person—gay, joyous. But then, when was he ever home? On Friday evening, on the Sabbath. All week long he was taken up with business—he had no time to be sitting home. Even at night there was no rest. Long Serel could not fall asleep for hours; she fussed, paced the room, read aloud the whole of the Prayer Before Sleep, as well as the Confessional. Now and then Zorech gnashed his teeth, but did not say anything. Only once had he said something rude to his mother-in-law, and Miriam had all but wept her eyes out then. He wouldn't indulge in any more foolish things like that now; he might gnash his teeth, but he wouldn't say anything any more.

About the admonitions delivered by his mother-in-law, he knew nothing. He could see that Miriam was growing paler and paler, and becoming even thinner; he would see her clutching at her breast and gasping for breath. And he would smile gaily in expectation of a joyous event. At times he had the fleeting thought that he ought to call in a doctor, but he had not done so and was afraid even to hint at it—afraid of frightening Miriam. For some time back she had begun getting frightened by all sorts of things, especially at night—the mewing of a cat, the barking of a dog out in the street. If she heard a knock on a door somewhere, or some rustle, she would start shaking all over and then cry out—and first thing you knew she'd be lying there barely breathing, practically in a faint! If he were to bring in a doctor she would, God forbid, become ill in earnest.

He had often led the conversation around to this matter:

"What is wrong with you, Miriam? What's hurting you?"

* The torment wherein the sinner is tossed from one end of the world to the other. —*Translator.*

191

"When you're home," she would answer him with a feeble smile, "I feel fine. I do hope nobody puts the evil eye on us!"

She was horribly afraid of the evil eye—there were not a few things in her life some people might find enviable! When, on Sabbath after dinner Zorech dozed off, she would often tiptoe up to him, ever so quietly, and puff at him lightly. For if it was summer, the window was open—and many a thing might befall him; some passerby might put the evil eye on him! It seemed to her that everybody must envy her, that there was nobody better or more goodlooking than her Zorech—no, not even if you were to crisscross all Poland in search of his like!

There just wouldn't be a thing to say against him (she reflected), if only he were stricter about observing . . . *that* one point; just a little stricter, at least! But again, he was a man, after all (as her mother said) and he had all of 613 religious observances to follow. So that point was of no great importance to him!

Zorech maintained that she was ailing, but she stubbornly denied it. If only he were to stay home—stay home all the time! He would listen to her and smile. Did he at all surmise the real reason for her ill health? But as for complaining against her mother—that was something she would never do; he would never find out what suffering she had to go through when he was away from home.

However, on the evening we are now picturing, it would be Sabbath soon; Zorech could leave now—let him go to the synagogue. On the Sabbath Miriam was not afraid, and on that day her mother always refrained from delivering any admonitions for her benefit. On the Sabbath our mother is a kindhearted mamma!

"Miriam, dear," said her mother after Zorech had left, "it's the Sabbath today; wash yourself, dress up. When, after the service, your husband enters the room with the angels you must run to meet him with a joyous mien, with glowing eyes, in peace and amity and with all good wishes. For that you will be found worthy—"

"Of a good kiss from Zorech," Miriam finished, laughing.

This ending was not particularly after the mother's heart, but then it was the Holy Sabbath already and she refrained from uttering any harsh word. She sat down to the Old Testament, put on her spectacles and began to read aloud.

Miriam had often listened attentively to her mother reading—

some of the stories were much to her liking. During previous read-ings, her laugh had rung out like a little silver bell when she heard how Abraham, as a youth, had smashed the stone idols of old Terah; or she had become all a-quiver: would Isaac surmise that it was Jacob who brought him his meal and not Esau? Tears had come to her eyes over Jacob's encountering Rachel at the well, and she had felt a deadly hatred toward Laban for having duped Jacob. There, let somebody try to fool her Zorech! She had been all on edge during that reading but had calmed down when Jacob got both Leah and Rachel as wives; after all, she knew that these events all occurred long before the days of Rabbi Gershon's for-bidding a multiplicity of wives.

Today's scheduled reading, however, was only about gift-offer-ings. All sorts of objects for the inner temple were brought. This held but little interest for Miriam; she was tired and wanted to sleep. Her head drooped; her eyelids closed . . . she dozed off. A kind, charming smile appeared on her face; it became slightly flushed.

"Miriam!" her mother's voice suddenly awoke her.

"What is it, Mamma dear? I'm listening."

"No, I didn't mean that—"

"What then?"

"According to my reckoning . . . do you understand, my daugh-ter—*it* is due today—"

"It isn't time yet, Mamma dear!"

"Watch out, daughter—don't make any mistake!"

Miriam again fell into a doze; the mother went on and on read-ing about the plates of silver and the silver spoons. And then she awakened her daughter again.

Alas—*it* had already happened!

"What a pity," said Serel. "The Sabbath is spoiled. But, perhaps you're not quite certain? . . ."

She sighed and again plunged into her reading. Miriam fell asleep, but her little face was no longer covered with a rosy blush; the smile no longer appeared on her rosebud lips.

In the meanwhile Zorech had finished his prayers and was in a hurry to leave the synagogue, lest someone detain him. He crossed the street at a run. When he reached his door he stood still and listened closely to what was going on within the room. His mother-in-law was reading; while Miriam, as absorbed in the stories as always, must be listening. He wanted to give her a pleasant surprise by appearing suddenly.

He opened the door quietly. His mother-in-law failed to hear him; Miriam was asleep. At a single leap he was by her side and kissed her, with holiday greetings.

"You Godless sinner!" Serel cried out.

Miriam lost consciousness. They had ever so hard a time bringing her to.

The holiday was spoiled. . . .

The Eighth Circle of Gehenna

WEARY AND CAREWORN I kept tossing in my bed, trying to recall how it had all come about.

I had attended a meeting and had addressed it. My speech had been a veritable broadside; I had let them have it, full force.

I had harangued the assembly, fully relishing every word of mine; I was the hero; I fought for all that is noble and commendable in life. I was the champion of liberty, of all the righteousness and happiness that awaited us in the *remote future,* of a millennium that was drawing ever closer to us! I had snatched the mask of the face of hypocrisy and exposed it to the public ridicule; I stripped it naked and exhibited its festering sores and its degeneracy.

Then, suddenly, I had fallen silent. My erstwhile fervor was all gone, my fire was extinguished and my tongue became paralyzed. What had happened to me?

Well, as I had been holding forth I had unwittingly raised my eyes and caught sight of my reflection in a mirror on a wall across the room. There was a peculiar glow in my eyes—a gleam of evil. Not at all my eyes, and yet they were familiar: I had looked into such eyes somewhere before, at some time. Then it dawned on me I had been present in a barracks when a soldier was being flogged. His barrack-mates, who were administering the lashes, had had just such eyes—eyes that seemed to say emphatically: "Today *we* are whipping you; tomorrow *you* are likely to turn the tables against us. Let's throw in a few more lashes, then, just to even up the score!"

It was no gallant champion of the future that I discerned in that mirror, but a condemned man whose eyes were scourging others!

I was bewildered and petrified. As for the auditors—well, they breathed a sigh of relief, as if each one had shed a load. They felt like cattle in the field after a hailstorm, like children groping in darkness, who are suddenly confronted by a friendly light, like helpless cripples hugging a wall, who are enabled to snatch up their crutches again and be free to resume their tottering progress. I saw a young man take a young lady's hand and heard him plead: "May I?" She nodded her pretty head and added smilingly: "Yes, of course!"

And I had fled ignominiously.

Now I was lying in bed, weary and downhearted. The moon, floating across the sky, was peeping in at my window. It is said that moonlight is conducive to soul-searching, to introspection. That is absurd! I care not a straw about that.

But, alas, what was that? Two eyes seemed to emerge from the wall and to stare at me. The moon must be a sorceress—this was one of her pranks. . . . And yet, whose eyes were these? Were they the eyes of a soldier flogging a comrade-in-arms? Or, perchance, the eyes of a phantom accosting me in a desert mirage, to proffer me a drink of cold water?

The eyes still gazed at me, but there was neither anger nor sympathy in them. They seemed set in a wan, wasted face. Then, little by little, the head of a patriarchal Jew emerged; his beard and ritual sidelocks were white as snow, and he was wearing a skullcap.

"Who may you be?" He seemed oblivious to my question, however. "Who are you, old man?" I persisted.

"I? I am the Shevat Mussar," * the spectral figure replied, stirring.

Delighted by the drollery, I fell in with the moon's mood:

"Peace be unto you, Shevat Mussar!"

Whereupon he acknowledged my salutation with "Unto you be peace!" and seemed to draw nearer to me. He was of slight build but held himself erect in an unassuming way. Although there was a certain naïvete about his eyes they were regarding the scene with an air of confidence, apparently without any misgivings whatsoever. And his voice, too, was well modulated, without the least quaver. He was quite articulate: each word seemed to have a special meaning of its own.

"So you're the one who described the Gehenna?"

"I am the one."

* *Shevat Mussar*, literally the Rod of Reproof, the title of a well-known Hebrew ethical treatise dealing with the Gehenna, published in 1719—*Translator*.

"And did you depict it correctly, without amplifying or minimizing? You ought to know by now what it's like, having seen it with your own eyes."

"I saw it also during my lifetime," he remarked evasively, not in the least perturbed.

"During your lifetime?"

"Yes—in my dreams—"

"And is Gehenna actually as you had pictured it—as you saw it in your dreams?"

"Not exactly; they have enlarged it—it was found necessary to add an eighth circle—"

"What for? For whom?"

"The eighth circle," Shevat Mussar explained, "is intended for you and the likes of you; for all the *new* sinners, the *modernists*, as you wish to be known."

"Come, why the distinction?"

"Listen carefully. Once upon a time the soul and the body were engaged in endless contention. The soul, an integral part of Providence, was constantly yearning and languishing for the starry heavens, the high realms, whereas, the coarse gross body was drawn earthward—it was hankering and itching for the morasses of sinfulness, of immorality. And so, whenever the soul triumphed all went well, but when the body won, it met with retribution, since it had actually transgressed.

"Now, what does bodily punishment consist of? Well, for one thing, one can inflict pain by means of boiling pitch or fire, or water, or serpents; also by penal servitude in the desert, in the wilderness, among ruins, and so on. In addition to that, there are the seven circles of hell, wherein sinners are punished, according to their respective transgressions.

"However, things are different in this day and age. It is the souls that make common cause now, conspiring and rebelling! The souls wage war against heaven, against the Almighty and His creation. They find universal fault; they wish to transform all things, and to turn everything topsy-turvy.

"So it isn't the bodies that transgress now, but the souls. You and your sort are impatiently straining for the end; you are champing at the bit and your eyes are popping out of their sockets in your haste to bring about the millennium before it is due. You carry on with a high hand, as though the world were yours exclusively, and all men were at your beck and call. There was no room for your kind in the seven circles of Gehenna."

"And there is no boiling pitch in the eighth circle of Gehenna?"

"There's nary a vat of it!"

"And neither fire nor water?"

"No."

"And no scourging with serpents either?"

"There's nothing of the sort."

"And one is allowed to eat, drink and sleep there?"

"Why, one may even *read* and *write* and *publish* there."

"But just what does the punishment consist of?"

"Behold, a massive cloud is drifting toward the moon from the west. As soon as this cloud eclipses the orb of night, I will vanish. However, now, you can still discern me by the moon's light, and since the cloud's progress is slow, I shall try to explain things to you briefly. Listen carefully, then. Let us say that someone like you, for instance, a man who is constantly impatient, is set naked before a mountain of snow. As he faces the mountain, he is overcome by the idea of melting the snow away. The initial idea is transformed into desire, then into passion—he simply *must* carry it out. Whereupon, he presses himself against the cold countain, breathes upon it, burrows into it with all his body and soul, so to say. The snow must melt, come what may—it must be turned into water. Water is motion, water means happiness—"

"Is he goaded on in his task by devils?"

"What for? His inordinate desire is good enough. And so he burrows into the snow ever deeper; however, each time he pauses, the snowbank freezes harder than ever. He toils and moils amid the snow, but no sooner does the white substance thaw a little, then it freezes anew."

"And—"

"And so he turns the snow into ice."

"How terrible!"

"Another man is set down in a field where the earth is as hard as rock. The sky is resplendent; there isn't even a cloudlet in it—but neither is there any sun, or moon, or stars. And, come to think of it, is there really any sky? There is merely a blue curtain stretched above the earth. And so he drags his feet over the hardened earth, all alone, as if in a desert. After all, he is the only living being there endowed with sentience and intelligence.

"It is only a question of time before he becomes very lonely; he craves for fellowship, for human life around him, and since these are lacking, he must create them, he must resurrect other lives. Only one mortal, he has suffered for thousands; he had exerted influence over tens of thousands and has thought for them. Indeed, his soul is the symbolic soul of millions! Is he not a creator? Is he not capable of bringing things about even as the Lord did?

"No sooner said, than done: he picks up clay and proceeds to knead the lump. But what does he aim to create? Why, birds with wings. Man, bereft of any wings, is as nothing. In due time, he will create eagles, too, but in the meantime it will have to be small, common birds. His first creations are inanimate little winged things. He breathes into them his own soul and, lo and behold, the birds become alive! He is beside himself with joy, and he cries out to them: 'Take to the air, my little birds! Fly up to the sky!'

"But the birds do not fly. They merely hop about on the ground, searching for little worms to sustain their little selves. But there are no worms around, and so they starve to death. And when, on occasion, a very few of the birds do take to the air, they happen to be a male and female, and merely bill and coo.

" 'Fly higher—soar through the skies!' the man urges them.

"But the birds merely keep on billing and cooing. In his rage, the man pelts them with clods and kills them. The same fate meets the other birds he fashioned. The ground becomes strewn with carrion, with the bodies of dead birds, heaped upon one another."

"Unhappy mortal!"

"Still another transgressor I could tell you of was pitched headlong into a kennel of wild dogs.

"Did they pounce upon him and devour him alive? God forfend! Though ravenous, the hounds would not harm him: after all he was their friend, he communed with them. He was the prophet of the canine breed. At first he addressed them in their own speech and, once they had grasped his message, he began to include a few words of human speech, adding to them as he went along. Thus did he stand, haranguing them, his eyes fixed upon those dogs, casting a spell over them and restraining them.

"Everything is subject to evolution. Species change: Dogs may evolve into human beings. Here one was rearing on its hind legs, and beating the air with its forepaws. A second followed this example; even in their barking one could already detect a milder tone, an inflection as of the human voice.

"And the man went on with his harangue, holding the dogs spellbound with both his words and eyes. Look, they are all standing erect like human beings! There, one has lifted a forepaw as though it were a hand, pointing it at heaven. And in the eyes of that dog over there is a gleam, something akin to a *will*, to a realization of self. Before long, the eyes of all the dogs will become animated and gleam thus. They have become oblivious of hunger, of their being famished dogs. Before long, they will become conscious of *thought!*—of great, wondrous thought. . . ."

"And then what?"

"However, that was never destined to happen. The Angel of Destruction lost no time in flinging a bone into their midst, whereupon the entire pack fell to scrabbling for it. Only when the bone had disappeared could the prophet of dogdom start haranguing them all over again—and thus did it go on, forever and ever—"

"And I glimpsed still another transgressor at the foot of a high mountain, with a wondrous light beaming on the summit thereof. The man was drawn to that dazzling light. If he could but attain to that alluring, that entrancing height (he mused), how happy he would be!"

"Did he ascend to that height?"

"*She* restrained him. There was a woman reclining at the foot of that mountain and, at his first attempt to climb up, she fixed him with her eyes. And these eyes, too, held a magic gleam; one could discern heaven within them, and the sun, and the stars, and an entrancing radiance.

"And he retrieved his steps!

"Thereupon she closed her eyes. And thus did he go up and down, alternating between one radiant splendor and another, between this refulgence and that."

"But why didn't the man take the woman along with him?"

"She was not what she seemed to be. The cloud is drawing very near the moon. Let me tell you about the eagles and the pighides—"

"But what are those things yonder?"

"Oh, what do they matter? As I was saying, the souls of some of your prophets are transformed into living eagles—eagles broad of wing but with the skin of swine. And those metamorphosed prophets of yours take to the air and soar to great heights. They yearn to conquer heaven, to triumph over the Heavenly Throne.

"But as they wing upwards, their swine skins crack, and when the open wounds become too painful, they plunge into the mire of swamps, where they try to assuage their pain. And this alternate process of rising and falling goes on continuously."

But at this point the moon vanished—and the Rod of Reproof vanished along with it.

When I awoke and lighted a candle, I found a postcard on the night-table.

"You are cordially invited to attend a meeting—," it read.

I tore the card into small bits.

The Bass Viol

O NE DAY a homeless young man appeared on the streets of the Polish town of Tomashov, which is on the border of Galicia. No one knew where he came from or where he found shelter.

It goes without saying that alms are given any man who holds out his hand. But since this strange fellow would accept no money —and no food—the people in the town lost interest in him. Nevertheless, they gradually became aware of his quaint ways. His eyes seemed to peer far ahead, yet were oblivious of his immediate surroundings; also, the lobes of his ears would twitch as though they heard a hundred noises, even though silence hung as heavy as the moment preceding the blowing of the ram's horn in a House of Worship. He was always deep in thought and would start as if he had just been aroused from a coma whenever anyone accosted him; the simplest question would throw him into confusion and he would falter in his speech while beads of perspiration appeared on his brow. Whenever someone sent him on an errand, he would disappear for days at a time, and when he did show up you couldn't make head or tail of what he had to say. This peculiar behavior was not due to shiftlessness, however, but rather to fits of depression.

"Have you delivered the message?" he would be asked.

"I just got around to it."

"And what were you doing up to now?"

It turned out that, while on his errand, he had come across a field-mouse; the little animal was squeaking—it had probably lost its way. Then he had become fascinated by a chirping bird, and he had run after it. He had been woolgathering and had either forgotten or had failed to grasp the answer he was to bring back. Then he would grin innocently and hold out his gaunt hand for a piece of bread—it seemed he had gone without a bit of food the whole time he had been away.

One tedious summer day, when almost all business activity in the town was at a standstill and the local shopkeepers were sitting on their doorsteps twiddling their thumbs, one of them caught sight of the destitute stranger and called him over for questioning —anything for a bit of fun.

"Come inside, young man," the shopkeeper suggested. But the young man hesitated, so the tradesman stepped outside and proceeded to cross-examine him.

"What's your name, young man?"

"My name?" he echoed. "Abraham—I *think* it's Abraham."

"You're not quite sure?" The young man seemed dubious. How could one be absolutely sure when there were so many things in this world? "And what's your last name?" the shopkeeper went on, snickering.

Completely baffled by the question, the newcomer asked innocently if a family name was a necessity.

"Indeed it is!" the shopkeeper enlightened him. "There are quite a few Abrahams and they have to be distinguished somehow. Whose son are you?"

"My father's."

"And what's your father's name?"

"I called him father."

"And where does your father live?"

"Same place as yours," and he pointed to the sky.

"A driveling idiot," the shopkeeper reflected. "And have you no other father?" he persisted.

"No."

"Do you have a mother?"

"What does one need a mother for?"

The interrogator was convulsed with laughter, and the young pauper asked if he were free to go.

"You can go as soon as you tell me where you come from," the shopkeeper replied.

"From a village."

"What's the name of the village? Is it far from here?"

That was something Abraham could not answer. All he knew was that he trudged for days and nights without number before arriving here.

"Can you say your prayers?"

"Prayers?" the young man was at a loss. And, after a long lecture from his tormentor, Abraham divined that prayer meant having a private conversation with the Father.

The young man said that he could recite the "Hark, O Israel!" prayer and proceeded to tell how, while he was making his way through a forest he had come upon an old man who had enlightened him as to who his Father was and how he was to commune with Him and who finally taught him to recite "Hark, O Israel!" And although he had failed to understand the meaning of the prayer, the ancient had assured him that the Father knew it's meaning and that He was greatly delighted by it.

"And when do you converse with your Father?" asked the shopkeeper.

"Twice a day." Abraham added that he played music.

"What instrument can you play?"

"Any instrument at all."

He used to play on a shepherd's pipe; then he had mastered the art of making and playing wooden whistles. And when people in the town from which he came presented him with an ocarina, he played that as well.

"And suppose someone were to give you a fiddle?"

Abraham's eyes lit up. What wouldn't he give for a stringed instrument—especially a huge bull fiddle like those the town musicians carry on a strap! How he would play on it!

"It's quite possible that such an instrument could be obtained for you," the shopkeeper said with a straight face. "However, let's hear you play something first."

Without further ado, the young man got an ocarina from his tattered pocket and began to play. Just a few notes, and birds came flying from all directions, fluttering their wings and chirping joyously. Abraham greeted the birds with a smile and put the ocarina back in his pocket.

The shopkeeper seemed unaware of what was going on. His wife, however, came running out of the house, followed by the maid, to see who was playing, and heads appeared at the windows of the houses nearby.

"What did you live on in the woods?" the shopkeeper asked.

"Mushrooms," the young man answered.

Evidently he had some idea of nourishment. "And how did you get along in your village?"

He lived on whatever the good folk gave him.

"Who gave you anything?"

It seemed that the peasants gave him an occasional handout—sometimes even the priest and the innkeeper would give him something.

"And what did they give you?" the shopkeeper asked, positive that the best was yet to come.

They gave him cabbage soup every now and then or borsch, meat or bread, the lad explained sheepishly. He would hold on to the bread and give the other things to the small wild creatures.

"But why only bread?"

Bread was what he liked, he explained; he had an aversion for any other food. The ancient in the woods had, by the way, questioned him on the same subject. And when he had explained that he ate only bread, the old man had professed great liking for him and, what is more, taught him how to commune with the Father. The lad, in turn, had come to worship the old man, and it was because of him that he could say "Hark, O Israel!" so fervently.

"And suppose the old man had asked you to steal or to rob?" the shopkeeper retorted.

Why, he would not have hesitated, although the ancient was not likely to urge anything like that, he was such a good-natured man.

"But just the same, suppose he had bidden you to kill a man?"

The lad would have done the old man's bidding.

"And would you have no fear of your Father?"

"Why should I?"

"Aren't you afraid of being punished?"

The lad's face beamed for the first time:

"You are making fun of me—a father doesn't punish his children!"

By now, it was time for the pre-sunset prayers, and the shopkeeper went to the synagogue where he could inform the others of the clever way in which he had questioned the young stranger.

The story would have caused quite a stir in the Jewish community, had it not been for a greater sensation. This community supported a troupe of musicians, consisting of two fiddles, a flute, a clarinet, a drum and bass viol. It was a pitiful small-town *capella* which played at Jewish weddings and during the Purim and

Hanuka festivals. Every now and then it also filled in at gala affairs of the lesser Polish gentry. Needless to add, it was scarcely a metropolitan symphony orchestra.

One winter morning, the wretched Tomashov orchestra was homeward bound from one of these second-class Polish fiestas. The players had partaken of the flowing bowl but not of the food, which was ritually unclean. They straggled along the road, yodeling, singing, and cursing. The bass viol player, who was an old man, was staggering under his load, barely able to plod through the snow, and he pleaded with the others not to leave him behind. They paid little heed to him, however, and, since it had begun to snow, quickened their pace. On reaching town, each musician hastened to his home and was fast asleep within minutes. It was not long, however, before each one was awake again—the old bass viol player had not turned up and his wife was wailing and clamoring:

"Where is my husband? What have you done with my husband?"

When the befuddled and sleepy musicians realized that something was amiss, they retraced their steps in search of their lost companion. But a new blanket of snow had covered all tracks, and the search party had to admit failure on its return. There was still the last hope that the unfortunate old man might have had enough presence of mind to find refuge in some peasant hut.

Within a few days, the snow melted a little. Then, on Friday, when the Jews repaired to the public baths and the topic of the missing man was still uppermost in everyone's mind, a peasant cart carrying the frozen body of the bass viol player rolled into the marketplace. Working against time, the townsmen managed to bury him just before the blessing of the candles, thus coming perilously close to transgressing against the holy Sabbath; they were far from desirous, however, of becoming involved in any post-mortem investigation.

The following morning, the widow resorted to the drastic step of interrupting the services in the synagogue to remind the congregation of the plight of her five orphaned children. The elders called a meeting that same evening and invited the musicians. Since there was no communal provision for such emergencies, the musicians were urged to do without a bass viol and to donate the share of the deceased to the widow. The musicians protested vehemently, maintaining that even though a reduced orchestra might do for Jewish weddings—if such was the wish of the elders— the Polish gentry would never engage an orchestra without a bass viol. The Rabbi, however, contended that the matter of sustaining a soul in Israel transcended the issue of playing dance music for the gentry. The defiant players argued that the spiritual leader of the community—begging his pardon—did not know beans about music.

Voices were raised in protest; they called the musicians heartless ruffians. It was at this critical moment that the shopkeeper who had questioned the hapless young fellow pounded on the reader's desk, called for attention and proceeded to tell the congregation all about him and his yearning for a bass viol; in all probability he would be able to play it. Now then, if he were to marry the widow, the marriage would cut the Gordian knot, and the community would not be taxed even one extra copper.

He had probably meant the thing as a joke but the suggestion caught the fancy of the congregation. The widow agreed and so did Abraham, and within a month the two were married. Hardly knowing how it had all happened, the young unfortunate had acquired a wife with five children and a bass viol with a bow.

The newlyweds lived in harmony. Abraham rarely entered the house; he slept on the threshold and roamed for days at a stretch, turning up only on important occasions or when he felt the pangs of hunger. In the latter event, he would tap at the window and his wife would hand him a piece of bread, whereupon he would vanish until hunger drove him back again. When inquisitive neighbors questioned her concerning her domestic bliss, she told them with a smile that she was delighted. What could an elderly woman wish for, after all? Her new husband neither ate nor drank at home and never scolded her. Furthermore, she collected his entire earnings directly from the orchestra. What else could one ask?

Abraham, too, was happy as a lark. At the outset, he had had difficulties with the orchestra. He would strum right on, long after the others had stopped, as though he were accompanying some far-off band that only he could hear. In time, however, his companions learned to take this in their stride. Whenever they played for the gentry, one of the other players would simply restrain Abraham's bow when each dance was over, but at Jewish affairs he was purposely given free rein and the gathering would roar their approval. This was particularly the case during wedding feasts.

It need hardly be said that the community was delighted with its find. At weddings, he used to sit unobstrusively, facing the wall in order not to look at the women. Nor would he touch any of the viands, always bringing along his own supper of bread.

Without realizing it, he also rendered a special service to his fellow-townsmen by summoning them to the synagogue services. He got into the habit of playing the solemn *Hearken, O Israel* at dawn, at sunset, and at midnight. The dawn and sunset rendition originated from beside a stream that ran through a meadow on the outskirts of the town, while at midnight he played in the marketplace. The moving strains of the bass viol would echo through the silent night and find their way through doors and shuttered windows to the hearts of men. Even those Jews whom the loud call of beadle had failed to rouse to the penitential prayers would respond to the call of Abraham's bass viol by getting out of bed and going to the House of Worship.

Whenever he played offkey at a ball, some Polish patrician would leave his partner and make a dash for Abraham to pluck a few hairs of his ear-locks; the town's Jews poked fun at him during their celebrations; yet, when his plaintive music was heard at midnight, many would comment with a sigh: "A poor, senseless creature, alas—yet there's something about the way he plays," or: "Poor soul—he yearns to commune with the Almighty, and this is the only way he knows."

The placid life of Tomashov was interrupted one day by a festive occasion, the kind that happens only once in a lifetime.

Two illustrious families—that of the *parness,* the leader of the great Jewish community of Lublin on the one hand and the Grand Rabbi of Cracow on the other—were to become related through a marriage. A significant matter, this, for Tomashov was located between Lublin and Cracow.

The leader of the Jewish community of Lublin was eager for the wedding to be in keeping not only with his own prestige but also with the status of the spiritual leader of Cracow. He therefore ordered a barrel of gold coins be brought up from the cellar to defray the expense of the wedding. Next he sent caterers to

Tomashov to arrange everything in a manner befitting an alliance between two such distinguished houses.

The caterers had to find a place spacious enough to accommodate a large number of guests, which included prominent merchants, the leading citizens, and the distinguished scholars and rabbis from the two cities as well as those from Tomashov itself. And, naturally, not only was the orchestra from each metropolis engaged but the Tomashov band as well, though it was anything but first class.

There was a huge barn on the outskirts of Tomashov, used for storing and drying timber through the winter months. It was empty just then, since the lumber it had held was by this time floating in barges down the Vistula River, heading for Danzig. The caterers took over this Noah's ark of a barn, refurbishing and decorating it with all sorts of drapes, pictures, and paper lanterns in keeping with the occasion. Long tables were set out (those for the women apart from those for the men) to accommodate at least four hundred guests. The entrance for the women was also separate from that of the men, and there was a special entrance adorned with the crown of the Torah for the Sage of Cracow and the other guests of honor.

On the day of the wedding, the influx of guests exceeded all expectations, and many had to be put up in the homes of the leading citizens, who considered it an honor to extend their hospitality.

The erstwhile lumber shed was now lighted by candelabra and colorful paper lanterns. The guests sat down to a feast at which the brilliance of the women's jewelry and finery vied with the hallowed splendor of the Torah, reflected in the men of learning, headed by the Sage of Cracow.

As soon as the waiters served the heaping platters of highly seasoned fish, the chatter of the women blended with the tinkling of the silver knives and forks and with the learned discourse at the Rabbi's table. Suddenly the three orchestras struck up a *frailichs,* a wedding tune so lively that the very flames of the candles seemed to leap and join in the merriment. The Grand Rabbi of Cracow, reputed to be a connoisseur of music, leaned back, beaming with joy.

From the sprightly *frailichs* the musicians glided into the leisurely, enchanting melody of a *wallach.* Hardly anyone was aware of the transition. A solo played by the first violinist of the

Cracow orchestra animated every heart in the place. All three orchestras accompanied the soloist. The music created the impression of a gentle stream, rippling and murmuring in honor of the bride and groom and the Sage of Cracow. And above that stream a bird seemed to be hovering and—lo and behold!—it was warbling liturgical chants, now mellow and sweet, now plaintive. It reminded the celebrants that no matter how great the present festivity, the Jews were still in exile and that the Divine Glory was in exile together with them. Before long, however, the pensive guests, beholding the men of learning and the Grand Rabbi, burst once more into joyous song. And the musicians, overwhelmed by their fervor, let themselves go completely. This jubilation, this paean, seemed to transport the guests into a realm of bliss.

Suddenly all the three orchestras fell silent, as though their instruments had been put out of commission. All the instruments, that is, but one: Abraham, facing the wall, went right on strumming his bass viol. All eyes riveted on him; the assembly was spellbound. Abraham's bow went on and on. This was a prank that the musicians had planned, by way of amazing the guests, but it evidently backfired. The musicians were waiting eagerly for the gathering to roar with laughter, but instead everybody kept staring —first at Abraham, then at the Sage of Cracow, for they were reluctant to laugh at or to ridicule anyone in the presence of the Rabbi. Inwardly they were bursting with laughter, but were awaiting their cue from the Rabbi whose sable-trimmed hat shaded his half-closed eyes. Had he dozed off by any chance?

Abraham kept right on playing and the guests were becoming fidgety. Suddenly all eyes turned to the central entrance. There was a commotion there, and the sound of much trampling outside. The attendants hastened to the door and called out, rather perturbed:

"No, not now—there will be another supper later on, especially for the poor."

The commotion was caused by a horde of beggars, it turned out, who were eager to gain admission. The Rabbi of Cracow looked up, as if to voice his opinion—undoubtedly to invite the poor brethren in. But at that moment an old man in tatters with an unkempt gray beard appeared in the doorway. To all intents and purposes he was a typical beggar, except that his eyes had the gleam of a prophet and there was authority in the gesture as he held up his hand. The attendants fell back, reluctantly, yet with great deference. The strange figure with the compelling eyes advanced to the center of the room, followed by a crew of beggars. All the guests, including the Sage of Cracow, were dumbfounded. Abraham, however, was still bent over his instrument and kept right on playing, unaware of what was going on.

As the patriarch was about to speak, the guests leaned forward, all eyes and ears.

"*Chetzos*—the midnight prayer!" he began and, after a moment's hesitation, went on: "Rabbi of Cracow, Abraham is playing for the midnight prayer. I see you are disposed to doubt it. Well, you shall judge for yourself. In order that you should be found worthy of hearing Abraham play for the midnight service, it was ordained that your house should become united through marriage with that of the *parness* of Lublin—and that the event should be celebrated in Tomashov, which is situated midway between your respective cities. And, through your merits, the other guests as well will be privileged to hear him, but not as appreciately as yourself—since you, Rabbi, are a connoisseur of music."

And as Abraham kept on playing and the assembled guests sat spellbound, the strange beggar waved with his right hand toward the ridge of the roof, whereupon its halves parted and swung open in opposite directions. The moon and millions of twinkling stars suddenly became visible. The stranger waved his hand again, and the sky itself split asunder, revealing a streaming radiance accompanied by a symphonic chant. It was the celestial host chanting the Midnight Prayer. Angelic choirs and musicians took part in the heavenly service, and Abraham's playing was in harmony with the heavenly chant.

The guests were stunned.

Once more the old man waved his hand; the sky closed up, the music ceased, and the twinkling stars reappeared. Then came his final signal, and the two halves of the roof came together at the ridge again. The guests did not move. Abraham continued his solo for a few moments, and then the instrument slipped from his grasp. He stood up, faced the audience, and began to recite the solemn prayer, "Hearken, O Israel!" with the same ecstasy he had evinced in accompanying the celestial chant. And, his prayer done, he collapsed.

The mysterious old man picked him up:

"Carry him to the House of Worship!" he bade the attendants.

As soon as they had removed Abraham, the strange figure proclaimed solemnly:

"Rabbi of Cracow, it is not only a wedding that you have come to solemnize but also a funeral. Abraham has been summoned to the Kingdom of Heaven—its orchestra was in need of a bass viol."

The next instant the mysterious old man and his tattered horde disappeared.

The following day Abraham died in the House of Worship and the Grand Rabbi of Cracow together with all the other guests attended his funeral.

It was rumored that the mysterious ancient was none other than Leib, the son of Sarah—the saintly Rabbi Levi Yithok.

Morning in a Basement

O LD MENASHEH had barely finished his prayer and a few Psalms when the wan break of a summer day was already peeking in at the tiny basement window.

With sad, weary eyes Menasheh contemplates the newborn day. He cracks his long knuckles and closes his psaltery, extinguishes the small kerosene lamp, and walks over to the window. He gazes at the pallid strip of sky over the narrow alleyway, and the shadow of a wry smile appears on his greenish, wrinkled face, framed in its silvery beard and ritual sidelocks.

"I have paid my debt," he reflects. "Many thanks to Thee, Creator of the Universe! Come," he sighs, "what need hast Thou of one here, Creator of the Universe? Dost Thou need an extra prayer, an extra Psalm—is that it? As if Thou didst not have enough!"

He turns away from the window and reflects that to his way of thinking, it would be better if his granddaughter Rivka had his bed; the way things were, she had to sprawl on the floor among the rags which were the stock-in-trade of his son, Hayim. According to his conscience, it would be far more just if the glass of milk which sustains him for almost the whole day, were to go to Soreh, his daughter-in-law, who bustles about the marketplace from morning to night without so much as a cup of broth the whole day. Nor would it hurt any if Yankel, the latest offspring of the family, were to get this milk. True enough he, who was an old man, needed little, but things would be so much easier for the whole family if he needed *nothing at all.*

Hayim's clothing was all threadbare. Hannah, Menasheh's oldest granddaughter was sickly and anemic. Greensickness, the doctor had declared, prescribing tincture of iron and codliver oil— and a little wine. They are saving money for her, knotting it in a handkerchief all by itself; they've been saving it for months but

213

still it was all too little. Poor Hannah wasn't growing at all; neither did her mind mature; it was just at a standstill. She was all of seventeen now, yet she understood no more than a twelve-year-old.

"Creator of the Universe, why hast Thou placed me as a burden upon their shoulders?"

He listens closely to the harsh and abrupt breathing of Hayim in his sleep. He can see how wearily Soreh's long hand, which had just been rocking the baby, hangs down off the bed. He notices that Yankel is stirring in his cradle. "He'll soon be yelling and will waken his mother!"—and with small, hasty steps he runs up to his grandson and begins to rock the cradle.

"But," he reflects, turning to the window, "perhaps it is Thy wish, God, that I should bide long enough to be gladdened by Yankel—that I may teach him his prayers, that I may instruct him in reading—is that it?"

There is a bloom on Yankel's tiny cheeks as he sleeps. A sweet smile hovers over his rosebud lips as they open and close. "The glutton—he would like to suck even in his sleep."

At this point the old man notices that Rivka is extremely restless in bed. She is lying on her straw pallet, her chest covered with a soiled, polka-dotted bedsheet. He cannot see what she is using for a pillow. Her delicate face, her long, exquisitely carved neck rest demurely against the background of her tangled, vividly red hair which is spread over the whole pillow. The strands stir with her every breath and reach right to the floor.

"The very image of my dear wife," reflects the old man. "Hot blood—dreams. May the Lord preserve her and grant her many years!"

"Rivka!" He approaches her and touches the bared arm thrust out from under the sheet.

"What is it?" Rivka awakes in fright, opening her large blue eyes.

"Shh!" he calms her with a smile. "It's me. You can use my bed."

"What about you, Grandpa?" she asks.

"I'm not going to sleep any more—one doesn't sleep much at my age. I'm going to make the tea. You must have heard last night —they're getting up early. Your father has business to attend to in town, and your mother must do the marketing for the engagement party at the Pimsenholtz house."

"I will make the tea, Grandpa."

"No, Rivka—go and sleep in my bed. You can sleep for quite a while yet. Your mother said you're not going to the factory today; she'll need you. You may as well catch up on your sleep."

"A-ah!" Rivka yawns. Now she has recalled everything. Last evening Father had come home with good tidings—God had sent him a decent lot of old rags. Mother had also brought good news: the Pimsenholtzes for whom she did the marketing were having an engagement party at last, even though the prospective bride was not entirely satisfied: but there would be a celebration just the same.

These tidings held no promise of any great pleasure for Rivka. True, she would catch up on her sleep, and going to market with her mother was more pleasant, of course, than working at the factory, but at the same time lugging the baskets with eggs and chickens—and running after a hen whenever one escaped—was not the most agreeable of occupations.

There was no escaping it, however. She wrapped herself in the bed sheet and got into the old man's bed. He watched, thinking: "The very image of my old woman!"

By the time the old man had gotten the fire going, shaving off a few extremely thin bits of kindling, placing them in the range, sprinkling pea-coals over them ("Coal comes high!" he reflected while doing this), pouring kerosene over it and placing an old tin teakettle, all covered with rust, on the opening in the kitchen —by the time he had done all this Soreh had managed to give Yankel the breast, expressing as she did so, the desire to see the day when Yankel would be pronouncing the benediction over milk.

Pale Hannah had also awakened and was sitting up in bed; behind her mother's back she is playing peek-aboo with her little brother. Framed by thick ashen-colored hair her tiny face, with its pale cheeks and dreamy eyes, bobbed from right to left. But her movements were languid, her smile wan and her gaze much too fixed to distract Yankel the Glutton (as they called him) so early in the morning from his mother's breast. He was too occupied: he was looking at his sister but had no time to play with her.

One of his hands was tucked in under him in his mother's lap; with the other he was holding aside the edge of her unbuttoned chemise to keep it from his face and was regarding his sister imperturbably and indifferently—she'll be around whenever he wants her.

Hayim has already wrapped himself in his prayershawl and put on his phylacteries and is praying as he paces the room. He frequently stops, glowering at Soreh as if he wanted to tell her something, but then he looks at the old man and resumes his pacing.

He is in awe of the old man, who thinks that the present is still like the good old times when a Jew could pray properly, reciting word for word from the prayerbook. Now there are seven dealers for every pair of worn-out-pants! True, he had taken precautionary measures yesterday: he had closed the deal for six roubles (less five kopecks) and had left a deposit of seven zloty and twelve groszen; he had given three kopecks to the caretaker as he was leaving, not to let in any dealer in old rags before he came back. However, he is uneasy. Who knows, before he can find a partner for the deal.

At last he is drinking tea, holding the glass on his palm and blowing on the tea before each gulp. He does not know what to do—it is hard to find a partner! Whom can he turn to? A usurer? He will skin him alive! The keeper of the general store? He will get the last copper out of him. But even if he should find a partner Hayim will have to give up half the profits to him—even though he, Hayim, does all the haggling.

There are occasions when he can get a few zloty out of Soreh—but today it's impossible! She had told him the day before that she wouldn't have money enough for her marketing. However, maybe she will trust him for one day with something from Hannah's savings. Just the same he is afraid to broach the subject. He has tried more than once only to come a cropper each time. He sneaks another glance at Soreh, and it strikes him that this is the most propitious moment. She has just put Yankel back in his cradle and is dressing as she stands near it. Her smile is so tender that the thing may work, after all.

"I was thinking last night," he opines, "that this will be a very good buy. I think I'll make something on it—"

"May God grant it," Soreh responds. "Let it be lucky for Yankel's sake. Ever since he was born it has been a little easier to earn something—"

"I think," Hayim turns to her with an ingratiating smile, "that this is a lucky stroke for Hannah. Do you know, Soreh, I was thinking as I was buying the lot that at least one third of the profit ought to go to Hannah. And, just as the thought came to me, the lady became as soft as silk and began coming down on the price, one five-kopeck piece after another.

"So much the better," Soreh smiles at him. And, it seems to him that she has regained her youthfulness, her freshness. If conditions were only better. . . . But he has no time to think of such things.

"And so, Hannah is my partner!"

"Fine! What could be better?"

"Yes," he mumbles, "if Hannah is a partner . . . after all, I'm counting on her luck, but since she's a partner. . . ."

"Well, what about it?" Soreh asks, pricking up her ears and looking at him closely. "He's surely leading up to something," she suspects. "He's after something."

"What about it? Only this—I want her to be a partner in fact—to have her put some of the capital into this deal."

"What? What are you saying?" Soreh cannot believe her ears, and receiving no answer, flies at her husband.

"Bandit! Monster! There's a father for you—There's a husband! He knows how sick the girl is that I would not touch her money. It's her money—money gotten for her with blood! Now and then she carries a basket for me, so I occasionally give her a little something—"

Soreh cannot calm down. Hayim wants to say something in answer to her, but the old man will not let him:

"It would be better if you kept quiet, Hayim. Keep quiet—can't you see that Soreh is right? Go, find yourself a partner. Don't take advantage of people—live and let live."

Without a word Hayim puts a slice of bread and an onion in his sack, and leaves the house.

"Have you ever seen how birds pick up crumbs out in the yard?" the old man admonishes him as he leaves. "When a crumb is extra *large* it take two birds to pick it up!"

Rivka sleeps in the old man's bed no less restlessly than before. A persistent thought will not let her sleep soundly. *She has met someone!*

Once, toward evening, as she was going home from the factory, she had collided with a young man on the sidewalk. She kept right on going, thinking that he would make way for her, but he re-

217

fused to budge, staring her right in the face with his laughing eyes and making her blush all over. It was she who had to step aside, after which she ran all the way hime. As she was turning into the little street where she lived, she looked over her shoulder and saw that he was still standing there and following her with his eyes, his dazzling white teeth still bared in the same smile.

"I'll tell Hannah about this," she thought, but then decided against it: what would Hannah, the poor ailing thing understand!

A few days later she saw him again. Her heart began to beat faster; embarrassment kept her from raising her eyes and she walked past him quickly, yet so clumsily that she almost slipped on the side walk! As she passed him she felt (so it seemed to her) that his gay radiant smile was gliding over her bared neck. This frightened her: it seemed to her that all the passers-by noticed, and she fled in great haste.

On one occasion he appeared out of nowhere. She gasped, but he still stood there, barring her way.

"I think young lady," he said, "that I have the good fortune of being acquainted with you."

He had called her *young lady!* Nevertheless she was angry and stepped back from him, impatient and frightened. However, she had to admit that he had a most pleasant voice. A voice of gold, her heart told her.

Since then they had seen each other almost every evening, but she didn't speak to him. And every evening he accompanied her from the factory to her home; they walked side by side, without exchanging a word. Often she could not resist the temptation and would glance at him out of the corner of her eye. He would respond to her with a smile that was more radiant than ever. What extraordinary eyes he had. At times it seemed as if golden rays were shooting from them.

Meanwhile, the girls at the factory had found out all about this; they had observed everything and the talk began. They laughed and poked fun at her.

"The young are foolish," one of the girls remarked. Today she runs away; tomorrow she will start running after him."

"You'll never live to see the day," Rivka reflected.

"She'll stick her tongue out, like a sheep after salt—"

Rivka bit her lips but said nothing.

"And what a handsome chap," the banter went on. "What eyes,

what hair—and his nose is simply sculptured! He's got a watch-chain hanging from his vestpocket with at least ten gold charms dangling from it!" (Rivka felt flattered at this.)

"It may be pinchbeck," one of the girls remarked.

"Of course!" Rivka reflected sarcastically.

"Oh, now, now, what are you saying!" others chimed in with what Rivka was thinking. "One can see he has well-to-do parents."

Others said:

"So you don't want an affair—you've got time! But you might at least be clever about it. Speak kindly to him, accept small presents, let him treat you to supper, give you candy and theatre tickets."

"Of course!" one of the girls laughed. "Grab all you can. But don't let them lay their hands on you—oh, no, may the devil take them!"

Finally there came the voice of the forelady; she had a long, bony face, a pointed chin, and her greenish eyes were crossed:

"My, my, my!" she said. "Just think what the likes of her has to lose! The wedding canopy is simply waiting for her. I guess there's just no counting her dowry; the matchmakers are wearing out her threshold and the suitors are coming in droves—she has to beat them off—"

Rivka pressed her lips still tighter; head sank and scalding tears fell on her hands as she worked the sewing-machine.

And it is all these things that will not let her sleep. No, she will not take anything—not a thing. Especially not theatre tickets. Once she had been detained rather late at the factory by rush orders. Her mother had come running, more dead than alive. When she caught sight of Rivka, her eyes started blinking and tears gushed forth from them like a fountain. Her grandfather was standing in the factory hallway near the staircase, wringing his hands.

"Glory be!" he was muttering. "Glory be to God!"

It was Soreh's turn to get ready to leave for the city. She put the glass of milk for the old man on the table and moved Yankel's cradle close to him. She still had to see to at least some of the domestic details, but just the same she managed to complain to the Grandfather how bad times were.

"Surely, you must have heard, Father-in-law! The engagement party must take place . . . the time is all set. They sent me a telegram to buy everything. But the bride is creating scenes all the time. She doesn't want to marry! She doesn't want a husband from the provinces. Says she has a Warsaw fellow, a Warsaw fashion-plate!"

Hannah, who all this time had been lying and staring at the ceiling, watching the flies take off one after the other and fly away in all directions, suddenly sat up on hearing her mother's words and her eyes, which were generally dull, took on an unexpected glitter. Obviously she was listening with great interest.

She would earn something, however, her mother felt sure.

"The engagement will go through, with God's help. Old man Pimsenholtz will show him yet. His bloated old lady won't keep her mouth shut either. Has she got sharp claws!

"First of all, their cook told me, they searched all of the daughter's things, found the letters of some fly-by-night dandy, and burned them. After that, did she get it! She got plenty! They dragged her around by her hair—"

Hannah felt that her eyes were getting moist, and that her face was reddening and becoming distorted with compassion. She fell on her pillow, weeping. Soreh became frightened; the old man hastened to her.

"What is it, Hannah? What's the matter with you?"

"I feel sorry, Mama—I feel sorry—"

"Sorry for whom, my daughter?" Soreh asked, forgetting everything else.

"For the girl who's getting married. She's so good, so kind-hearted. She gives me money all the time—the money that I give you. She pets me; sometimes she kisses me. She wants to teach me how to write—"

"That's all we need!" Soreh says angrily. "May my enemies have such things for their perdition! And does she want to turn your head too, so that you won't listen to your mother?"

"No, Mother dear!" Hannah answered, weeping. "You needn't be afraid of anything like that. I'll always listen to you. No matter what sort of a bridegroom you may pick for me—"

There is a sound of sudden ringing laughter. It is Rivka, laughing at the naïvete of her sister.

"You wicked creature!" Soreh screamed at her. "The child is ill—dangerously ill. Watch out you don't laugh out of the other side of your mouth—"

"Don't curse her, Soreh," the old man tried to calm her. "After all, she too is still a child."

"Get up, my fine lady!" Soreh shouted at Rivka as she left the room. "Give Hannah her tea; sweep up the room—"

Old Menasheh has drunk his milk and seated himself at the little window. All you can see through the small pane are long, narrow shadows, cast by the legs of the people passing by on the sidewalk. The nearer it is to noon, the more rapidly do the shadows shift, and the sadder does the old man feel. People are hurrying, running, buying and selling, working; he alone (so it seems to him) is no longer good for anything.

He picks up a Psaltery. In a quavering voice he reads a verse in the ancient tongue, then a verse in Yiddish, and with a trembling foot rocks Yankel's little cradle. Rivka, half dressed, is sitting on Hannah's bed; the two of them are drinking tea. Next to Rivka, blooming with health and life, Hannah seems even sicklier, even paler and smaller. They are having a heart-to-heart talk.

"I won't breathe a word of it, Hannah—tell me the story!"

"Swear."

"I swear—"

"By what?"

"By anything you like."

Hannah wrinkles her forehead and then says:

"Swear by Yankel's health."

"I'll swear by Yankel's health," Rivka repeats after her.

"About what?"

"That I'll keep secret whatever you confide to me."

Hannah plunges into deep thought.

"You sit there," she says. "I can't sit—I'd better lie down and look at the ceiling, for otherwise I forget things, I become confused. When I'm lying down and looking upward I see everything before me . . . everything appears clearly before me—"

"Very well, lie down, Hannah—"

"You lie down, too. Put your ear close to my lips; this is a dreadful secret! I don't want Grandfather to hear."

And Hannah wrinkles her forehead still more. She is breathing hard, as if she bore a great weight. She throws herself back on the pillow. Her interest thoroughly aroused, Rivka hastens to put the tea tumblers on the table and lies down next to Hannah.

The old man interrupts his reading of the Psalms and says, turning toward the bed:

"Wouldn't it be better to tidy up, Rivka?"

"Right away, right away, Grandfather," Rivka answers. "Hannah wants to tell me something."

The old man smiles sadly and shakes his head and begins again to chant the Psalms in Yiddish.

And Hannah begins her story, her eyes staring and hardly moving, which rather frightens Rivka. It strikes her that Hannah is telling the story not from memory but that she is seeing something before her eyes, and that her story deals with what she sees. And her voice comes from deep within her, and her breath is so hot.

"The cook had gone off somewhere," Hannah begins her story. "I was left in the kitchen all by myself, waiting for Mother—she was to come for me. Rivka," she suddenly breaks her story, "when did we have wheat porridge with honey?"

"Yesterday," Rivka answers her in a petulant voice.

"It must have been yesterday, then—yes, yesterday. So I'm sitting there and drinking tea. The cook always gives me tea. Whenever I come, she gives me tea. And it's such a pleasure to drink tea there. With a silver teaspoon, all shiny. The tea warms your whole body. And as for sugar—are you listening?—you put it right in the tea. I wanted to bite off a little at a time and sip the tea through it, but she wouldn't let me, that cook; sugar's good for you, she said, and watched me so that I would put all three lumps in my tea! The cook gets a whole pound of sugar all for herself— a whole pound a week! And she takes a lot of it herself, besides. Mother says she takes it out of a silver sugar bowl that stands in the front room. It stands with the lid up—I saw it myself! But I'm not going to take any. There's a picture of a reindeer on the sugar bowl. Old lady Pimsenholtz told me it's a reindeer. With such huge, branching horns—it really is a reindeer—"

"Well, then you were sitting in the kitchen?" Rivka reminds her.

"Yes, I was sitting on the bed there. My, what a bed the cook has! Three big pillows, the slips as white as snow. With woven lace and red showing through. Big mother-of-pearl buttons, each like a big silver coin. A quilted satin cover, with a big circle in the middle of it, just like a well. Surrounded by eagles with enormous wings. Lying on top of the bed is an extra blanket, green, of silk. Like a high-born lady, the cook is, but she's kindhearted. Invites me to sit on the bed, at the foot—she turns back the cover. She loves me, she says—and do you know why, Rivka?"

"Why?"

"She says she once had a girl just like me. They didn't call her Hannah, but she was my age—so she loves me she says. Why did you shudder, Rivka?"

"Just so. Go on with your story, Hannah!"

"I'm sitting and drinking tea—and she walks in—"

"Who?"

"The bride: the one that got a beating."

"A beating? What do you mean?"

"Come, haven't you heard? Yes, yes—they beat her because she doesn't want to marry the other man."

"Oh, yes! Well, then, she walked in—"

"She walked in, pale as could be, and her eyes all red. She was wearing a blue silk dress in the house—you hear, Rivka?—brand-new, with red dots. With two long broad ribbons of satin, also red, dangling behind and tipped with silk fringes. There were diamonds in her ear-rings. Her hair was done magnificently—high up on her head it was gathered into a crown, and in the center of the crown there was a dove with spread wings—you understand?—the dove was fashioned out of her own hair. The hair in the back was held by a golden clasp in front, too. Or maybe there were even two clasps in front. And there was still another gold clasp on her sash—it was enough to blind you! Every time she turned she simply glittered!"

Hannah falls silent.

"And that's all?"

"Wait—this is a great secret, Rivka!" And fearfully, she adds: "God will punish you if you tell!"

Rivka assures her that she will not tell. Hannah places her hand under Rivka's head, clasps her closer, and goes on with her story in a softer, more repressed voice.

"She saw me and rushed toward me, sobbing."

"What did she want from you?"

"She wanted a favor from me."

"A favor? A favor from you?"

"She shoved a silver half-rouble into my hand—that same half-

223

rouble which I gave mother yesterday—and something else. . . ."

"What else, Hannah?"

"A letter. And she told me to deliver the letter in the strictest secrecy."

"And you took it?"

"Wait! She told me the address and made me memorize it—for I don't know how to write. Herman—I've already forgotten his second name . . . and I've forgotten the street too. But I think it was Number Forty—"

"You took it and delivered it?" Rivka asks her, concealing her apprehension.

"Not so quick!" Hannah replies. "I had to look for the house a long time."

That, however, is not what Rivka's interested in.

"Is he a bachelor?" she asks sharply.

"How should I know? Probably he is."

"Does he live all by himself?"

"Looks that way . . . yes. He opened the door for me himself. As soon as I had pressed the white button. She told me to do that."

"Did he take the letter?"

"He did!"

"Did he give you any answer?"

"No, he didn't. He would answer by mail, he said. But he was so happy over the letter. In his joy he invited me inside, made me take a chair—"

"What for?"

"He was so glad! He even stroked my hair—the way mother does sometimes, on Sabbath or a holiday, when she has time. Then he laughed and even kissed me . . . on the lips, right on the lips. Then my eyes: 'Beautiful eyes,' he said—"

Rivka lies as if she were turned to stone. Hannah becomes thoughtful for a little while, then concludes:

"But later, when he wanted to unbutton my blouse and put in his hand I grew ashamed and ran off—he had forgotten to lock the door—"

"Glory to God, Glory to God," Rivka whispered with stifled sobs.

"What are you saying, Rivka?"

"Nothing Hannah."

224

"But do tell me one thing, Rivka—why did he want to put in his hand?"

"Keep quiet!" Rivka cuts her short in fright.

Fortunately, the old man does not hear them. He is plunged in his Psalms. He recites a Psalm and immediately translates it:

"For there is no faithfulness in their mouth; their inward part is very wickedness; their throat is an open sepulchre—a pit, that means to swallow one up—they flatter with their tongue—"

Rivka listens to him; her face is pale and her teeth are clenched. Hannah, thoroughly frightened, is watching her.

The Magician

O NE DAY a magician arrived in a small town in Volynia. And, although this happened at a time just before Passover, a time crowded with all sorts of excitement when every Jew has more cares than hairs on his head, the arrival of the magician nevertheless created a sensation.

An enigmatic fellow, tattered and torn, his head covered by an opera hat (crushed, true enough, but an opera hat just the same), with a Jewish face (his nose alone testified sufficiently to his origin) yet no beard; he carried no passport. Who could tell what sort of man he was? If they asked him, "Where do you come from?" he would say, "From Paris!" If they asked, "Where are you bound for?"—"London!" he would say. "How did you ever happen to land here?"—"Oh, I just wandered over here!" He did his traveling on foot, apparently. And he never showed his face in the House of Prayer—he stayed away even on Sabbath. But if people pestered him or formed a crowd around him, he would vanish, just like that, as though the earth had swallowed him up—and then he would reappear at the other end of the marketplace.

He hired a hall and began giving exhibitions of his tricks. And what tricks! He swallowed live coals right in front of everybody, just as if they were dumplings; he pulled ribbons out of his mouth —ribbons of all colors—red, green, or whatever color you called out—and each ribbon as long as the suffering of the Jewish folk. Out of his boots he pulled sixteen pairs of turkeys, each one as big as a bear—live turkeys that scattered all over the stage. He would lift his foot, scratch the sole, and there would be a rain of gold coins—until he had scraped up a whole bowl of gold pieces! This evoked much applause, whereupon the magician would whistle, and rolls and Sabbath loaves came flocking through the air just like birds dancing up and down or hopping about in the Quarrel Dance. Then he whistled once more and everything vanished, just as if it had never existed! No loaves, no ribbons, no turkeys—nothing at all.

Oh, well, everybody knows that the Evil Power can also put on a show of miracles! The Egyptian wonder-workers had probably evinced even greater artistry. But the main question was, why was the magician himself so poor?

The man could scrape gold pieces off the soles of his boots, yet he could not scrape together his rent. He had merely to whistle to bake a batch of rolls and Sabbath loaves, he pulled turkeys out of his boots, yet his face was gaunt—the face of a corpse looked healthier—and hunger was like a flame in his eyes! People made jokes about it; a fifth question had been added to the four traditional ones asked at the Passover supper.

But before talking of the Passover, let us leave the magician and pass on to Hayim-Jonah and his wife Rivka-Bailah. Hayim-Jonah had at one time dealt in timber. On one occasion he had bought a forest for cash but had been denied the right to fell the trees and had lost his shirt on the deal. He had secured a position as clerk to another lumberman but then had lost it, and he had been out of work for several months now. He and his wife had managed to get through the winter somehow—Lord, let no other man experience such a winter! But then, after winter came the Passover. Yet everything had already been pawned, from the candlesticks to the last pillows. And so Rivka-Bailah said to her husband:

"Go to the Benevolent Society and ask for money to buy matzoth."

But Hayim-Jonah's answer was that he placed his trust in God and was not going to humiliate himself before people. Rivka-Bailah rummaged through all the nooks and crannies in the house and—a miracle from Heaven!—found an old tarnished silver spoon that had been lost for many years. So Hayim-Jonah went to the marketplace, sold the spoon, and carried the money he had gotten for it to the fund for the poor.

"They're poor people," he said, "who are in even greater need than we."

Time was passing quickly; there were only two short weeks left till Passover, yet Hayim-Jonah did not lose hope.

"The Lord," he said, "will not abandon us."

Rivka-Bailah kept silent; she knew that a woman must defer to her husband. Yet as the days sped by, Rivka-Bailah could not close her eyes all night through, weeping with her face buried in the straw pallet so that Hayim-Jonah might not hear her. And they still had not as much as a crumb for Passover! In the daytime things were even worse for Rivka-Bailah than at night, for at night she could at least ease her grief by weeping, whereas in the daytime her cheeks must appear rosy even if she had to pinch them. The neighbors watched her and their pitying glances pierced her like needles. Some questioned her: When was she baking the matzoth? When was she preparing the beet-juice? Those who were on a more intimate footing with her would say: "What's the matter with you, Rivka-Bailah? If you're in need we'll lend you the money!"

But Hayim-Jonah wanted no "gifts from the hands of men," and Rivka-Bailah would not go against his wishes. She tried to decline the offerings gracefully, while her face burned with shame.

The neighbors saw that things were in a bad way and went to the rabbi to find out what was to be done. The rabbi heard them out, sighed, thought, and at last declared that Hayim-Jonah was a man of learning and a Godfearing one. And if he was not without hope, then there must be hope.

Rivka-Bailah was left without so much as a candle for the holidays.

And at last it was Passover.

When Hayim-Jonah came home from the synagogue he saw that all the windows on the square were aglow with the joyousness of the holiday—his house alone stood there like a young widow among the merry guests, like a blind man among those who can see. He did not let his heart sink however; "if the Lord wills it, there will be a holiday in my house as well!"

"A happy holiday!" he said gaily as he entered the house. "A happy holiday to you, Rivka-Bailah!"

And Rivka-Bailah's voice, choked with tears, came to him from a dark corner; "Happy holiday! May you have a good year!" And her eyes gleamed like two dying embers.

"Rivka-Bailah, the holiday is here; it is the eve of the exodus from Egypt—do you understand? There must be no sorrowing. And besides, what's there to feel sorry about? If the All-Highest did not wish us to have a holiday feast, we must accept that as our due, as a blessing, and share the supper of others. Very well, then —we shall go! They will accept us anywhere. Today all gateways and doors stand wide open. Let everyone that wants to do so come and eat, say the Jews. Let's go. Put on your shawl; we'll walk to the first Jewish house we come to."

And Rivka-Bailah, who always did as her husband wished, made a supreme effort to restrain the sobs that were straining at her throat, threw a tattered shawl over her shoulders and was ready to go. But at that moment the door opened, and a voice said:

"A happy holiday to you!"

And they answered, although they could not see who had entered.

"I want to be a guest at your supper," said the man who had entered.

"We haven't a supper for ourselves," answered Hayim-Jonah.

"I have brought the supper with me," said the voice.

"Are we going to hold the service in darkness?" Hayim-Jonah asked with a sigh.

"There will be light as well!" answered their guest.

He waved his hand—two pairs of silver candlesticks holding lighted candles appeared in the middle of the room and hung in midair! The room became light. Hayim-Jonah and Rivka-Bailah, amazed, beheld the magician and could not utter a word because of their astonishment and fear. Clutching each other by the hand they stood there gaping and staring. Meanwhile the magician turned toward the table that was standing in a corner and said: "Well, now, my fine fellows, come here and spread a cover over your table!"

Immediately a snowy cover fell from the ceiling on the table and covered it, while the table itself moved to the middle of the room and stopped right under the silver candlesticks, which sank onto it.

"Now we need couches to recline on!" said the magician.

Whereupon three benches made their way toward the table and arranged themselves on three sides of it. The magician ordered them to expand their width and thereupon they transformed themselves into easy-chairs.

"Get softer!" the magician bade them—and they became upholstered with red velvet, and at the same instant snow white pillows plumped down upon them from the ceiling. The couches were ready! Next, a platter with all the ritual ingredients appeared on the table at his bidding, followed by red cups and decanters of wine, matzoth, and everything else that was needed for a merry feast—even the books of devotion, well bound and with gilt edges.

"And do you have water for the washing of the hands?" asked the magician. "If not, I'll order it—it'll be brought!"

Only at this question did the hosts recover from their astonishment.

"Is this permissible?" Rivka-Bailah asked Hayim-Jonah in a whisper—and since Hayim-Jonah did not know what answer to make to her she counseled him to go to the rabbi and ask.

But he said that he could not leave her alone with the magician —let her go by herself, to which Rivka-Bailah replied that the rabbi would not believe a simple-minded Jewish woman; he would think that she had gone out of her mind. And so the two of them set out together to see the rabbi, leaving the magician alone with the Passover feast.

And the rabbi's answer was that everything created by enchantment had no real content, inasmuch as all spells were merely for the deception of the eyes. And he ordered them to go home, and if the matzoth would allow itself to be crumbled, if the wine would let itself be poured into the cups, and the pillows on the couches were actually palpable, why, everything was well. In that case everything was a gift from heaven and they could avail themselves of it. Such was the rabbi's decision.

When Hayim-Jonah and his wife returned, the magician was no longer there, but the feast stood just as they had left it, and the pillows turned out to be real, the wine flowed freely into the cups, and the matzoth crumbled without any trouble.

They understood, then, that the Prophet Elijah had visited their home. Joyously they celebrated the holiday!

The Treasure

TO SLEEP with a wife and eight little children in one tiny room in sultry July, even on Sabbath eve, is no pleasure. Little wonder then, that Shmerrel, the woodcutter, awoke past midnight, sweltering and gasping for air. He made his ablutions hurriedly, donned his old coat, and dashed barefoot from his infernal abode. Outside, everything was tranquil. The windows were shuttered and a serene, star-studded sky hung over the slumbering little town. Sensing that he was alone with God—praised be He!—Shmerrel spoke to Him:

"Lord of the Universe, it is high time Thou didst hear me and bless me with just one treasure out of Thy treasure house!"

No sooner had he spoken than he noticed a tiny flickering light flitting in front of him. "That must be it," he reflected, "the answer to my prayers." He was just about to pursue the light when he recalled that running on the Sabbath was forbidden. Therefore, he merely walked after it. And remarkably, the flash of light slackened its pace to his, so that the distance between them neither diminished nor increased. As he jogged along, a voice seemed to urge him on from time to time: "Don't be a fool, Shmerrel! Slip your coat off, make a dash, and throw it over the light!"

However, it dawned on him that this was nothing but the prompting of the Evil Spirit. And, though he had removed his coat, with a view to snaring the light, he slowed his pace in defiance of the Wicked One. But, to his great joy, the light also slackened its pace.

Tagging along leisurely after the little light, he found himself on the outskirts of the town. The path twisted and meandered across fields and meadows but the distance between Shmerrel and the light never varied by a hair. And even if he had flung his coat ahead, it would have fallen short of the mark.

Meanwhile, he gave free reign to his imagination: if only he could get his hands on this treasure, he wouldn't have to be a woodcutter in his declining years. He would obtain a pew for his wife in the synagogue—in the section reserved for women—so that she would not be humiliated by being seated in a corner on Sabbaths and holy days. On Rosh Hashonah and Yum Kippur, the poor soul could barely hold her own. The rearing of her children had all but undermined her health. He would buy her a new dress and present her with a string of pearls. As for his children, he would send them to a select school and seek an advantageous match for his oldest daughter. At present, the girl had her hands full carrying baskets of fruit for her mother, with hardly a chance to even comb her hair. And what beautiful hair she had, what marvelous eyes!

To get his hands on this treasure was surely a divine commandment!

But again, for a moment, doubt assailed him; perhaps it was all the instigation of the Evil One. If such luck were not to fall his way, he would do just as well without it. If all this were happening on a weekday there would have been no problem. If his son, Yankel, were here he would not stand idly by, either. But when it came to the young people of today—who could tell what they were up to on the Sabbath? His younger son was no prize, as it was. He was forever irritating his religious teacher—let the latter try to box Yankel's ears, and Yankel would probably pluck out his beard, hair by hair. But who had time and the patience to understand the young ones? The ax and saw claimed his attention all day long.

Breathing a sigh of relief, Shmerrel plodded along. Now and then he would look up and soliloquize: "Almighty, whom art Thou subjecting to temptation? Shmerrel the woodcutter? If it be Thy will to dole out a trifle, then do it and get it over with!"

Just then it seemed to him that the light had slackened its pace somewhat. He heard a dog bark. Mentally, he traced it to the neighboring village of Visoki. Through the early morning mist, he could make out clusters of white spots—the whitewashed huts of the Visoki peasants. He suddenly realized that he had overstepped the Sabbath limit—the distance beyond which no pious Jew must go on foot during the Sabbath, and he halted in his tracks.

"A Sabbath limit," he pondered, and then said to the light:

"You're not going to lead me astray? God could never have or-dained such a thing. He does not mock man. Someone must be playing a practical joke on me!" And, irked at the Adversary, he wheeled about and headed straight for home. He would keep the whole matter to himself, he decided. In the first place, his family would not believe him, and they would certainly make fun of him. Furthermore, what was there to brag about? The Lord of the Universe was aware of everything—let that suffice. And, prob-ably, his wife would be resentful. His children—they hadn't a stitch to their backs—would surely be angry. Why should they be forced to violate the commandment of honoring their father? No, he wouldn't breathe a word about any of this—not even to the Lord. If he had acted rightly, the Lord would not be un-mindful of it.

Suddenly, he felt a strange joy, and contentment flooded through his body. Money was, after all, nothing but filthy lucre; wealth was sure to lure one from the path of righteousness. And he felt disposed to thank the Lord for not tempting him in that fashion. He almost began to chant "Our Father, Our King," which he recalled singing as a boy, but, somewhat abashed, restrained him-self.

As he tried to think of another liturgical melody, he was as-tonished to see the light still leading him and moving even closer to the town. The distance between him and the light had still neither increased nor diminished, and it was as if both of them had simply gone out for a stroll in honor of the Sabbath. The sight warmed his heart. The sky was becoming light, and the stars were fading here and there. A glow appeared on the eastern horizon, spreading out into a stream of crimson.

The tiny flame, undeterred, advanced toward the town, then turned in the direction of his street. There was his house, the door wide open: evidently he had forgotten to shut it. The little flame actually made its way right into the house, no mistake about it! He followed close behind and saw it creep under his bed. Everyone was sound asleep; he tiptoed over, bent down, and caught sight of the light spinning like a top. Without further ado, he flung his coat over the light. By now, the first morning rays were stealing in through a chink in the shutter.

Sitting down on the bed, he vowed not to divulge a word to any-one about this until the end of the Sabbath. Otherwise, God forbid, the holy day might be profaned. His wife would not be able to curb her curiosity—and his sons would surely never control theirs. And that would be the end of the secret. In the synagogue, in the House of Study, in the streets—a great to-do would spring up about his sudden riches, his good fortune. Worshipers would become remiss in their praying, their ablutions and in their benedictions. He would be the cause not only of his family's transgressions but those of half the community as well. No, he would not breathe a word! And, stretching out on his cot, he pretended to be asleep.

Because of his prudence in not overstepping the Sabbath limit, when he bent down at the end of the Sabbath and removed his cloak from under his bed, he came upon a sack bulging with thousands upon thousands of gold pieces—a genuine treasure-trove. He had become as rich as the proverbial Croesus.

He lived out his remaining years in great happiness, with not a care in the world. Yet, notwithstanding all his wealth, his wife always remonstrated with him:

"How can a man be so heartless as not to utter a word of his good fortune to his own wife—not a single word? And I used to cry and implored the Lord as I recited 'God of Abraham'! We were destitute."

"Who knows," he would comfort her, his face beaming, "perhaps our good fortune is due entirely to your reciting 'God of Abraham'."

Seven Years of Plenty

H ERE IS THE STORY of something that happened at Turbin. Once upon a time there was a porter living in Turbin, and they called him Tevyeh. He was extremely poor. On a certain Thursday, he was standing in the marketplace, the skirts of his kaftan tucked within the rope that girded him, watching to see from what direction help would come to him or how he might earn a little something for the holy Sabbath. Yet all the shops around him were empty; no one entered them, and no one came out. There were no buyers in sight for whom he might carry something. And Tevyeh lifted his eyes to heaven, silently imploring the Lord not to send him a sad Sabbath so that his wife Sarah and their little one might not have to go hungry on that holy day.

Hardly had he said this prayer when he felt someone tugging at one of his coattails from behind. He turned around and beheld a foreigner in hunting clothes, with a feather in his hat and green piping on his jacket.

"Listen, Tevyeh," the stranger spoke to him, "you have been allotted seven years of plenty—seven years of happiness, good luck, and riches. You have but to wish it and this very day the star of your happiness will shine forth; before the sun over your head sets you will be able to buy up all of Turbin, together with all its outlying parts. But at the end of the seven years you will again become the poor man you are now. On the other hand, should you wish it, these seven years of plenty will come only toward the end of your life, and you will die a rich man."

Now this person, as it turned out later, happened to be Elijah the Prophet who, as he occasionally did, had assumed the guise of an outlander. Tevyeh, however, took him for an ordinary wizard and answered him:

"Leave me in peace, dear man! I—and may no one say it of you —I am very poor. I haven't the wherewithal to celebrate the Sabbath, and I surely have nothing to pay you with for your counsels and efforts."

But when the German refused to go away and had said his say once more and again and a third time, his words penetrated to Tevyeh's comprehension.

"Do you know, dear man," said Tevyeh, "if you are really concerned about me, and are not merely mocking my poverty—if you are truly expecting me to agree—then this is what I have to say to you. I've made it a practice, whenever I'm faced with any proposal, to hold counsel with Sarah, my wife, before I do anything. I can't give you a positive answer without her consent."

The foreigner, after commenting that it was a good thing to hold counsel with one's wife, suggested that Tevyeh go and have a talk with her, and promised to wait for his answer.

Tevyeh looked about him once more; there seemed no prospect of earning anything. Having decided that he would not lose anything even if he left, he adjusted the skirts of his kaftan and set out for the outskirts of the town where he lived in a small house, almost out in the open country.

Sarah, catching sight of him through the open door (all this took place in the summertime) ran out to meet him with great joy, thinking that Tevyeh had brought the wherewithal for the Sabbath meal.

But all Tevyeh said was: "No, Sarah! The Lord—blessed be His Name!—has as yet sent me no earnings. However, a certain German came to me—"and Tevyeh repeated to her the words of the stranger, to the effect that seven years of plenty had been assigned to him, and that it was necessary to decide when these years were to come—right now or before his death.

"Go, dear husband," said Sarah, without much hesitation, "and tell the stranger that you wish the seven years of plenty to come right now."

"Why, Sarah?" asked the astonished Tevyeh. "After seven years we'll become poor once more, and life is harder for anyone who becomes poor than for anyone born in poverty."

"Don't fret about what is to come, husband. Take what is given you, and say Blessed is the Lord each day! Besides, we need a teacher for our children. They have been expelled from school and are now wasting their time playing in the sand."

This was enough to make Tevyeh run back to the stranger with the firm resolve to ask for the immediate beginning of the seven years of plenty.

"Do stop to think, Tevyeh," said the stranger. "You're healthy and strong now and can earn something, much or little, depending on circumstances. But what will happen when you grow old, become poorer, and have no strength to work?"

"Listen, stranger!" Tevyeh replied. "My wife Sarah wants the plenty to come now. 'In the first place,' she says, 'Blessed is the Lord each day, and therefore there's no use in worrying about the day to come; and in the second place, the children have been expelled from school—' "

"So be it!" said the German. "Go home. Before you set foot in your house, you will have become rich!"

It occurred to Tevyeh to ask just what would happen at the expiration of the seven years, but the stranger had already vanished.

Tevyeh set out for home. And, as we have said, he was living beyond the town, almost in the open country. As he approached his house he saw his children playing in the sand. And he saw that it was not sand they were digging out of their small pit but pure gold. And the happy days began—the seven years of plenty.

Time flies, however; the seven years passed swiftly and the German appeared to announce to Tevyeh that the seven years of plenty were over and that his gold would go back into the ground that very night—all the gold that was in the house, and even those riches which they may have concealed.

On his arrival, the stranger found Tevyeh standing in the marketplace, as he had been at their first meeting. Tevyeh, just as before, had the skirts of his kaftan tucked in his belt, waiting to earn something. And the stranger said to him:

"Listen, Tevyeh—the seven years are up."

And Tevyeh answered him:

"Go and tell that to my wife Sarah, because the riches were in her hands all these years."

So the two of them went beyond the town, came to the house, and found Sarah in her old dress smiling merrily.

The stranger repeated his announcement to her.

She told him, however, that they had never seen the plenty, that they had never considered this gold their exclusive property, inasmuch as property is something that a person acquires through the labor of his hands. When riches come without sweat or callouses, they are only a gift which the Lord entrusts into one's keeping. Out of all that money, she had spent only enough to pay for the schooling of her children. The children were learning about the glory of God, and therefore it was no sin to spend God's money for such a purpose. But she did not avail herself of the riches for anything else. However, if the Lord God had now found a better guardian for His riches, then it was His holy will to take them and to hand them over to someone else.

Elijah the Prophet heard her out—and vanished. He transmitted her answer to the All-Highest Court, and the All-Highest Court handed down the decision that a better guardian could not be found. And the seven years of plenty did not cease until the death of Tevyeh and Sarah, his wife.

A Woman's Wrath

THE TINY ROOM is as somber as the poverty within its four walls. There is an orphaned hook sticking out of the ceiling, bereft of its big brass lamp. An enormous, lopsided oven, girt with an apron of coarse sacking, is sadly facing the blackened hearth, which harbors an overturned pot and a broken spoon. This tinny creature has found an honorable death, having fallen in the fight against yesterday's dried up porridge.

The handsomest piece of furniture in the room is a tall bed with torn curtains, through the holes of which bare pillows peep out, their eyes bleary with feathers. There is a cradle, where one can see the large red head of a sleeping baby; near by a tin trunk, its lock hanging open—next come a table and three stools. All this furniture had once been painted red; now the roomful is a dirty gray. Add a wardrobe, a water-cask, a slop-pail, a poker, and a coal shovel and you will see there isn't room for one more pin.

And yet, there are two people—a man and a woman.

The woman is middle-aged, sitting on the trunk that takes up all the room there is between the bed and the cradle. To her right is the only window, with its greenish pane; to her left, the table. She knits a stocking and rocks the cradle with her foot as she listens attentively to the man, who is seated at the table reading the Talmud. He reads in a choppy and nervous chant. Some of the words are mumbled, others are drawn out; some he blurts out in one breath, others he skips over altogether; certain passages are lovingly emphasized, others are read by rote, until they sound like peas rolling out of a sack. And all the while he never sits still: now he snatches his bandanna out of his pocket, which at one time had been red and whole, rubbing his nose and wiping the perspiration from his face and forehead; then he will drop the bandanna on his lap and start twisting his ritual locks, or twitching his grizzled goatee. Now he has plucked a hair from it, which he places on the folio volume before him, and takes to slapping his knees. Aha—he has found the bandanna again! He seizes it, pops one corner of it into his mouth and begins chewing it, at the same time crossing and recrossing his legs.

And all this while his pale forehead is crisscrossed with wrinkles; deep furrows lie across the bridge of his nose—his elongated eyelids all but vanish under the overhanging skin of his forehead. Suddenly he imagines that he has felt a stabbing pain in his chest and smites it with his right hand; he snatches a pinch of snuff and begins to sway still more, until his voice rings out and the stool under him groans.

The baby sleeps through all this: he has become used to such concerts.

As for his wife who has aged so prematurely, she sits there and cannot get her fill of rejoicing over her spouse. She does not take her eyes off him, and is on the alert for every sound of his voice. From time to time she sighs, as she reflects: If he were only as good for this world as he is for the *other*, things would be fine and bright for her even here—yes, even here! Oh, well (she consoles herself), whom will you ever find who is worthy of tasting both repasts?

She listens still more attentively. Her wrinkled face is also changing from moment to moment; she, too, is nervous.

Just now immeasurable gratification had suffused her face—so much delight had she derived from his Torah. But suddenly she recalls that today is already Thursday, that there isn't a copper for the Sabbath—and the glow of Paradise on her face grows dimmer, until the smile disappears altogether. Then she glances through the green window and takes a look at the sun. There isn't as much as a spoonful of hot water in the house. The knitting needles stop; a somber shadow overcasts her face. She glances at the baby: by now his sleep is uneasy—he will be waking soon. The baby is ailing, yet there isn't a drop of milk for him. By this time the shadow on her face has turned into a cloud; her knitting needles begin to shake, and bob up and down. When she remembers that Easter is almost here, that the candlesticks and her earrings are in pawn, that the trunk is empty and the brass lamp has been sold—the knitting needles begin to dance at a deathly speed; the cloud turns to lead; lightning flashes in her small gray eyes, which one can barely glimpse under her headkerchief.

But *he* still sits there and reads on. He does not perceive that a storm is about to break—that she has let the stocking fall out of her hands, that she is beginning to crack her gaunt fingers while her forehead wrinkles in pain, one eye closing while the other is regarding him with such murderous keenness that, were he to notice it, he would be chilled to the bone with terror. He does not perceive how her livid lips quiver, how her jaws work as if in an ague as she restrains herself with all her might. But the storm is about to break and the least little thing will bring it bursting from her lips.

And this does happen.

He is reading: *"Shma minei—tloss . . ."* and translates the passage in a long-drawn out chant: "Therefore, it follows hence—" He is about to say "Thirdly—" but the word *follows* suffices. Her long-aching heart seizes on the word; it falls like a spark of gunpowder. Her much-enduring patience explodes. The unfortunate word opens all the sluices and shatters all restraints. Frenziedly she leaps toward her husband with foam-flecked lips, ready to scratch his eyes out.

"It *follows,* you say—it *follows,* does it? Ah, my God, if you would only *follow* along with it!" she screams in a hoarse voice. "Yes, yes," she goes on, hissingly, "it will be Passover soon . . . today is Thursday . . . the baby is ailing . . . and there isn't a drop of milk in the house!"

She is all out of breath; her flabby bosom is heaving; sparks fly from her eyes.

He seems to be petrified. Jumping up from the stool, pale, gasping in fright, he begins retreating toward the door. They stand facing each other—his eyes glassy with fright, hers blazing in wrath. He soon notices that because of her rancor she has no control over her tongue or her hands. His eyes narrow more and more. Popping a corner of his bandanna in his mouth he moves back a little more, and mutters, breathing with difficulty:

"Listen, you woman—do you know the meaning of *bitul Toirah* —do you know what it means to hinder one's husband in studying the Torah—eh? Always harping about earnings, eh? There, who provides for the fowl of the air? Still no faith in God! Temptation everywhere—everywhere concern over *this* world only. . . . You are a stupid woman—and a malicious one! Not to let one's husband study—why, hell is the punishment meted out for that!"

She is silent and he grows bolder. Her face is becoming ever paler, she is trembling more and more, and the more she trembles and the paler she grows, the firmer and louder does his voice sound:

"Hell! Everlasting flames! You'll be hung by your tongue—you'll receive all the four punishments of the Supreme Tribunal!"

She is still silent; her face is as white as chalk. He feels that he is not acting right, that he ought not to torture her thus, that this is dishonest, but by now he is no longer able to hold himself in check. All the rancor that had been lurking in his soul is now poured forth without restraint.

"*Skilo!* There, do you know what that means?"—and his voice becomes thunderous. "It means being cast into a pit and stoned to death . . . *Sreifo!*" he goes on—and is amazed at his own daring. "That means having a spoonful of molten, boiling lead poured down your throat. *Hereg:* that means having your head lopped off by a sword—like this!"—and he waves his hand in a circle about his neck. "And now we come to *chenek*—that's strangulation—do you hear? Strangulation! *Bitul Toirah*—you understand? All this for *bitul Toirah!*"

His very heart contracts with pity for his victim, but then, this is the first time he has ever gained the upper hand. This intoxicates him. Such a foolish woman! Up to now he hadn't known at all that one could throw such a scare into her.

"There, that's what *bitul Toirah* means!" he cries out once more—and then falls abruptly silent: after all, she may come to herself and grab the broom! He dashes back to the table, slams the folio volume shut and dashes out of the room.

"I'm going to the synagogue!" he calls out to her, by now in a gentler tone and shuts the door behind him.

The shouts and the slamming of the door have awakened the ailing baby. He slowly raises his heavy lids; his face, yellow as wax, becomes distorted, and a wheezing breath issues through his tiny nose.

She, however, seems petrified. She is still beside herself as she stands there and does not hear the baby crying.

"Aha!" escapes from her sunken breast at last in a voice hoarse and strangled. "There's no place for me either in *this* world or the *next*—They'll hang me, says he; they'll use boiling pitch and molten lead on me, he says. *Bitul Toirah!* Nothing matters—*to me* nothing matters!"—and there is a gurgling in her tortured breast. "Starvation *here* . . . nothing to wear . . . no candlesticks . . . nothing at all . . . the baby is starved . . . not a drop of milk. . . . But over *there* I'll be hanged—hanged by the tongue. *Bitul Toirah,* says he. So they'll hang me—" and she breaks into laughter, despairing and shrill. "Very well, let me be hanged, but let it be here, right now! Nothing matters—why wait?"

The baby breaks into still louder crying, but she hears nothing.

"A rope, a rope!" she cries out, and her wandering eyes search all the corners. "Where is one to get a rope? May he fail to find even my bones! Just as long as I get out of this hellish place. Let him know what's what! Let *him* become a mother—let him! Let me perish! One can die but one death—the end is the same. Let there be an end, once and for all! Give me a rope!"—the last word escapes her like a call for help in a fire.

She recalls where the rope is lying . . . yes, under the oven: they were thinking of using it to hold the oven together through the winter: it must still be there. She dashes to the oven and finds the rope. Oh, joy—she has found a treasure! She glances toward the ceiling—the hook is right there. All one has to do is to scramble up on the table. She scrambles up on it. But, from her vantage point, she sees that the baby is on his feet, that he is leaning over the edge of the cradle, wanting to clamber out. There, he'll fall at any moment!

"Mamma!" the baby barely manages to utter faintly—his throat is none too strong. A fresh outburst of rage seizes her.

She drops the rope, jumps down from the table, dashes over to the baby, tosses his little head back on the pillow and shouts malevolently:

"Monster! He won't even let me hang myself! Won't let me hang myself in peace, even! He wants to be suckled, now—to be suckled! Oh, it is poison you will be sipping from my breast! Poison! There, you glutton!" she gasps and thrusts her withered nipple in the baby's mouth. "There, sip away—torture me!"

The Times of the Messiah

L IKE ALL JEWISH TOWNS and small villages in Galicia, the little
town in which my parents lived had its madman.

As usual, the madman feared no one: neither the community,
the rabbi, the judges, nor the bath-house keeper and the man in
charge of the cemetery—all people of whom even the very rich
stand in fear. On the other hand, the whole little town, along with
its elders, its bath-house keeper, and the man in charge of the
cemetery, looked askance at the madman. All doors were locked
to him. Even though the poor fellow had never injured anybody
by so much as a word, or ever laid a finger on anyone, everybody
took occasion to scold him; some people beat him, and little boys
threw muck and stones at him.

I always pitied this unfortunate. Something drew me to him. I
wanted to talk to him, to console him, to show him some kindness;
but to approach him was out of the question. Many of the lumps
of muck thrown at him would have fallen to my lot. I was a child;
I had decent clothes, brought back from Crakow—and, perhaps,
from as far as Lemberg; I took care not to get hit by the stones or
to get any of the muck on my clothes, and so I kept aloof.

The little town in which my parents lived was a fortress. It was
surrounded by high walls, behind which there was a rampart and
a moat. There were cannons upon the walls, and armed soldiers
guarded them, grimly and silently pacing back and forth. As soon
as night fell all the gates would close, the iron bridge would be
drawn up, and all connection between the little town and the rest
of the world would be cut off until morning. A reinforced guard
was always stationed at the gate.

At noon; we are all free and can move about at will; one can
enter the little town without asking the military commander's
permission; one can go swimming in the river outside the town,
or lie in the meadow near the river and stare up at the sky—it's

244

nobody's business. But night comes, and the little town quiets down; now no one will venture from the town or enter it. Glory be (I used to think), the crescent moon is not forbidden to appear on the horizon!

As long as I live I shall not forget the twilights in that little town. Together with the evening shadows a sort of a fear would come over the place; the people and the houses would suddenly slump. There, they're drawing up the bridge, its iron chains squealing as they move the enormous pulleys; their screech, their harsh, choppy yapping, go through and through me; then, with much rumbling, the gates close. And so, every evening. And each time, at this point, legs tremble; a dull fatigue creeps over every face; the light goes out in the eyes of the people; their eyelids narrow, as if they were filled with lead; the heart all but swoons and beats quietly, ever so quietly. Then, the patrols appear on the streets; their long sabres rattle over the cobblestones, their scabbards glisten, and all you hear is the challenge: "Who goes there?" You must answer "A friend," for, otherwise, God knows what might befall you. Some of the inhabitants prefer to lock themselves in at nightfall; they are even afraid to put their nose outdoors at this time.

Here is one adventure I had. I had been swimming in the river outside the town. I can't tell whether I had become absorbed in some sight or had been dreaming or had simply forgotten that night follows day—but suddenly I saw that the bridge was being drawn up; there, the gates were closing—their rattle grated on my ears and found a painful echo in my heart. All was lost! I would have to spend the night out under the open sky. And here is the amazing thing: at home, lying in my soft bed, I dreamed every night of the untrammeled freedom beyond the walls of the fortress; and yet, when my dream was realized, I felt only fear. Each rustle, each shadow made me afraid.

I buried my face in the sand.

Was I asleep or awake? Really, I don't know! But suddenly I heard somebody breathing close to me. I leapt up. Yes, I was not alone; two deep dark eyes, which I knew well, were looking at me kindly.

It was the madman.

"What are you doing here?" I asked in a stifled voice.

"I never pass the night in the town," he answered sadly, and his look was so gentle, his voice so kind, that I forgot I had been afraid.

I suddenly recalled that madmen were at one time regarded as seers; and in the Orient they are still so regarded. I asked myself: Was the man standing before me a phophet? Are they tormenting him because of his divine gift? Aren't they casting stones at him, even as at a prophet? Doesn't there dwell in his soul a prophetic yearning for better times? And, can it be that, he actually does know about the times to come?

And so, I fell to questioning him, while he answered me, so softly and gently that it seemed that all this was but a waking dream, a dream on a summer night in the vast expanse of fields.

"Do you believe in the coming of the Messiah?" I asked him.

"Of course!" he answered quietly, with assurance. "The Savior of the world is bound to come. He will come! All men await him —even the sky and the earth sense his coming. If if weren't for that, no one would want to live, no one would do a stroke of work. And yet, people live and want to live; because they all feel that the Messiah is nearing, that he is bound to come, that he is already on the way—"

"Is it true," I asked him, "that before his coming there will be bloody wars because of a false messiah? That men will kill men like wild beasts, that all the earth will be soaked with blood, that rivers will flow from east to west and from south to north, that birds and beasts will be slaking their thirst with human blood, that all the ways and roads, all the fields and meadows, will be flooded with torrents of human blood? And lo, at that very time the true Messiah, the Savior of the world, will appear—is that true?"

"It is, it is!"

"And men will recognize him?"

"Everyone will recognize him; none shall be mistaken. His mission will be apparent in his every smile, his every word, his every glance. There will be no armed host about him; it is not on a steed that he will appear, and there will be no sword in his hand—"

"What then?"

"He will have wings. For, by that time all men will have wings. And this is how it will come about. Suddenly a child with wings will be born, then a second, and a third . . . At first, people will be frightened by the winged children, but after a while they'll get

246

used to them, and there will arise a generation of winged children, and that generation will not want to wallow in the mire and fight over a worm ..."

For a long while the madman spoke on, and I no longer understood him. But his voice was so sweetly appealing that I drank in the sounds of it like a sponge. When he fell silent it was already growing light; the gates of the fortress were opening; the drawbridge was being lowered.

From that night on life in the fortress became more oppressive to me, and still harder to bear. The old walls and towers, the squealing and grating of the chains against their pulleys, the iron bars of the gates, the guards and patrols, the hoarse, angry challenges, "Who goes there?" and the lying, fawning answer, "A friend"; the cowardly faces, the half-extinguished eyes, the marketplace with indolent shades timorously wandering over it—all this was weighing down upon my soul. I was seized by profound melancholy, and I resolved to set out to meet the coming Messiah.

I got on the first cart that came my way.

"Where do you want to go?" asked the driver, turning around.

"Wherever you want. As long as it's as far from here as possible!"

"How many hours do you want to ride?"

"For as long as the horse has strength to go on!"

The driver twitched the reins and we started off.

And so, we rode on and on; by now the fields were not familiar, the forests were different, so were the villages, and the towns. The difference, however, was purely external; inwardly everything was the same. Everywhere one beheld the same sadness, the same timorous and lying looks in human eyes, and heard the same quavering, cowardly voices. Over everything there hovered the same melancholy mist that obscured every beam of light. Everywhere there was the same attempt to shrink into one's self, to become smaller, less conspicuous. And I kept shouting to the driver to go on. But I was dependent upon the driver, and the driver was dependent upon the horse. The horse demanded feed, and we were forced to halt.

I entered a country inn. It was a large room, divided in two by an old curtain. In the half nearer the entrance three men were seated at a table. They did not notice me, but I had a good view of them. I was looking at three generations. The oldest man was gray as a loon—he had an erect bearing and was reading, without glasses, a large book that was lying on the table before him. His face was calm; his eyes confident.

The man sitting to the right of him was somewhat younger—his son, apparently, for he looked quite like the first man. But his face was more mobile, more nervous—at moments it looked more tired. This man, too, was reading, but with the help of glasses; the book was of smaller dimensions, and he was holding it closer to his eyes, his arm elbowed on the table. He was middle-aged; his head and beard were merely touched with gray. From time to time he looked at his father, but the old man paid no attention to him.

To the left of the old man sat the youngest of the three, probably a grandson—a young man with black glossy hair and an ardent, absentminded gaze. He, too, was looking into a book, but the book was a small one, and he was holding it close to his eyes. Quite often he put it aside altogether. With fear, mixed with deep respect, he would occasionally glance at the old man, cast a slightly ironic look at his father, and listen to what was going on behind the curtain. Someone was sighing and moaning behind it, just as though a woman were giving birth there.

I wanted to cough, to attract their attention. But at that moment the curtain parted and two women emerged: a little crone with a sharp, bony face and a stern gaze, and another, rather younger, with a gentle, full face and kindly eyes. They stood there, looking at the men and waiting. The old man did not notice them: he had blended into one with his book. The middle-aged man did notice them, but he was reflecting how he might attract his father's attention. But the youngest one jumped up at once:

Well, Mother, Grandmother—what's what?"

The middle-aged man rose uneasily from his place; as for the oldest, he merely moved the book away from him and lifted up his eyes to look at the women.

"How is she doing?" the youngest man asked in a tremulous voice.

"Everything is fine," the crone answered calmly.

"Fine, fine!" the youngest man echoed her.

"Mother, you haven't even congratulated us!" remarked the middle-aged man.

The old man thought a while and then asked:

"What has happened—is it a girl, or what?"

"No!" answered the crone. "It's a boy—"

"Is it a still birth?"

"No, he's alive," answered the crone, but one could not detect any rejoicing in her voice.

"Is he a monster? A cripple?"

"He has some marks or other on his shoulderblades—"

"What sort of marks?"

"The marks of wings. Clear marks of wings!"

"Wings?"

The old man was perturbed, while his son was amazed; the grandson was the only one to leap up in joy:

"How splendid! Let those wings grow, let them grow to their fullest—great powerful wings . . . how splendid this is!"

"What is there to rejoice about?" the middle-aged man voiced his wonder.

"It's a dreadful deformity!" sighed the old man.

"But why?" asked his grandson.

"Wings," the old man answered sternly, "bear one aloft; with wings it is difficult to maintain one's hold on earth."

"As if that mattered greatly!" the grandson ventured to remark. "What of it—man will not then be attached to one place; he will not have to be scrabbling all his life in the mire, he will live above the earth. . . . Come, isn't heaven better, more beautiful than the earth?"

At this the old man actually paled, while the middle-aged man remarked:

"Foolish little fellow—what is one to live on in the heights of heaven? One cannot be fully fed on air alone. . . . You can't become an innkeeper there, and you won't find any land you can lease. . . . In the clouds one can't trade even in rabbit-skins. There—"

But the old man broke in on him:

"In the heights," said he in a voice as hard as steel, "there are no synagogues, no houses of prayer, nor any books; there are no roads there, nor any trails blazed by our ancestors, and one is forced to wander, without knowing the true path. . . . You feel yourself as free as a bird, true enough—but woe to the free bird if it be overcome by gloomy thoughts, if it is seized by doubts—"

"How is that?" the youngest man leapt up from his seat, and his eyes lit up, while color mantled his face.

But he did not have an opportunity to speak; the little old grandmother broke in on him:

"You foolish men!" said she. "You surely have found something to argue over. For what about the rabbi? Come, will he grant permission to perform the rite of circumcision upon the child—will he allow a winged child to be of the Jewish faith? . . ."

I leapt up. My night beyond the confines of the city, my trip, and the child with the marks of wings—all these were but a dream.

Beryl the Tailor

I T WAS DUSK on the eve of Yum Kippur. In the synagogue in Berditchev, the graybeards had already recited the preliminary prayer and returned to their pews. The venerable sage, Reb Levi Itzchok, garbed in a white linen robe with a prayer shawl draped over his shoulders, stood facing the Ark and was about to proceed with the chant of Kol Nidre.

All eyes were fixed upon him; there was an awed silence even in the section reserved for women. In all likelihood, the spiritual leader would address the Lord briefly in everyday Yiddish rather than in the time-honored Hebrew of the ritual—as he used to do from time to time.

But Reb Levi Itzchok remained standing at the cantor's lectern without uttering a word. What could this mean? Were the gates of prayer still closed? Or was he unable to command attention? He just stood there motionless, listening intently as though he expected some mysterious sounds inaudible to the congregation. Suddenly, he wheeled around, called out for the sexton, and asked him:

"Has Beryl the tailor come yet?"

The congregation was puzzled. The sexton mumbled that he did not know. The sage took in the assembly at a glance and observed:

"He's not here; he must be home." Then, turning once more to the sexton he issued his instructions: "Go and tell Beryl the tailor to come to the synagogue. Tell him it is I, Levi Itzchok, who have sent for him."

The absent worshiper lived within a stone's throw of the synagogue, it was not long before he arrived in his woolen gabardine without his prayer-shawl or white linen robe. He seemed to be in ill humor and, half angry, half apprehensive, he blurted out:

251

"Rabbi, it was you who sent for me—and it's you I came to see."

Reb Levi Itzchok suppressed a smile:

"Tell me, my dear friend," he said, "what's all this fuss on your account in the world above? The heavenly hosts seem to hold you in great esteem. What have you stirred up there? All one hears is 'Beryl the tailor, Beryl the tailor,' over and over again."

"So!" Beryl exulted.

"So you want to lodge a formal complaint?"

"Indeed, I do!"

"Against whom?"

"Against the Lord Himself!" Beryl proclaimed. The worshipers, indignant at this blasphemy, were ready to pounce upon him. But Reb Levi, smiling, went on with his questioning:

"Would you care to tell us what your grievance is?"

"I certainly would. Moreover, I will submit the matter to your judgment right now, if you permit me to do so."

"Speak your mind!"

"Rabbi, during the past summer," the aggrieved tailor began, "I didn't have a stitch of work—may you be spared the same! Neither Jew nor—to make the distinction—gentile patronized me. I might just as well have turned up my toes—"

"The descendants of Abraham, Isaac, and Jacob are merciful and sons of the merciful," the Rabbi interposed. "You should have confided in someone."

"Not for the world, Rabbi! I'll neither ask for charity nor accept it from anyone." And he went on to say that he had as much faith in the Almighty as the next fellow, but just the same he had to send his daughter to the next town to work as a domestic, while he bided his time at home, waiting impatiently to see what Providence would do.

"Just before the Feast of Tabernacles," Beryl rambled on, "the door opened—at long last help was in sight. A special messenger from the landed proprietor came for me—there was a fur coat that needed re-lining. Well and good! The Lord is benevolent. I was escorted to the manor and handed the coat and a number of fox pelts. Rabbi, you should have seen those pelts! You couldn't find any better!"

The time was drawing near for the solemn service, and Reb Levi Itzchok decided to prompt Beryl:

"Very well; so you relined the coat, completing your work conscientiously—and then what?"

"Then—well, there were three small pelts left over."

"And you appropriated them?"

"That's easier said than done, Rabbi. There's a guard in a booth at the gates of the manor; at the least suspicion you are searched—they even take your boots off. And if, God forbid, those pelts were ever found on me—well, the squire has dogs and whips—"

"Well, what did you do?"

"Beryl the tailor, I'll have you know, is nobody's fool. Why, I made my way to the kitchen door and asked for a loaf of bread."

"The bread of a gentile, Beryl?" the Rabbi broke in.

"It was not for eating, God forbid, Rabbi! As soon as I got the loaf, I retraced my steps to the workroom, scooped out the soft bread, kneaded it a bit so as to let it absorb the sweat of my hands, and then flung it to the watch dog—for dogs are fond of human sweat. Then I thrust the three small pelts into the scooped-out loaf and started to leave.

" 'Hey, little Jew, what are you carrying under your arm?' the guard called out. 'A loaf of bread,' I told him, showing it to him. Then, as soon as I had left the estate behind me, I turned off the beaten path and took a short cut across the fields. I was as happy as a lark: for one thing, I would have a palm branch and a citron all of my own for the Feast of Tabernacles. Those small pelts were a treasure.

"Suddenly I felt the ground shaking and heard the sound of hoofbeats; someone was after me. My blood ran cold; they must have inspected the coat and checked the number of pelts. There was no sense in trying to escape the messenger, who was riding one of the squire's thoroughbreds. No sooner had I flung the loaf into the cornstalks and made a note of the place than I heard the man calling me: 'Berko! Oh, Berko!'

"I immediately recognized the voice of the landowner's Cossack rider. Rabbi, I was frightened out of my wits—but you know Beryl the tailor! When I turned around to face him, I seemed unruffled. However, it proved to be a false alarm; I'd merely forgotten to sew a hanger on the coat. So the Cossack helped me mount his horse and back we went. I thanked the Lord for the narrow escape, sewed the hanger on, and retraced my steps to where I had hidden the loaf—but there was not a trace of it! It was long past the harvest time; no human being would go tramping that way. Nor could any bird possibly snatch up the loaf. I guessed at once who had done it—"

"And who could that be?" Reb Levi Itzchok asked searchingly.

"He!" Beryl answered, pointing heavenward. "The Almighty— it's His doing, Rabbi. And I know the reason: the Lord of the Universe looked askance upon His slave, Beryl the tailor, spiriting away remnants."

"Well, of course, according to law—" the Rabbi began.

"Law, indeed!" Beryl parried. "It's common knowledge that custom takes precedence over law. Furthermore, it was not I who introduced this practice—it's been a custom from time immemorial. And if the Lord of the Universe is such a proud and exalted squire," Beryl argued, "and doesn't want His poor and humble servant, Beryl the tailor, to help himself to remnants, why, then let Him grant me a livelihood, let Him furnish me with maintenance, the way a squire usually does! And if there's neither maintenance nor helping oneself to remnants, well, I refuse to serve the Lord any longer. I've taken a vow, come what may!"

The congregation, aroused, was stirring in an ominous way, but Reb Levi Itzchok calmed the worshipers and said to the rebel indulgently:

"Go on, Beryl!"

"There's nothing more to say. I came home—and ate without even washing my hands. And no sooner did my wife open her mouth than I shut her up. And when I went to bed, I omitted reciting the usual prayer. My mouth started to recite the prayer instinctively, but I clenched my teeth. When morning came my attitude was still the same: no ablution, no praying, no prayer shawl and phylacteries. 'Let's have some food!' I called out— whereupon my wife ran out of the house and headed straight for her father's, in the next village. Very well: I would do without a wife. Fact is, I was actually pleased. For she is of the weaker sex —no use of involving her in this mess. And I kept on with my plan: I avoided the Tabernacle; I acquired neither the citron nor the palm branch. I take a drop once in a while, but just the same I didn't go through the Benediction of the Cup during the Holy Days. When the Rejoicing of the Law was celebrated, I put on sackcloth, as Mordecai had done after the harsh decree, as recorded in the Book of Esther. Just to spite Him!

"The Penitential Days rolled around. I was in low spirits. The beadle's voice, calling the townsmen to prayer, echoed in the night, and I was itching to go to the synagogue. But Beryl the tailor is a man of his word: I pretended not to hear. New Year came—but I remained firm in my resolve. When the blowing of the ram's horn sounded, I stuffed my ears with cotton. Rabbi, my heart was simply rent—it was pitiful. I went around unwashed, and it made me sick just to look at myself. There was a small mirror on the wall—I turned it round, so as not to behold such an eyesore as my face. I heard my townsmen heading for the stream, for the ceremony of casting out their sins—" At this point the speaker paused, and it took him a little while before he could go on. "But I am in the right, Rabbi! I won't budge an inch!"

"Well, what do you wish for?" asked Reb Levi Itzchok, "Is it a livelihood?"

"A livelihood? What does that amount to?" Beryl became indignant. "He should have provided me with sustenance *before* this. *Everyone* is entitled to that much: the bird is fed and so is the worm. A livelihood is just bare subsistence. Beryl the tailor demands far more than that."

"Be more specific, Beryl."

Beryl deliberated for a moment before replying:

"Rabbi, isn't it true that on Yum Kippur only transgressions against the Almighty are forgiven?"

"That is true."

"But there's no forgiveness for wrongdoing against one's fellow men?"

"No."

Beryl drew himself up to his full height:

"I will not yield," he asserted sternly; "I will not return to the service of the Lord until He will, for my sake, grant forgiveness this year for such sins as well. Am I right, Rabbi?"

"Indeed, you are!" Reb Levi Itzchok concurred. "Don't give up—you're bound to win."

The spiritual leader wheeled around to face the Ark, cast a glance upward and, after a moment's meditation, declared:

"Beryl, your wish has been granted. Go and get your prayer shawl and white robe!"

Marriage

I REMEMBER the time in the summer when, as a little girl, I used to play hopscotch and make mud pies. In winter, I spent days on end sitting by the cradle of my little brother who was delicate from birth and died at the age of seven during an epidemic. In the summertime my poor brother would sit outdoors until evening, warming himself in the sun and watching me play. In the wintertime he never left his crib, and I would tell him fairy tales and sing songs for him after my other brothers had gone off to Hebrew School.

Mother was busy all day every day. Poor mother—how many occupations she had! She bought and sold things, baked cookies, helped at weddings and circumcisions, was an attendant at the ritual baths, performed the measurement of the graves,* served as a reader in the synagogue and, in addition to all these things, did the marketing for well-to-do housewives.

Father worked as a clerk, at three roubles a week, for Reb Zainvel Terkelbaum, who was in the lumbering business. Those were happy times: the *melamedim* [religious instructors] received their fees, the rent at home was paid almost regularly, there was enough bread. Now and then mother would cook porridge for supper— a real holiday in the household.

Most of the time mother came home late, tired and in a vile temper, her eyes red from weeping. The housewives, she complained, would not pay what they owed her. First of all they told her to lay out her own money, then they suggested that she come tomorrow, or the day after, to collect. Meanwhile there were new purchases, but when the time came to settle accounts, the housewife "didn't remember" whether or not she had paid for a certain pot of butter. For the time being the butter would be left out

* During a critical illness, the grave of a Jew noted for his piety would be measured, and candles corresponding in length to the length of this grave would be donated to a synagogue—*Translator.*

of the calculations. It would be necessary to ask the lady's husband, who had been present at the time: he had a memory like an elephant, and would surely remember the amount. The next day it turned out that the husband had come back late from the synagogue and the lady had forgotten to ask him; the third day she announced triumphantly that she had asked her husband but that he had become angry at her because she was pestering him about trifles: that's all he had to do—listen to female accountings! And it was left up to her to recall the amount. Then it began to be clear to her that she had almost certainly taken that pot of butter into account, and finally she was ready to swear that she had done so. And when poor mother got up courage enough to remind her once more about the butter, the lady would call her impudent: mother was making things up, the lady would say, trying to cheat her out of a few extra coppers. She was warned that if there was another peep out of her about the butter she would do better never to show her face again.

My mother, who came from a well-to-do family, would have been a housewife herself now, on the same footing with the others, except that the landowner had helped himself to her dowry. Thus, she found her life hard to bear. She would come home sobbing, throw herself on the bed, and lie there for a long time until she had no tears left. Then she would get up and cook beans and dumplings for us.

Often she would take her misery out on us—that is, on me. She never scolded the sickly Beryl; and rarely scolded my other brothers who were going to Hebrew school—as it was, the poor fellows used to come home with black and blue marks on their faces and sometimes with black eyes. But to make up for such forbearance, she would pinch me or yank my braid; "Would your hands wither if you were to make the fire and boil a pot of water?" But when I complied, she would scold me with even more intensity: "Look at her—what a housewife she's become! She's made the fire just to waste fuel. What does she care that I have to break my back! She'll make a beggar of me yet!"

My father often got his, too—but behind his back. My mother would seat herself on the bed with her face toward the window and, fixing her eyes in the distance, would sigh deeply. "He has nothing to worry about. He sits there in the forest like a count or something, breathing all that fresh air, lolling on the grass, and swilling buttermilk—even cream, for all I know—and here my stomach is shrinking from hunger!"

Just the same, those were good times. We didn't have to go hungry, and after a week filled with all sorts of unpleasantnesses Sabbath would come. Father usually came home for the Sabbath, and mother bustled about, smiling when she thought no one would see.

Often on Fridays, just before she said her prayers over the lighting of the candles, she would kiss my head and I understood that she loved me. But when father wasn't expected for the Sabbath, she would call me a witch, pull almost every hair out of my head as she combed it, and hit me several times on top of that. But I didn't cry. I knew that it was not me but her bitter lot in life that mother was reviling.

At last the trees were all chopped down, father came home, and the lack of a piece of bread began to be felt in the household. Actually, the need affected only father, mother and myself; little Beryl needed next to nothing—he would take a sip or two of soup, and then stare at the ceiling again, and the other children, poor darlings, were going to Hebrew school so it was imperative to give them something hot to eat. But I had to go hungry quite often.

Father and mother were forever recalling the past with tears in their eyes; I, on the contrary, felt considerably better during a hard spell. Ever since privation had come to reign in our house mother grew to love me considerably more. Now, when she got home, she did not yank me by the hair and no blows fell on my thin body. When we sat at a meal father stroked my head and tried to divert my attention from the fact that I wasn't getting my full share. I was proud that now, when it was necessary to fast, I was fasting on the same footing with father and mother, and I considered myself an adult.

It was at this time that Beryl died. Here is how it happened. One morning mother woke up and said to father: "Do you know, Beryl must be better; he slept all through the night and didn't wake me up once."

I caught these words (I was always a light sleeper) and joyfully sprang off the trunk on which I slept and ran to have a look at him—I loved him very much. I was hoping to see a smile on his peaked little face—I found a dead body. We all had to sit for a week in mourning.

Soon afterwards, father took sick and a doctor "of the second class" began calling at our house. As long as we were able to pay, somehow making ends meet, he used to come to us himself; but when the last pillows, the hanging lamp, and my father's books of devotion (which my mother would not allow to be touched for a long time) had all gone to pay for medical expenses, the doctor began sending his assistant.

This assistant went very much against my mother's grain; he sported a tiny curled mustache, dressed after the new fashion and, besides all that, hardly let a minute go by without interpolating Polish words into his speech. I was afraid of him—to this day I don't know why—and each time he was expected I would run out of the house and wait outside until he left.

One day one of our neighbors fell ill (he was also poor and evidently, just like ourselves, had already managed to sell all his household belongings), and the doctor's assistant (whose name I don't recall) went from our house to that of our neighbor. As he was going through the yard he came upon me, sitting on a log. As I sensed his approach a chill went through me, and I felt my heart beating faster.

He came up to me, took me by the chin, and said in simple Yiddish: "Such a beautiful girl as yourself must not be untidy and must not feel embarrassed before a young man!"

He released me, and I ran back into the house. I felt that all the blood had rushed to my face and I huddled in the dark corner behind the oven, under the pretext of counting the dirty linen. This happened on a Wednesday.

On Friday I reminded my mother, for the first time in my life, that my head needed a washing.

"My God!" my mother wrung her hands. "Why, it's three weeks since I've combed her!" But the next moment she flew into a rage: "You witch!" she screamed. "A husky girl like you can't take care of herself! Another girl in your place would have washed not only herself but the other children as well."

"Don't scream, Soreleh dear!" my father implored her. But my mother's wrath was becoming more and more intense.

"Do you hear me, you witch? Wash your head right away, this very minute! Do you hear?"

I was afraid to walk up to the oven where the hot water was

standing since, in going past my mother, I might get a kick. It was my father who saved me, as usual.

"Don't scream, Soreleh, dear," he repeated, moaning. "My head is aching as it is."

My mother's wrath subsided as if by magic. I crossed the length of the room without interference and took off the pot of hot water. As I was awkwardly washing myself I saw my mother go to my father and then point to me with a deep sigh.

"Merciful God!" she said softly—my ear, however, caught every word. "She's growing by the hour, the poor thing; she glows like gold—but what's the good of it?"

My father sighed heavily by way of answer.

The doctor had told my father more than once that he wasn't so very ill. Due to his worrying so much he had gotten an inflammation of the liver, which had become swollen and was pressing against his heart—that was all! The main thing was, he had to drink milk, avoid any unpleasantness, go out of the house as often as possible, meet people and, in general, find some occupation. But my father complained that his legs were played out. Why, I did not find out until later.

Once, at daybreak (this was in the summertime) I was awakened by mother and father talking.

"You must have done a great deal of walking, my poor darling, when you were working in the forest."

"I should say so," answered my father. "The trees were being felled in twenty places at once in that forest. The forest, you see, belongs to the landowner, but the peasants have certain rights in it—the deadwood and the windfalls belong to them. When all the trees in a forest are felled they lose rights and are forced to buy lumber and firewood. Of course they wanted to get an injunction and turned to the proper authorities. But they didn't realize what was happening until it was too late. As soon as Reb Zainvel noticed that the peasants were scratching the napes of their necks, he lost no time in sending out a call for forty more lumberjacks. It was a nightmare: trees were being felled all over and one had to be everywhere at once. Well, what could you expect? My legs used to swell up until they felt like logs."

"How a human being can sin!" mother sighed. "Yet I was thinking that you didn't have a thing to do there."

"Guess again!" my father smiled bitterly. "I had to be on my feet from before daybreak until far into the night."

"And all that for three roubles a week!"

"He promised me an increase. In the meantime, as you know, his lumber rafts became waterlogged and sank, and he started complaining that he was utterly ruined."

"And you believed him, just like that?"

"Could be—"

"He is forever becoming ruined," my mother grumbled, "but meanwhile his wealth keeps growing and growing."

"Do you happen to know what business he's in now?" asked father, who had not set foot out of the house for almost a year.

"What business should he be in? He's trading in flax, and eggs; he has opened up an inn—"

"And what is his wife doing?"

"She's ailing, the poor thing."

"What a pity. She's a fine woman."

"She's a treasure. The only housewife who doesn't want a copper that doesn't belong to her. She would even pay promptly, if she meant anything at all to him."

"That's his third wife, I think?" asked father.

"Why, of course!"

"You see, Soreh, there's a rich Jew for you—and he has no luck in marriage . . . every man has his own troubles."

"And she's so young!" mother put in. "Only a little past twenty."

"Who can ever tell! He must be over seventy—and yet he's so strong."

"I should say so! He can still crack nuts with his teeth."

"And he doesn't wear glasses."

"And the way he walks—the floor shakes under him—"

"Yet I must lie in bed."

I felt a flush go through me when I heard this.

"God will help us," mother consoled him. "The only thing, there's our daughter," she sighed, glancing as she did so at the trunk on top of which I slept. "She's . . . she's becoming a woman —may she be spared the evil eye. Did you see her, just now?"

"Of course!"

"Her face . . . it glows like the sun!"

261

"You know, Soreleh, we are sinning before God," said my father after a brief pause.

"In what way?"

"Why, in regard to our daughter. How old were you when we were married?"

"I was younger than she."

"Well?"

"Well what?"

At this point there were two knocks on the window. Mother jumped out of bed. It took her only a moment to tear off the cord that held the two halves of the shutter together and throw open the window, the fastenings of which had gone long ago.

"What's happened?" she shouted out into the street.

"Reb Zainvel's wife has passed away."

Mother staggered back from the window.

"Blessed be the Righteous Judge!" said my father. "It isn't hard to die—"

"Blessed be the Righteous Judge!" my mother echoed. "We were talking of her just now—"

I was going through a very upsetting time just then, without knowing what the matter was.

There were periods when I could not sleep all night. There was a pounding as of hammers at my temples; my heart beat as if it were frightened, while at other times such a warm and joyous feeling came over me that I wanted to embrace everything and everybody, to kiss them, and to hold them close to me.

But whom? My brothers would have none of that—five-year-old Jochanan became balky and screamed that he didn't want to play with a girl. As for mother . . . well, to say nothing of my being afraid of her, she was always ill-tempered and full of cares. And father was ailing more than ever. In a short while he had turned completely gray, his face was covered with wrinkles, and his eyes had such a helpless look, there was such a mute appeal in them that it took only one look at him to make me run out of the room in tears.

It was at such times that I recalled my Beryl. He was the one in whom I could have confided, whom I could have kissed and held close to my breast. But he was lying in the dark ground and . . . at that point I would burst into tears.

Truth to tell, tears came to my eyes for no apparent reason. Sometimes I would be looking out of the window at the court-yard, watching the moon as it floated nearer and nearer to the whitewashed enclosure. And suddenly I would be overcome by a feeling of pity for the moon; my heart contracted, and tears coursed in torrents down my cheeks. Or else I wandered about all wilted and pale of face, with dark circles under my eyes. There was a buzzing in my ears; my head was heavy. And it would begin to seem that the best thing of all would be to die. As such times, I greatly envied Beryl. He was just lying there, and nothing could upset him.

Very often I would dream of my own death: I was lying in a coffin, or flying through the heavens in nothing but my shirt and my hair all loose, looking downward and watching what was hap-pening upon earth.

That was just about the time I drew away from all the girls with whom I used to play hopscotch; I failed to acquire any new friends. One of the girls I knew began coming out on the Sabbath in a satin dress, with a watch and chain pinned to her bosom; her wedding was to be celebrated soon. Others were also reaching the marriageable age. Matchmakers and the relatives of the bride-grooms were wearing out their doorsteps. The young ladies were coiffured, bathed, dressed up, while I was still running around barefoot in an old skirt and a faded calico blouse which was com-ing apart at the seams in several embarrassing places and was patched with calico of another color. My contemporaries turned away from me, and I was ashamed to be on terms of friendship with girls younger than myself, and playing hopscotch no longer interested me.

For these reasons, I would not go outside in the daytime. Mother never sent me on my errands, and whenever I volunteered to run and get something, she would not let me go. I would often steal out of the house toward evening and stroll past the ware-houses or sit by the river bank. In the summertime I used to sit thus far into the night. At first, my mother occasionally came out after me, yet she never approached me. She would stop at the gate, look about in all directions, and go in again. I thought I heard her sighing as she watched me from a distance. But with time that, too, stopped.

I would sit like that for hours at a time, listening to the tiny river and to the splashing that came each time the frogs plopped from the bank into the water, or gazing at some radiant cloud in the sky. At times I half dozed with my eyes wide open.

Once I heard a sad song in the distance. The voice was young and vigorous, and it found a melancholy echo throughout my being. Just a little Jewish song, it was.

"That's the doctor's assistant singing," I reflected. "Another would not be singing such songs but chanting psalms instead."

It occurred to me that I ought to go into the house, so that I should not listen to such songs, and that I ought to avoid meeting the doctor's assistant. Yet I could not move. I was in a daze; a faintness came over me, and I remained where I was even though my heart was pounding alarmingly.

The song came closer and closer; it came to me from across the river, then from the bridge, and at last I heard the singer's footsteps on the sand. Once more I wanted to run away but my legs refused to obey me. Finally he came to where I was sitting.

"Is it you, Leah?"

I did not answer. The noise in my ears was deafening, the blood was pounding more and more at my temples and it seemed to me that I had never yet heard a voice so kindly, so gentle. He was not disturbed by my silence; he sat down beside me on the log and looked straight into my face. I could not lift up my eyes, nor did I see his gaze, but I knew that my face must be flaming.

"You're a beautiful girl, Leah; I feel sorry for you."

I wanted to burst into sobs, and I ran away.

The next evening and the one after that I no longer left the house, but on Friday, my heart grew so heavy that I had not the strength to resist going out; it seemed to me that I would smother indoors. He must have been waiting for me in the shadow behind the house, for as soon as I had seated myself in my usual place he sprang up before me as if out of the ground.

"Don't run away from me," he said. "Believe me, I will not harm you."

His smoothly flowing and tender voice reassured me. He began another pentle, plaintive song and once more the tears came to my eyes. I could not restrain myself and began softly weeping.

"Why are you crying?" he asked, breaking off his song and taking my hand.

"You sing so sadly," I said, and took my hand away.

"I am an orphan, all alone in a strange place."

Someone appeared on the street, and we hurried off in different directions.

I remembered that little song and hummed it every night as I lay in bed. I would fall asleep to it and awaken to it. But just the same, I cried often and regretted having become acquainted with the doctor's assistant, who dressed like a non-Jew and went without a beard. If only he would have behaved like the old doctor himself and were a pious Jew. I felt certain that father would die, God forbid, from grief as soon as he found out what was going on, while mother would do away with herself. The secret lay like a millstone on my heart.

Whenever I happened to go near my father's bed to hand him something, whenever my mother came home, I remembered my transgression, and my arms and legs would begin to tremble, while every drop of blood drained from my face. Nevertheless, I promised myself every day that on the next day, I would go out to see him. I had no reason to avoid him: he no longer took my hand or called me a beautiful girl, but only talked to me and taught me songs. Once he brought me something: a carole-pod.

"Take it, Leah!" I refused. "Why?" he asked in a sad voice.

"I'd rather have a slice of bread!" I blurted out.

I don't remember how long we kept seeing each other like this. One day, however, he came in an unusually sad mood. I immediately noticed this and asked him what was wrong.

"I must go away."

"Where?" I asked, and my voice sank.

"I have to report for military service."

"They're going to take you for a soldier?" and with that I clutched at his hand.

"No," he said, squeezing my hand hard. "I'm not well—I have a weak heart. But I must report."

"Are you coming back?"

"Of course." For a minute or so we kept silent. Then he said: "But this will drag out for several weeks." I said nothing and he kept looking at me with pleading eyes. "Will you miss me?"

"Yes." I could barely hear my voice.

"Let's say goodbye to each other."

"May you be well," I said in a tremulous voice, my hand still in his.

He bent down, kissed me, and left quickly. I remained standing there for a long while, as if in a coma.

"Leah!" I heard my mother's voice—tender, joyous, as it used to sound at the time when father was still well. "My little Leah!"

It was a long time since she had called me that. I felt feverish and, my lips still warm from his kiss, I dashed into the house. But I failed to recognize our room. Standing on the table were vodka, cookies, and two borrowed candlesticks with lit candles. Father was seated in a chair, his elbow leaning on a pillow. Each wrinkle on his face seemed to rejoice; borrowed chairs were ranged about the table with strangers sitting on them. Mother embraced me, kissing me, and clasping me to her breast.

"Congratulations, my daughter, my little daughter, my little Leah—congratulations!"

I could not understand what was going on around me, but my heart contracted and pounded with fear! When mother had released me from her embraces father called me over to him. All my strength left me. I sank on my knees before him and put my head on his breast.

"My child," he began, stroking my head and running his fingers through my hair, "you won't have to endure hunger and need any more . . . you won't have to go in rags and without shoes, my child. You'll be rich . . . you'll pay for the schooling of your brothers—they won't be put out of Hebrew school any more. And you'll help us also; I'm going to get well—"

"And do you know who your bridegroom is?" mother asked me joyously. "Reb Zainvel himself! Reb Zainvel himself sent a matchmaker!"

I don't know what happened to me, but I woke up in bed, in broad daylight.

"Glory be to God!" mother cried out.

"Glory be to His Holy Name!" father uttered after her.

And they fell to hugging and kissing me—they actually gave me some jam! Did I, they asked, care for some water with syrup? Or for some wine? I shut my eyes again and broke into muffled sobbing.

"That's fine!" my mother brightened up. "Let my child have

a good cry. It's all our fault—telling her such good news so abruptly, so unexpectedly! She might, God forbid, have had a stroke! But now, glory be to God! Cry, my child; ease your soul. Let all your grief flow away with the tears, and let a new life begin. A new life!"

Every human being has two angels—an angel of good and an angel of evil—and I felt certain that the angel of good was bidding me to forget the doctor's assistant, to eat the jam sent over by Reb Zainvel, to drink his syrup and to outfit myself at his expense. The angel of evil, however, bade me declare to father and mother, once and for all, that I did not want all this—that I did not want it, no matter what the benefits. As yet, I did not know Reb Zainvel. It may have been that I had seen him once but had forgotten it or had not known that it was he. But sight unseen, I hated him.

For two night running I dreamed that I was going under the wedding canopy. My bridegroom was Reb Zainvel. I was led around him seven times . . . but my legs had turned numb. My bridesmaids lifted me high and were carrying me. Then I was led home. Mother came out to meet me—dancing. Then the wedding supper was served. I was afraid to lift up my eyes. I felt certain that I would see a blind, one-eyed man, with a long, long nose. My whole body was bathed in cold sweat. Suddenly he bent over and whispered in my ear:

"Leah, you're a beautiful girl!"

But his voice was the voice of another. I opened my eyes a little and saw the doctor's assistant.

"Shh!" he whispered to me with a mysterious air. "Don't say anything to anybody; I enticed Reb Zainvel into the forest, shoved him into a bag, tied a stone to it, and threw him in the river." (My mother had once told me a story like that.) "Now I am here to take his place!"

At this point, I would wake up in horror. A wan ray of moonlight stole through the chink in the shutter and lit the whole room. Only then did I see that the lamp was hanging from the ceiling, that father and mother were sleeping on featherbeds, father smiling in his sleep, and mother breathing evenly. And my angel of good said to me: "If you will be a good and dutiful girl your father will get well, your mother will not have to work so much and so hard in her old age; your brothers will become learned rabbis and well-known men—you will pay their instructors."

"But," the angel of evil whispered to me, "it will be Reb Zainvel who will be kissing you. He will cling to you with his moist lips and embrace you with his bony arms. He will torture you just as he tortured his previous wives and drive you to an early grave. As for the other man, he will come back and suffer; he won't teach you any more songs and you won't be spending all your evenings with him. It will be Reb Zainvel you'll be sitting with!"

"Never! Never, never, never! Tear up the marriage contract!"

There was no more sleep for me that night.

Mother would be the first to awaken. I wanted to talk with her, but I had always turned to my father for help. At last he awoke.

"Do you know, Soreleh dear, I feel well, altogether well. You'll see—today I'll be going out."

"Praise be to His Holy Name! And it's all due to our daughter —to her saintly intercession."

"The doctor was right, it seems—the milk tastes very good to me."

Again the good angel spoke up inside me:

"If you will be a good and dutiful girl, your father will get well; but if one sinful word escapes your lips he will die through your fault."

"Listen, Soreleh dear," my father resumed, "you've done enough trading."

"What nonsense are you spouting?"

"You heard me! I'm going to Zainvel this very day. He will give me a job, or else he'll lend me a few roubles. We'll open a shop. I'll stand behind the counter a little, and so will you; then I'll start trading in grain—"

"May God grant it!"

"Of course He will! Today, when you'll be buying materials for the wedding clothes, get some for yourself as well—make it enough for two dresses while you're at it. And why shouldn't you? After all, you can't go to the synagogue the way you are when the bridegroom will be called up on the dais to read the Torah."

"Whatever are you saying!" said mother. "It's more important to get something for the children. Rubin is running around barefooted—last week he got a splinter in his foot and is still limping. Winter is coming on; they need shirts, sweaters, and overcoats."

"Get enough for everybody!"

"You hear that?" said my good angel. "Should you utter the sinful word your mother will be left without a new dress, and you know that her old one is all worn out and hangs about her in tatters. Your brothers will be running barefoot to Hebrew school, and in the summertime their feet will be crippled by splinters."

"Speaking truthfully," mother declared, "everything should definitely be decided in advance—for you can't call him the kindest of men. We must decide how much he's going to leave her, because there will be heirs beyond all counting. If there's no regular will, let him at least write a simple letter. After all, how much longer can a fellow like that live? Another year or two—"

"When a man lives well," father sighed, "he lives long."

"Long, indeed! Don't forget he's seventy. Sometimes . . . sometimes it seems to me that the skin under his ears is dying—"

And the angel of evil whispered to me:

"If you remain silent, you'll be married to a dead man; it'll be a dead man gets you—"

My mother sighed.

"Everything is in the hands of God," said father. Mother sighed again, and father went on: "And what could we have done? Come, was there a better way out? Of course, had I been well and able to earn something, if there were any bread at all in the house—" He did not finish. It seemed to me that my father's heart burst into sobs.

"If she were younger, I might have done something extreme. I know . . . I would have taken a chance in the lottery—"

My seventy-year-old bridegroom furnished the money for the wedding finery; to my father he gave several hundred zloty and a promissory note made out to me in the amount of a hundred and fifty zloty, over and above everything else.

It was an advantageous match, everybody said.

Now I acquired girl friends. The one with the satin dress and the watch and chain used to drop in on me two or three times a day. She was happy because I had caught up with her, because we were both to be married during the same month. I had other friends as well, but this one did not leave me alone for a minute:

"Why those others are just nobodies," she would say. "Who knows how long they're going to stay old maids."

Rivka's betrothed came from a distant town, but he was going to live with her family for two or three years. All that time we would be bosom friends; she would be dropping in on me for a cup of chicory, and I would do the same for her.

"And, when I give birth," Rivka asked me once, "will you be sitting at the head of my bed?" I said nothing. "Oh, it's nothing!" she said. "Things like that happen even when the husband's seventy . . . Ah," she went on consoling me, "if God's willing, even a broomstick will shoot! And even if it shouldn't happen, how long do you think he can last? After all, no man can live forever. I swear by my luck—you'll be such a young and handsome widow that the men will simply smack their lips!"

Rivka did not wish Reb Zainvel any ill, even though he was rather a vile person! He had been a tyrant to his last wife, but she was ailing, whereas I was as sound as could be. Me he would treat well—and how!

He came back.

Father had actually gotten better, but one day he wanted to be cupped—he was apprehensive about going out of the house unless this were done. He felt that because he had been confined to bed and chair so long all his blood had become congested. It had to be stirred up! Besides, his back ached a little—and cupping was a time-tested remedy for that.

I shook as if I had the ague: it wasn't the doctor but his assistant who did the cupping.

"Will you go for the doctor?" father asked me.

"What are you saying?" mother interrupted. "The girl is engaged—" It was she who went for the doctor.

"Why are you so pale, my daughter?" father asked.

"It's nothing."

"You've been that way for several days now," father persisted.

"You're imaging things."

"Mother says the same thing."

"It's nothing, really."

"Today," father tried to cheer me up, "you'll be trying on your wedding finery. Aren't you glad at all?"

"Why shouldn't I be glad?"

270

"Why, you don't even know what they're making for you."

"They took my measurements, didn't they?"

Mother returned with the doctor himself. My heart felt easier, yet at the same time something pained me: "You may never see him again," a voice within me said.

"What a world this is, to be sure," sighed the doctor as he entered, grunting and gasping. "Reb Zainvel is marrying a young girl, while Leizerl, the son of a synagogue elder, is going to be a recluse—he's run away from his wife!"

"Leizerl?" my mother echoed.

"He and none other. And an old man of sixty like myself must be on my feet from morning till night, while a young man like my assistant falls sick for no reason at all."

"You ought not to employ a goy like that," mother put in.

"A goy? What do you mean by that?"

"What do I care?" my father cut the doctor short. "Better do what you have to do."

My father was a kindhearted man. It always seemed to me that he wouldn't have the heart to hurt a fly, yet just the same one could feel in his words a profound contempt for the doctor. Since he was bedridden, he was happy whenever anyone dropped in to talk with him; the doctor was the only person for whom he had no kind word. He was constantly cutting him short and urging him to attend to the work at hand. Now I became so acutely aware of this that my heart contracted. It occurred to me that father would have treated the doctor's assistant with even more contempt.

"What's the matter with him?"

"He says he has heart trouble."

Just what sort of illness that was, I didn't know—probably it was something which at times made the patient take to bed. Nevertheless, I felt partly to blame for it.

That night I cried in my sleep; mother woke me and sat down at the head of my bed.

"Calm down, my child, let's not wake your father."

We went on talking in whispers. I noticed that mother was greatly agitated. She was eyeing me searchingly and wanted to find out something, but I firmly resolved to tell her nothing—at least as long as father was asleep.

"Why were you crying, my child?"

"I don't know, mother."

271

"Are you well?"

"Yes, mother dear. Only, sometimes my head aches."

She was leaning over me with her elbow on the bed. I moved over and put my head on her breast.

"Why does your heart beat so hard, mother?" I asked.

"From fear."

"Are you afraid in the night, too?"

"Both night and day—I'm afraid all the time."

"What are you afraid of?"

"I'm afraid for you."

"For me?" Mother did not answer, but I felt her tears rolling down my face. "Are you crying, mother dear?" The tears fell faster. I resolved still more firmly not to tell her anything.

"Did Rivka say something to you, by any chance?" she asked me after a short silence.

"Did she tell me what, mother?"

"About the man you're going to marry."

"How should she know anything about him?"

"If she knew him she wouldn't be talking, but you know how this town is—what won't they talk about . . . out of sheer envy. A rich Jew and, although he's old, he's still vigorous enough to marry a young girl. Surely, they must be wagging their tongues? Wasn't she telling you that he had tormented his last wife to death?"

I replied, with complete self-possession, that I had heard something of the sort, but that I couldn't remember from just whom.

"Most probably from Rivka—may her mouth grow crooked!" mother said angrily.

"Why, then," I asked, "did his last wife die so suddenly?"

"Why? She had heart trouble."

"Do people die from that?"

"Of course!"

I felt as if someone had struck me over the head with a club.

I became a model daughter. Everybody sang my praises. Not only my father and mother but even the tailor could not understand why I didn't ask for anything for myself. Mother did as she liked; she bought whatever pleased her, picking the material and the dresses according to her taste. Rivka tore her hair: how could one possibly rely on mother in such matters—a woman of the old school? Why, I wouldn't be able to show myself on the Sabbath in the synagogue or out on the street—or anywhere! "You're ruining yourself!" she always wound up.

It occurred to me that my life had been ruined long before this, and I waited calmly for the Sabbath of Consolation, when my bridegroom would be called up on the dais to say the *Kiddush* over the wine. Next would come the Call to the Torah, and then the wedding.

My father's health really did improve. He occasionally left the house; little by little he began acquiring information about the grain quotations. Discussing a loan with my bridegroom, as he had planned to do, he considered as yet premature. He was going to invite Zainvel to supper on the Sabbath of Consolation, and after supper he meant to hint about the loan.

"Since our circumstances have improved," father remarked one day, "we ought to send over what we owe the doctor, even though our credit is good with him. He isn't dunning us, and he comes himself now instead of sending his assistant, but just the same it's time to pay him what we owe."

I don't know how much we sent; it was Avramehl who was commissioned to deliver, on his way to school, a few zloty to the doctor. But just the same, the doctor's assistant came to see us!

"What? Didn't I send enough?" asked father.

"No, it isn't that, Reb Jehudah—I've come to say goodbye."

"To me?" father asked in surprise.

As soon as he came in I sank—no, I almost fell—on the nearest chair. But, on hearing the last words, I quietly stood up, and it flashed through my mind that I must protect him, that I must not allow him to be insulted. Matters did not come to that, however.

"I used to drop in on you," he began in his soft, melancholy voice, which went to my very soul. "Now I am going away forever. I thought—"

"There, there, that's fine," my father broke in on him, but this time more amiably. "Sit down, young man—that really is fine of you—your remembering old people. Very fine! Leah," he turned to me, "you must give him some refreshment—"

The young man sprang up, all pale, with lips quivering and eyes flashing. However, his face changed again on the instant and resumed its melancholy air.

273

"No, Reb Jehudah, I don't need anything, thanks. Goodbye!" He did not offer his hand to anybody and barely glanced at me. It seemed that he was accusing me, that he would not forgive me— just *what* I did not know myself. This time, I lost consciousness.

"This is the third time she has fainted!" I heard mother saying to father.

"It's nothing: at her age things like that do happen. But, God forbid, Reb Zainvel should find out; he would back out of the marriage . . . he's already had his fill of sickly wives."

I did not become sick.

I fainted only once more, during the bridal supper, when I had my first real look at Reb Zainvel.

And that was all.

Even yesterday, when the doctor, as he was leaving the room of Reb Zainvel, my husband, whose ingrown toenails he cuts every month, asked me whether I remembered his assistant, and told me that he had died in a hospital in Warsaw—even then, I did not fall in a faint and shed hardly a tear.

"You're kindhearted," he said, and only then did I feel that my cheek was wet.

And there you have the whole story.

I am well. It is five years now that I'm living with Reb Zainvel. *How* I live—that's something I may tell you about some other time.

The Miracles That Failed

O H, SOMBRE, impenetrable and silent nights—devoid of sleep, of dreams, of solace.

The wan, gray sky deprived of its radiant array is sprawled out wearily. The earth lies under a heavy mantle of dust, and the impotent fatigue of Creation and its Creator hovers everywhere.

Through the branches of stunted trees the impenetrable and silent night looks down; its water-gray eyes sap the last of my strength. Its breath touches me, and the blood in my veins turns to ice.

Oh, weary, frozen soul, seek warmth; go from house to house, from door to door, and pray for a spark—for a spark of fire to warm thyself.

I have grown deathly tired. There is nothing to live by—or for; yet it is beyond my strength to die; for how can I show myself in the world beyond?

I have grown deathly tired. Yet once upon a time I was strong; the beneficence of the Lord glowed upon me. But I transgressed and lost my strength; heaven was shut in my face and will bestow no new strength upon me.

As a prince, with gold curly locks, the anointed of God, I descended from the mountain heights, with a shining crown, in a radiant red mantle, bearing the golden harp of a king.

I descended from the mountain heights and lost everything in the lowlands.

My gold locks fell into the hands of Delilah.

Lilith, the queen of Hell, enticed and snared me with her spells; I chanted her praises to the strains of my golden harp— and one by one its strings snapped.

During bewitched nights, upon marshes strewn with flowers, I danced with the daughters of Lilith. And during these frenzied dances the golden crown flew from my head, and the mire swallowed my crown.

I wandered over twisting paths, and the thorny bushes along the way snatched the gleaming mantel from my shoulders.

Oh, nights devoid of sleep, devoid of dreams, of solace. . . .

God gave me a radiant soul; I wasted its sacred fire lighting penny tapers in the rainbow-hued gardens of pleasure. And the fire of my soul was burned out.

I changed the golden heart which He, Who overfloweth with Love, had bestowed upon me into small silver coins and bought the pitiful smiles of pitiful faces—and the golden heart ceased to be.

I am an extinguished flame. Heaven was shut in my face, and will no longer endow me with the glow of light or with new strength. God is not going to heed the imploring of impious lips that had sung the praises of Lilith, the queen of Hell, and had kissed the lips of her daughters.

I have become deathly tired.

There is nothing to live by, or for.

Yet it is beyond my strength to die; for how am I to show myself in the world beyond? They shall question me: Where are thy golden locks, and the crown that shone upon them? Where is thy gleaming mantle? How did the strings of the golden harp happen to snap—the harp of a king with which thou didst descend from the heights?

Oh, nights devoid of sleep, devoid of dreams, of solace!

With disheveled hair, in the garments of strangers gotten through begging, with a knotty staff in my trembling hand, I wander in search of the happiness that was once mine and I do not find it.

I have become tired, deathly tired from my seeking, and black thoughts pursue me like birds of prey.

Over hills and through dales, over fields and through forests, by meadows and along the banks of rivers I wander—day after day—day after day, yet my seeking is in vain.

I bend over the flowers in the green meadows—hoping to find only one that was nourished by my warm blood, but I do not

276

find it. Yet it was here, on these meadows, that my heart spilt the last of its blood.

I fix my gaze, filled with excruciating expectancy, upon the mirrored surface of the waters. Myriads of glittering images, reflected and intertwined in a fantastic dance, play upon the clear surface of the waters—and not a one of these images reflects the light of a familiar smile. And yet here, upon the surface of the waters, my soul expired.

It is not my colors that the flowers in the fields display.

I lift my gaze toward the treetops and in the mysterious rustling of their foliage I cannot hear a single sound of the chords of my sanctified harp.

And when I implore the thorn bushes to return the golden threads of my mantle, they laugh in mockery: "This wandering beggar seeks the golden threads of the king's mantle!"

It is hard for me here upon earth.

No matter where I go, I am haunted by recollections of what has been; here I found shelter for a moment, while there my heart poured forth its blood. But nowhere did the harsh earth allow me to sink roots. It did not preserve a single drop of my heart's blood, not a single ray of my soul, not a single sound of my king's harp—yet it had swallowed my crown.

It did not nourish the fragrant flowers I left upon its breast and these flowers of mine never fully blossomed.

This earth is jealous as a woman.

Upon its soft couch did I repose, but the dreams I dreamt were alien dreams; I longed for the far-off mountains hidden in mist. I wandered under its heavens, but constellations that showed me the way were still alien to me.

Earth allows me no shelter here. Her children and her foster-children are all alien to me.

With yearning and tremulous with hope I peer at all those I meet in my wanderings—and I feel the chill of the stranger is wafted from them. There is never a ray from a warm fraternal soul that might revive the flame that has gone out within me.

Cold, alien eyes. They hold neither joy nor my torments—nothing of that for which I suffered, nothing of that wherein I believed.

I have become tired, deathly tired in my search for the happiness I have lost, and I find it not.

None stops to greet the poor wayfarer, none offers him a hand in friendship. No one asks: "Wanderer, whither art thou going?"

You are an alien. Sadness and yearning becloud your eyes. Are you alive and, in punishment of your sins, condemned to the torments of exile, or are you dead and wandering without finding assuage for your sinful soul? None will give his blessing: "Whether thou be alive or dead, may the Lord console thee, O wanderer! May there be buds upon thy staff that will burst into blossom!"

But as for turning back home to the lofty mountains—I cannot turn back in the sackcloth of a beggar with a broken harp.

On the boundary between a forest and a field she is lying asleep.

Who is she? Why have I stopped? Why has my heart stopped beating?

On the boundary between a forest and a field she is lying asleep.

On her snowy mantle lurk, interwoven in lace-like tracery, the light and shade of the mysterious forest and the bounty-yielding field.

Who is she?

She is swarthy and pale, and wondrously beautiful. Whose vineyard is this Sulamith guarding?

The severe arch of her eyebrows is regally proud, and black as pitch; the rays of the sun glide playfully over her forehead, which seems carved out of ivory. An enigmatic smile flits over her half-open lips, scarlet and small—and her smile is delectable and pensive.

Her smile is trusting as her body clings to the soft green couch. Yet there is something disquieting that agitates her breast.

What is she dreaming of?

A new string has begun to vibrate sonorously on the old harp.

A tremulous hope has germinated in my heart. The power to wish, which had long since become extinguished, has awakened within me anew:

"Let her open her eyes!"

My wish came true. Slowly the long lashes parted and her big eyes cast a look upon me, a look proudly wondering and half-wrathful.

"Who has allowed me to gaze upon you?

"Oh, proud one! Even the stars did not ask me that, nor did the sun when I looked it in the eye.

"Do I know who thou art? Yes, I know. Thou art the one whom I have awaited these many, long years. Thou art the one of whom I dreamt during the still and pensive nights.

"My orphaned heart, drained of its blood and exhausted by tears, wasted in yearning after thee. And in the course of my wanderings, on a dark night when the last guiding star died out in the sky, when the last hope for an omen from on high vanished— it was then, in disquiet and amid frightful torment, that my soul begged for and, through prayer that all but failed, won thee from God!

"Drive me not from thee! Let a weary wanderer bow down at thy feet and reverently put his parched lips to the hem of thy gown as to a thing sanctified. I shall not defile it.

"I am full of sins. But sinful desires cannot touch thy regally proud and beautiful brow. Even as the enchanting reflection of the clear blue of heaven upon the eternal snows of Mount Hermon in the Holy Land is the smile that flits over thy pale face.

"Within thine eyes . . . cherubim with glittering words guard the gates of Eden from man, driven therefrom for that he had sinned; the glitter of these words of the cherubim is in thine eyes.

"Let a tired wanderer bow down and sing gentle praises unto thee.

"Heed not my weariness; look not upon my tattered garments; be not affrighted of my wanderer's staff.

"God is sending me His consolation. Fresh powers are awakening within me; the blossoms of hope have sprung to full blossom in my heart. The strings of my old harp have begun to vibrate, ready to break anew into the forgotten sounds of a hallelujah."

"I am mighty, I am rich.

"From the depths of the waters of Eden I shall bring up pearls for a necklace. In the impenetrable forests I shall find wondrous chords for melodious songs to thee. With the best flowers of all the fields, of all the meadows, I shall strew thy path. I shall purloin the most precious stones in the Lord's throne and shall adorn thy footstool.

"I shall create universes for thee."

279

"Who am I? Thou wouldst learn my name? It belongs to thousands of men; wherefore wouldst thou have the name of one amongst thousands?

"What am I?

"Without thee I am but the dim small rushlight at the head of a dying man.

"With thee I am a vivid flame of the Lord's hand; I am a pillar of fire, showing the way through the deserts to the promised land.

"Without thee I am an altar whose fire has died, fallen into ruin, forgotten by men and by God. The winds have long since scattered its ashes; the famished raven will on a rare occasion come to rest there, seek for the leavings of sacrifices upon it, find naught and fly off with a caw that sounds like a curse.

"With thee I am a high priest within the Holy of Holies, bearing a golden thurible, with a glittering diadem on my brow and an ephod of precious stones upon my breast. The little golden bells fringing the hem of my vestment pound in divine harmony. And, illumined by the beneficence of the Lord, I pray for creation, which is exhausted by sufferings.

"Without thee I am fallen, an outcast. An army of heroes marched by to demolish old worlds, to create new ones. I was one of the vanguard of that army—and I was left by the wayside. They abandoned a fallen comrade, some with tears of compassion, others with the spit of contempt, while others spurned me with a kick to clear the way for themselves.

"Thou hast but to wish it—and the ram's-horn of the Lord will be in my hands. Utter the word—and the blare of the horn will resound and new men of might, whose like has never yet existed, will appear for the creation of new, as yet uncreated universes— mighty men, men of flame with glittering armaments. And they will bend their knees before me and cast their banners and weapons at my feet for my blessing.

"Behold! The strings of the old harp have begun to vibrate; the staff has grown straight in my hands, new life awakens within me. Do not turn thy radiant brow from me, do not deliver me into the hands of death and its horrors."

"Wanderer, I understand thee not! Thy voice sounds strange in my ears; I understand not thy speech.

"From the height of mountain summits swathed in eternal

280

mist thou hast descended; wanderer, thou hast come down from the summits of the mountains, where the tempests contend eternally with the eagles. It may be that thou art one of the eagles, mighty and with broad-spanned wings; as for me, I am but a gentle swallow of the plain, and I understand thee not. . . .

"I hear thy words and I understand them not. A warm heart that is covered with blood quivers in them; a soul that has been exhausted by yearning is struggling within them; verily, like unto a sanguinary glow of a conflagration they are in the air before me; they frighten me. Yet I understand not thy sufferings.

"We are so alien to each other—so alien! Thou art an eagle of the lofty mountain summits; I am a gentle swallow of the valley: what wouldst thou have of me?"

And she arises and departs.

The glowing child of the valley has departed. She has left at my feet the sparkling diadem with which I had crowned her small head, and the radiant mantle I had placed upon her graceful body. The radiant swallow of the valley has flown.

"Greetings to thee! Greetings to thee, who hast come anew, proud and holy in the silvery glow of a quiet evening. Mayest thou be blessed. And blessed be thy appearance in the still, bewitched alley of acacias.

"The leafage of the snow-blossomed acacia softly quivers. And my heart, that had already become extinguished, grows young again. And again the fire has sprung into flame within my orphaned soul, and I have fathomed the enchanting mystery of the holy quiet of evening.

"Even as I, the blue height awaited thee with languishing love. Even as I, the silvery crescent and the joyous little stars yearned for thee. For thee did they weave out of delicate gold and silver threads the vision of the evening.

"Behold, it is for thee that the white acacia pours forth its fragrance. The sweet breath of the moon-flooded valley is wafted up to thee on the soft wings of evening and kisses, as a lover does, the hem of thy mantle. And knowest thou whereof the tiny bird sings so delectably? It sings of the delight of dying at thy feet.

"The tremulous light of the blue height flows timorously over thy beautiful brow. Happily the rays tremble upon thy face, but those that encounter the glow of thine eyes shyly vanish, timorous before their wondrous light—the light of the first seven days of creation which issues from them.

"Thou hast come, and behold! The wonder-working rays have transformed themselves into the strings of the golden harp, and the holy song of resurgence will break forth from them.

"By now thou art no longer a swallow of the valley. In the quiet of the night miracles have come to pass. The diadem shines anew upon thy small head, and the radiant mantle gleams upon thy body.

"Come, beloved, chaste, proud, and radiant! On this night of miracles we shall stroll, and by the light of thy eyes I shall find the sceptre and the crown.

"In the stillness of the night, blessed of God, miracles must come to pass."

"Man from the mountain heights, miracles will not come to pass!

"Thou hast implanted yearning in the gentle heart of the swallow. A tremulous heart drew me to thee. Now I am afraid of thee; let me depart!"

"Oh, child, be not affrighted! Wish, and thy will shall be consummated; from the lowlands of the valley with its pensive songs thou shalt be lifted up to the high mountain summits bathed in light."

"The height frightens me; we have already walked through part of the night, and my feet are tired."

"Think not of being tired, child—and be not afraid of me.

"In the still night, blessed of God, certain miracles have already come to pass. Look, in the glow of thy great eyes, to the music of thy words, I have grown mighty wings; I shall bear thee upon them to the distant snowy summits—"

"It is sadness, dear one, which thou hast implanted in my heart, that hitherto knew no care, and this sadness has grown greatly—and has impelled me toward thee. In the still nights I saw wondrous dreams. I dreamt of thy home, of the distant mountain summits, and I yearned for the glitter of eternal snows, for mountain roses that bend over a bottomless precipice."

"But now I am afraid!"

"Fear not, child! Thou art with me. A new, mighty strength is coming to birth within me. Come with me to the summits white with snow. But it is not the mountain rose we shall seek nor the gleam of snows upon mountain ridges that have congealed in eternal calm. Their gleam is that of white shrouds.

"People dwelt there once; they did not live rightly and lost their faith in life; they believed in death only, in white death, which cleansed one of all sins. They prepared their shrouds while still among the living; while they still had life they clad themselves in them, lay down on the calm summits of the mountains, closed their eyes and prepared themselves for death.

"And God, out of pity sent them slumber. And there they sleep. 'Until the ram's horn awakens them,' proclaimed the Lord, 'let them slumber!'

"Come, O Child, we shall arouse the dead. Behold, the ram's-horn of the Lord is in my hands. It shall sound forth and the dead shall awaken!

"Come, the clear song of the heavens resounds in thy voice; the wonder working strings are taut upon the golden harp.

"Come, we will sing to these dead and play for them a sacred song, the song of resurgence.

"Amid the beneficent stillness of night, blessed of God, miracles must come to pass!"

"Man of the mountain heights, the miracles will not come to pass. I am not what thou thinkest; giddy heights frighten me. I am afraid of thy miracles. The longing which thou didst implant in my indifferent heart has grown greatly and impelled me toward thee; it drove me from the comfort of a quiet home to a man of the mountain heights. But I cannot go with thee.

"My chest is weak; dear one, how shall I breathe upon the high mountains? There are no trees upon their barren slopes. Where can the weak-winged swallow of the valley find a resting place and weave its nests?

"And speak not to me of resurrection: the white blotches of the shroud blind me; they float in the air before my eyes and frighten me.

"The child of the valley is weak; she has not the strength to ascend a mountain. And do not lift me up, do not bear me up on thy wings; the breath is cut short on heights and I shall not keep my footing there—I shall fall into some abyss, while thou, in

the ardor of centending against whirlwind and tempests—thou
shalt not notice; thou shalt not know where and when thou didst
lose me.

"Hearken, man of the mountain summits, to the word of a
daughter of the valley! I am bound (by thousands of threads) to
the valley, to my quiet home; do not break these threads for that
will pain my heart.

"My soul has been woven by stars, by the bright little stars
that float over my quiet home. Lead me not away from them—the
glow of my soul shall go out like a taper under alien skies. And
my voice, which awakens the fire in thy heart—my voice is but the
echo of the softly purling rills of the valley. And the small golden
flame that flares up in my eyes is but the reflection of the golden
sands of the plain.

"It is not thy joy which makes me rejoice; it is not thy grief
which saddens me!

"In tiny sparks does my calm joy scatter, and my quiet grief
springs from sparse and stunted ears of grain that piteously sigh
as they slowly bend over the poor sandy field."

"I am bound to the valley by thousands of threads; I love its
lowlands.

"I love the glister of the golden sand and the small gnarled
trees that guard the gold. I love the plain with its green covering;
I love those gentle flowers of heavenly blue that smile up at me
from rustling grass.

"And when a melancholy mood comes over me I cast myself
upon the soft couch of the valley, on the boundary between a
forest and a field, burying my face among the lilies, breathing in
the moist aroma of the earth with its covering of flowers, and a
delectable peace floods my heart; then, too, whenever I have a
dream that is alien to me, a dream enigmatic and filled with yearning, I set out into the forest to see the sorceress of our valley, and
she beholds the future and replies—and her voice is the voice of
the cuckoo."

"Dear art thou to me, man of the mountains heights; I am
drawn and attracted to thee, but I cannot stay with thee nor go
with thee.

"Our ways do not cross. Thou art an eagle of the summits; I am a swallow of the valley.

"I am bound to my home (by thousands of threads); there is no breaking them.

"Leave me here. I have tired from the long road, from the search after sceptre and crown; sit thee down by my side. Thou hast a harp of gold; sing, then, a magic song to the swallow of the valley, to a weak child of the Exile.

"But sing not to me of mountain summits, sing not to me of rebirth—sing only of the delights of my quiet home.

"Sing me a song, a golden song, about the glitter of golden sand, guarded by softly rustling trees. Sing to me of the gentle flowers of the valley with their unassuming fragrance, the flowers that gaze so lovingly at me with their tiny blue eyes out of the softly whispering emerald grass. Sing to me of the poor, dear swallow of the valley, that is borne in the air by weak, tender and tiny wings; sing of the nests on lowly barns, where she shelters herself from the tempest and the wind.

"Sing to me of the stork that brings luck, that strides through a swamp on its long legs and has its home on the squat roof of a peasant's hut. Sing of forsaken parks grown over with woods, of the ruins of an ancient castle, where at midnight a bewitched clock awakens and chimes out the hours. Or sing to me of bewitched princesses, who can be freed from their spell only by the ardent kiss of love."

"And when I fall asleep, carry out my wish, dear one; do not take thy gift from my brow; I will be yearning for the sparkling diadem eternally.

"And do not take away the bright mantle. Forgive a weak daughter of the Exile—a swallow of the valley."

Closed are the wondrous eyes, vanished the spells of the still night. Anew my soul has become extinguished; anew sombre shadows are lowering over it and, anew, the flowers that have opened in my heart are fading and dying.

Vanished the magic spells of the silvery beneficent night. God has not taken pity upon me; He has not remitted my sins.

The mute harp, its strings gone, lies broken; my wanderer's staff has become sapless anew.

Slumber sweetly, bright and radiant child of the valley; let gentle, sweet dreams hover over thy head. Forgive me! Forgive the wayfarer who encountered thee on the road and implanted yearning in thy heart, which had not known any care before.

The night turns pale; star after star is becoming extinguished. The night shadows are tremulous.

The first golden ray has come to birth; the East is turning a rosette hue.

The joyous tidings are borne to the earth upon the wings of the dawn; the day has come to birth!

The day is bursting into flame; it is ablaze; it has brought the joy of new life to all Creation which had become exhausted by weariness—to all Creation, but not to me.

The Lord has not taken pity upon me; He has not forgiven me my sins, and will not save me from yearning.

Take up thy staff, wanderer, journey on. With a new wound in thy heart, with new sufferings.

No miracle has come to pass.

All for a Pinch of Snuff

THE DEVIL was lounging, his legs crossed, smirking in a well-fed sort of way, and, for lack of anything better to do, was leafing through a ledger of all living creatures, half-yawning as he did so.

Suddenly, he clapped his hands sharply. He had noticed that the page given over to the Rabbi of Chelm was completely free of any entries on the debit side. Not a one. Naturally, the servitors of Hell, devils every one, gathered on the run in answer to Satan's call; they stood at the portals like dogs with their tongues out and waited for orders.

"Send someone up to Heaven to find out if the Rabbi of Chelm has long to live."

The devils vanished as quietly as they had appeared, and not even a quarter of an hour passed before they were back with the answer. They had been to the Chamber of Life: the thread representing the Rabbi's life on earth was very short—you could hardly distinguish it with the naked eye: he would be called to Heaven almost any day now.

"My secretary!"

A bald little scrivener, waddling on chicken legs and with red-rimmed but slyly gay eyes, leapt forward, bowed low, and seated himself tailor-fashion on the hot, black pitch floor; out of one pocket he took his writing equipment: a new crow's quill and an inkwell filled with the scarlet blood of an arch-adulterer; out of another pocket he got a freshly prepared roll of parchment, made from the skin of a heretic; then he spat on his hands and gave Satan a look of utter submissiveness. He was all set.

The Devil propped his elbow on the arm of his easy chair and fell to dictating, while the scribe, licking his copious spittle, began writing in a cursive fashion. The quill scraped quietly along, until a missive was concocted, addressed to the Supreme Court, as follows: "Inasmuch as it is said in Holy Writ: 'There is no man upon earth who doth good yet sinneth not,' and inasmuch as the Rabbi living in Chelm is now nearing the end of his days without having sinned even once, and inasmuch as it is desirable to preserve faith in Holy Writ and not to lead the righteous into error, it is imperative that the Rabbi of Chelm be given over into the hands and power of Satan. . . ."

After a brief conference, the Supreme Court handed down its decision and conveyed it to Hell: "*Cf.* Book of Job, Chapter the First."

The Devil immediately grasped the gist of this decision: *Do with him what thou wilt, but guard his life: thy power does not extend to life.*

But it was not so easy for the Devil to fulfill his desire.

The Rabbi of Chelm had no wife—it was by now many years that he had been a widower; his children had been taken care of —besides, as it is said: "Fathers shall not be put to death for [the transgressions of] their sons." No hoof nor horn of cattle had he, nor any flocks—the old man did not keep as much as a nanny-goat; his flesh was unclean enough without that—he was forever itching and scratching. And, besides all that, torments were nothing you could astonish the Rabbi of Chelm with!

"If one could but arouse some petty passion in him!" the Devil reflected, licking his lips; he reached for a bell on the table—a bell made from the skull of a Free-Thinker—and tapped it: the chamber filled with devils.

"Whom should I send, and who will go, to turn the Rabbi of Chelm from the path of righteousness?"

"Me! Me! Me!" they all shouted.

They all wanted to go, knowing that with a little deal like that you could make your reputation right off. They argued so intently that they all but came to blows; they compromised finally by deciding to cast lots. Two imps won out. Everybody else wished them success and vanished.

One fine clear day the Jews of Chelm were gadding about the marketplace; they had gathered in knots and were discussing the squire's stand of timber, the fields and meadows belonging to the gentry, the grain crops of the peasants, the skins of rabbits not yet hunted down and eggs not yet laid, when the ground suddenly quaked. They heard the crash and clatter of wheels, and a vehicle came into view. Nobody knew to whom it belonged; the horses were maned like lions and all in lather; the carriage flew through the marketplace, the people barely managing to get out of its way. The coachman, wearing a broad red sash and small fur hat, was standing up on the box, without a whip, his head thrown back, clutching the reins tightly and holding the horses back with all his might, so that at moments they had to rear. Standing behind him was a richly garbed Jew in an embroidered kaftan, comely and benign of visage; in his right hand was a whip, with which he kept lashing the horses unmercifully, making them fly head-long, with his left hand he was pummeling the driver's back; every now and then he would let out a shrill whistle that would frighten the horses and make them gallop.

The driver, however, never stopped shouting: "Save me, good people—save me! Save me, fellow-Jews! Stop the horses!"

But stopping the horses was easier said than done—sparks were flying in showers from under their hoofs. The men were running after the carriage with frightened faces; the women had scrambled out of the shops and were screaming for help.

The road ran past the slaughter-houses; the dogs jumped out and leapt at the muzzles of the horses; the butchers and slaughterers ran up and grabbed the horses by their bridles. The animals shied, backed up, and stopped. The butchers and slaughterers surrounded the carriage, wanting to know what was up.

A bad business, it turned out. The passenger, who was dressed as a merchant, with a leather money-belt on him, was yelling that the coachman had gone out of his mind: he'd gotten the notion of stopping to feed the horses, for no good reason at all, and yet the merchant was pressed for time; he was in a hurry to get to a fair—he was a trader in diamonds. The people were inspired with respect for the trader and set upon the coachman. The coachman explained that he wasn't a coachman at all, but that he was the merchant. On the road, while they had been going through a forest, on their way from a distant region, the coachman had fallen upon him at night, had put a knife to his throat, compelled him to change his clothes for those of the coachman, and had robbed him of all his money, his precious stones and his documents. And that's why he had started yelling for help when he had caught sight of the people in the marketplace.

The other man denied everything: he maintained that nothing of all this had happened. The people turned the horses around (it was all they could do to drive off the dogs), and led both disputants off to be judged by the Rabbi. The latter began the interrogation by examining the witnesses, after which he summoned the plaintiff, who was dressed as a coachman. The Rabbi heard him out and said:

"Obviously, this is an altogether simple man. He speaks exactly the way horsemen do. And, besides, his voice is not at all like that of a merchant—it smacks of the forest, of the open spaces, and of horses!"

However, the Rabbi went on with the interrogation:

"Tell me, what goods did you have in the carriage?"

"Well, how should I know? I'm a simple man; the Lord helped me, and I turned to dealing in diamonds!"

"And how much money did you have in your belt?"

"I didn't count it. God frowns upon the counted copper."

The Rabbi became still more convinced that the coachman was lying. However, he merely sighed and fell to questioning the man dressed as a merchant, the one who had such a comely and benign appearance. The Rabbi began talking to him about Holy Writ—and the man turned out to be well-versed in it. But then he suddenly turned to the Rabbi and said:

"Rabbi, what's the use of all this long-winded talk? Look!" And with that he turned over his money-belt: there was a shower of gold pieces; diamonds burst into little flames on the table. "I'm not even averse to sharing the diamonds with you—if you will but decide in my favor!"

The Rabbi jumped up and began yelling in a high-pitched voice that was not his own:

"You robber!"

The people ran in—and they had to rub their eyes. There was no plaintiff there and no defendant, nor were there any gold pieces. Everything had vanished. There was no vehicle and there were no horses: the earth had swallowed everything.

The town kept mulling the thing over: had all this happened in a dream, or were there enchantments of some sort at work here?

In the meantime the Devil had been informed of the results.

"You blockheads!" said he. "On the sly he might even have taken the bribe. But not openly! For then this matter might have

ALL FOR A PINCH OF SNUFF

bobbed up again at some time. They might have called him to account, likely as not, and he would have landed in prison. What a fool you found, to be sure!"

The unsuccessful imps were condemned to sit in a barrel of boiling pitch. When a new conference was called no one begged to go. The affair was finally taken over by two of the older devils, one of them a shrewd article known throughout Hell, the other a devil who had also seen many things in his time.

It was a cold, dismal day in autumn; the rain was coming down in bucketfuls. Chelm was drowning in mire; the sky over it inspired one with melancholy thoughts. Some beggar—a beggar among beggars—appeared on the scene: a starving old man, all skin and bones; he walked on crutches, since one of his legs was shorter than the other. He shambled from house to house, from door to door, from shop to shop. In one house out of ten he would get a stale crust of bread, which he had not the teeth to tackle; in one house out of twenty a quarter-kopeck coin would be given to him, worn so smooth that it slipped out of his hands. Chelm had no relish for strange beggars—it had enough of its own, schnorrers of both recent and remote origin; it had also not a few of the poor who hid their poverty, widows and orphans of respected, well-known men, who were deserving of help.

The beggar wandered through the town for two whole days; the rawness and cold penetrating to his very bones. The wads of cotton quilting sticking out of his clothing dripped; his eyes popped out of their sockets. At last, this Jew keeled over as he was crossing the market square. His crutches flew to this side and that and the old man lay there, foaming at the mouth. The other Jews came running over; one spattered him with water, another brought him a small glass of wine, while a third had a spoon ready to pry his mouth open and pour in a few drops of the liquor. Some in the crowd waxed indignant over the hardheartedness of the townspeople, but in the meantime the beggar was dying.

After all, you can't allow a man to die in the street! The question arose where he was to be carried. Some of the householders made themselves scarce; others refused to take him in because they were already crowded themselves. The Rabbi happened to pass by, and he said: "Carry him over to my place. My place, of course!"

Never yet had he been so willingly obeyed.

They put the dying man on the Rabbi's bed, and he lay there unconscious. The Rabbi seated himself at the table with a book, but kept glancing at the sick man. Several Jews were milling about the house, in case they might be needed. Night came; the Rabbi was getting ready to stand up for the evening prayer when he heard the sick man calling him. He walked over to him, looked at him compassionately, put his ear close to the dying man's mouth and listened attentively, awaiting his last request.

"Rabbi," the other whispered with difficulty, "I am a great sinner, and I don't want to die this way—I want to confess—"

The Rabbi was about to call in some people but the sick man seized him by the arm:

"God save us—God save us! I want to speak to you alone!"

And he started telling the Rabbi how he had begged all his life, pretending utter poverty. He had worn out doorsteps, begging for bread for his wife and children—yet he had never married. He had begged for a dowry for his daughter, although he had been all alone in the world, through all his years, lonely as a wayside boulder. He had been collecting for a yeshivah, although not a single man of learning had benefited a copper from the money he had collected. He had gathered money to be sent to the Holy Land—yet had not sent a grosch there; he had carried on a trade in earth which he said was from the Holy Land—earth which he had actually dug from beside the first fence he had come upon. And so on. And then, after rummaging in the bosom of his shirt, he drew out a canvas pouch and added:

"There, that's how much I've hoarded!"

He opened the pouch: it was stuffed with bank-notes, and each one hundred roubles!

"I entrust this to you, Rabbi," said he, "as a reward for your good deed. Distribute it as you deem best."

The Rabbi leaped over to a window, flung it open and shouted:

"Come inside, fellow-Jews, and count the sums donated to charity!"—The Rabbi actually seemed younger by fifty years then.

The people ran in: there was neither money in evidence nor the man they had carried in; all they saw was the rumpled bed and two broken panes in the window.

And again they pondered: had they imagined all this in a dream, or were there enchantments of some sort at work?

292

When the Devil duly received a report of these events, he just stood and gaped:

"I guess you can't take him with that bait, either."

The devils were rattled.

But then Lilith spoke up:

"Just let me lay my paws on him. I have a time-tested method."

One day the Rabbi of Chelm felt unwell; he sent a servant after a doctor, to let his blood, and then stood up to say the pre-sunset prayer. As he was standing with his face to the eastern wall, the door opened and a young woman entered the room, ostensibly to ask whether the slaughtered chicken she was carrying could be used for food. The Rabbi prayed on; it was no great matter, the girl could wait. She walked about the room, but the Rabbi would not turn around. She, as if in absent mindedness, began to hum, and her voice was sonorous, like the trilling of tiny bells! But did the Rabbi bother to listen? Not he! Apparently tired, she perched on a bench, swaying, and the bench went *creak-creak* under her. It was no use—if a serpent were to bite him he still wouldn't stir! The girl began working up a temper, flitting about the room with even greater liveliness. The Rabbi finished his murmured prayer, whispering its conclusion. Then, seating himself at the table, he said quietly:

"Let me see the chicken." She wanted to hand him the chicken directly; but he told her, in the same calm voice: "Place it on the table. A Jewish girl," he added admonishingly, "should know how to conduct herself with a man." She placed the slaughtered chicken on the table. "Let's have your story!" said he.

She told him in detail how the chicken had been bought from a peasant woman, how they had brought it home, how the chicken had run off and how they had caught it again. During all this time she laughed and showed her little teeth, and her voice tinkled in all the corners, and her tiny teeth gleamed like mirrors, that's how white they were. Talking and laughing, she walked about the table. Her sleeves were short, as it happened, and rolled back; her arms were bare, her blouse was unbuttoned at the throat; while her body—she had used some perfume or other—gave off a most pleasing fragrance. And she resorted to all sorts of wiles: she would touch the table, or the bench, or else the Rabbi's hand. While he was inspecting the chicken, she kept scampering over and taking her stand behind him, looking over his shoulder and touching his head with her own round little face; her breath blew on his temples, warmed the nape of his neck—and all in vain! The Rabbi listened to her story once more, looked at the fowl, then consulted a book and pronounced the bird ritualistically clean.

"And as for you, girl," he added, "the sooner you find yourself a bridegroom the better!"

The girl, clutching the hen, soared out the window.

The Rabbi smiled; he had guessed by now what was going on.

There was a new conference in Hell. All sorts of expedients were proposed. Suddenly, a young fiend, fresh from school, who hadn't as yet earned a single feather in his cap or even one fang to hang about his neck as a decoration, thrust himself forward and asked:

"Is it possible that the Rabbi of Chelm has no desires whatsoever?"

"He has withdrawn himself from the world entirely!" they informed him.

"Has he no fondness for anything?"

"Well, for hot baths on Fridays, possibly—"

There was a pause before the young fiend resumed his questioning:

"Has he some habit, perhaps, some quirk about him—such as rolling bread pills, for instance?"

"We haven't noticed anything of the sort. And besides, what does his eating amount to?"

At this point, however, Lilith recalled that the Rabbi, irritated by her perfumes, had grabbed his snuffbox.

"That will do!" the apprentice fiend shouted. He obtained his leave of absence and vanished.

It was the wont of the Rabbi of Chelm, each Friday after his bath, to stroll beyond the town, out into the open fields; he had a favorite path, lying between a field of rye and a field of wheat, and as he walked he would read the Song of Songs. Since he was absent minded by nature, and feared he might exceed the distance of 2400 ells permissible to walk during the Sabbath, he had once and for all set limits for himself, and had marked a certain familiar sapling as his turning point. And so he used to read half of the Song of Songs on his way to the sapling, under which he would sit down, take a pinch of snuff from his birch snuffbox, rest a bit, and then turn back for the eve of the Sabbath prayer, reading the second half of the Song of Songs on his way back, and would return home just in time!

One day, a young fellow in a derby hat and green-striped trousers bobbed up near the sapling just before the coming of the Rabbi, tore it up by the roots, carried it a considerable distance, planted it on the new spot and seated himself behind it. Once he sat down—he was a skinny little fellow—you just couldn't see him.

In the meanwhile the Rabbi had reached the place where the sapling used to be; he had already gone halfway through the Song of Songs, but the tree was still a long way off, somehow! He felt vexed: this meant that he had read the Song of Songs sort of skimmingly, without due thought, and he immediately decided to do penance; he wanted the snuff so much, his heart actually ached for it, but he wouldn't take a pinch of it until he reached the tree! And so he plodded on. He had tired to such an extent, and he was pining for the snuff, so much so that there was a haze before his eyes. Finally—glory to Thee, O Lord!—he was sitting under the tree. When he snatched the birchbark snuffbox out of his bosom, his hands were trembling, but at that point there was a gust of wind or something of the sort behind him and the box fell out of his hands; there was another gust—of wind, probably—and the box rolled a little farther; the old man lay down on the ground, stretching out his hand—the little box rolled on lightly, and he pursued it: he longed frightfully for a pinch of the dear stuff. He crawled on all fours, but just couldn't catch that box. The young fellow behind the tree smirked; as soon as the old man had crawled off a little distance the imp pulled up the sapling and in the blinking of an eye carried it over to where it had originally been. But the box kept on rolling, rolling, ever so gently. The old man looked about him—and that tree was ever so far away from him! He looked at the sky; the little stars were already twinkling there! Why, he hadn't even noticed the sun setting—that's how he had been taken up with chasing after his snuffbox. True enough, even the night was not too dark. Well, now the way to town exceeded the prescribed distance for the Sabbath and he couldn't go back there; the ravens which had once provided for the Prophet Elijah would have to feed him as well. But get that birchbox snuffbox he could and must. And he crawled on, while the box kept rolling, and then . . . well, what's the use of drawing out a tale? The Rabbi exceeded the prescribed distance for walking on a Sabbath!

The imp was immediately entrusted with a more important assignment.

As he was taking his departure, he turned to his dark associates and remarked:

"If you set out to cross a *mountain* you won't fall. You're much more liable to trip over a *hassock*."

A Teacher's Tales

He Who Bestows Life Bestows the Wherewithal to Live Also.

Gentlemen! I, Jochanan, who am a *melamed,* come here to tell you a story. And the story I would like to tell will be like a little wheel inside a big one—one story interwoven with another. And I'm not going to make these two stories up out of thin air, as the saying goes. I am not, glory be to God, one of your writing fellows; and neither my father nor my grandfather, nor even my great-grandfather, ever were before me. I'm going to tell you the story in simple words, without a lot of pepper and salt, for he who tells the truth has no need of poetry. Such a man speaks simply in his mother-tongue.

There's also another thing I want to warn you about: I consider it likely that the tales I shall tell will show plainly that you've gone too far in many matters; that you rely far too much on your emotions; that there are in this world such things as were not dreamt of either by you or by your great sages. Yet, just the same, I beg you not to take offence. If you want to, you can believe; if you don't want to believe, it's up to you. I would, all the same, like to justify myself before our own people. It may, perhaps, seem that I am washing dirty linen in public—especially at this time when many people doubt everything. And, because of this there may arise, God forbid, some unpleasantness. I have some good news for these people. I want them to know that there's no abnegation here. What we have are mere inventions!(?)

The whole universe is nothing but faith. And, really, could it be otherwise?

The universe is great—immeasurably great; it is infinite! Yet our minds are *so very* tiny, that we are like men wandering about in the dead of night through the desert carrying candle ends that cast their light no further than our noses.

I stick to my point of view, that it is *impossible* to live without

297

faith. One cannot limit oneself to reason alone. And who thinks otherwise? Certain scribblers, perhaps, who make up books for the common folk—for cooks and chambermaids—fellows who think up fairy tales about cutthroats and robbers, about forged promissory notes and counterfeiters: anything to frighten people, anything to make their blood run cold. Well, it is these same scribblers who have invented godlessness, and who have done so to frighten people like chambermaids, cobblers, and poor tailors.

The truth of the matter is that there is no will without faith. To put it simply, a man who does not believe does not want anything. He is nothing but a clod, a graven image!

And if you see that people have desires, that they sacrifice these desires for the sake of higher things—if you see people drinking, eating, and building a hearth for a family, working by the sweat of their brows and constantly preoccupied with cares, you may realize that these people do have faith. They have faith in their own lives, at least. Yet it is possible to doubt even that. If you like, you can talk with a doubter; but nothing will come of it. It's a waste of time to argue with a fellow like that!

All men believe: that's the general rule. Where then, does the difference between men lie? Well, one man believes that, on the Judgment Day, the Leviathan will be dished up first and the Behemoth second, while another believes that the Behemoth will come first and the Leviathan after that, for dessert. But take an enlightened youth, one who believes neither in the Behemoth nor the Leviathan—well, *he* believes in ethereality! And what sort of thing is that? One of them explained to be that ethereality is something having neither substance nor soul—and it has no gravity or weight. I asked him if he had ever seen this ethereality. He told me that he hadn't, yet he believed in it. In short, there are men who do have faith in it.

Where then, I repeat, does the difference between men lie? In this alone—that each one of those fellows has *his own* rabbi, *his own* faith—his own little god, you might say. They're all eyeing one another with envy! They all go in for kissing—one will kiss the curtain of the holy ark, even though he has no conception of it; another will kiss a cabalistic book if it should happen to drop to the floor. Why, I myself have seen one of that crowd kissing *The Mysteries of Paris!* And yet, as I've heard from a reliable source, *The Mysteries of Paris* is a horrible fairy tale about somebody or other with a name that sounds like Harbonah *—only this fellow is not the Harbonah who is mentioned in the Book of Esther. And it was written by some French woodchopper, a good-for-nothing who gadded about the streets! They kissed other books of lies as well, composed by a French liar, while a certain scribbler from Vilna, one of your enlightened ones, copied these books into ancient Hebrew!

Gentlemen, I've lived a long while in this world, glory be to God. I've taught Hebrew lore not only in villages and small towns but in great cities as well. It's seven years now, glory be to God, that I've been a teacher in Warsaw and, thank the Lord God, I mix with people—I know what people are. I know some of the Worldly Ones who become indignant over every Hasidic trifle; I know Hasidim who consider other Hasidim of a slightly different persuasion as so many Godless fellows. I know many of these Enlightened Ones, great and small, those who know what's what and those who are simply scribblers—and I know ever so many free-thinkers! I know them all—but I have never yet seen one who was an actual unbeliever!

I will even venture to say that among all these Enlightened Ones, there isn't one who has anything all his own, his own system, his own point of view. In all this host, I haven't seen one who looked at things with his own eyes—with the exception, perhaps, of two or three great intellects among them. All the others—the whole pack of them—aren't worth an empty eggshell! They, too, are Hasidim—but of a different stamp. They believe in a rabbi *all their own*, and they are the worshippers of their sages, just as we are of ours.

I can swear to you by anything you like that they have nothing of their own. All they have faith in is their particular "genius." And they ape such a genius, without knowing the difference between what he has said after serious reflection and what he may have uttered just in passing, or in wrath, or out of sheer stubbornness. They act just as we sinners do; we're as alike as drops of water. And if one of these gentlemen should come to see me and announce that he is an infidel, I wouldn't make fun of him, of course; but just the same, I'd know that he is jesting, or simply wants to pull the wool over my eyes. It's precisely such a fellow who'll usually be afraid to venture out of the house by himself

* The old pedagogue probably has Marquis d'Harville in mind.—*Translator.*

at night. Or it may well be that he *has* to talk that way—his profession demands it. Why, what won't a man do for the sake of his daily bread! It's also possible that he is simply a fool, an idiot, who doesn't know that he doesn't know, and who doesn't know *what* to believe in. And, if that is the case, why should we be ashamed of what *we* believe in?

In what way are our people worse than the Enlightened Ones who do nothing but tell fairy tales about their great men? Can it be that we're inferior because our fairy tales are not made up? Or because we do not frighten the people with stories about cutthroats, robbers, counterfeit money and counterfeiters? Really, now, must one write of things about which no one ever thinks? And this is all the truer, because I don't want to tell you a story that came to pass ever so far away and at God knows what time; I want to tell you only what actually took place right here, in our own Warsaw, and not so very long ago, at that!

Bah! Somebody may come and say that that wasn't the way the thing happened; that the whole thing is a lie. Let him come—let him dare! I'm only a simple teacher, glory be to God—I'm no scribbler, God forbid; it isn't my business to lie, and I don't make my living by lying. In short, this story is honest truth. Perhaps someone will show up and interpret it otherwise. We shall see.

The Witty Answer of the Silent One—May the Kingdom of Heaven Be His. The Merits of My Brother, of Blessed Memory. A Good Beginning.

They tell a story about the Silent One of blessed memory. It seems that one day they asked him why he delivered no preachments to the people, as all men of righteousness do. And, after his wont, his only answer was silence. But at a moment when he happened to be in a good mood, and they pestered him and insisted, he smiled and answered them as follows:

"People," he said, "wonder at me because I *don't* deliver any preachments; but I wonder at *them,* and at how they are *capable* of delivering preachments. How is it possible to begin and end the reading of the Word of God, when the Torah has neither beginning nor end—when it is infinite?

"Yet, what do we see? It's a simple matter: people not knowing the Torah, say whatever pops into their heads; they begin when and where they will, and wind up the same way, inasmuch as that which they expound is not Infinity; it is not God's Torah! It's a Torah of *their own,* an invented Torah. But he who knows the Torah doesn't utter 'words,' since he knows neither where to begin nor where to end.

"Let's take an instance from life—a lawsuit, for example. They have summoned a witness, an honest man who cannot tell an untruth nor does he want to do so. When such a man stands up before the tribunal, he begins a long way off, going all the way back to Adam, and just can't get down to the business at hand—particularly when it comes to ending his story. But the man who tells a story of his own has decided on everything beforehand; he speaks glibly, knowing where to begin and where to end. And his story runs along smoothly, without any trouble."

This is applicable to our story, too. The scribbler who spins a yarn out of thin air, as the saying goes, knows how and where to begin and can end a tale at his pleasure. That's his business. He does just what he likes. If he likes, he draws the tale out, or he shortens it, if that's what he wants. I, however, am telling you facts as they are; it's a true story—and I still don't know where to begin and where to end. There's nothing new under the sun; everything has a connection with what has gone before, or else with the remote past, and so on. One doesn't know what came first; one has to start with Creation itself.

But, in honor of my deceased brother Zainvel-Yehiel, I'll begin with him.

All of Franciscan Street—all of it!—knows that my brother of blessed memory was a remarkable man of learning and an exceedingly pious man. He was a widower, and toward the end of his days was left with his daughter, an unmarried girl. Brocha-Leah, they called her. He lived in need; he no longer had the strength to teach; and he was left without any bread; and as for his daughter Leah, she was growing, not by the day but by the hour, like leavened dough. In short, he was in a bad way, and that's all there was to it!

But the Lord came to his aid. Several men of wealth, all men of note and held in high respect, whose children had studied under my brother, got together and decided to arrange a marriage for Brocha-Leah; as for my brother, after he had seen his daughter safely married, they would give him money for a journey—

301

let him go to the Holy Land. True, the journey wasn't crowned with success; on the way he fell ill and died—may the same never be said of any of you! Just the same, he had the happiness of beholding the town of Safed, where he met his end and was given back to the earth with all due honor. The Rabbi of Safed delivered a heartfelt eulogy. This oration appears in his book, *Precious Pearls*, and everyone who reads it is delighted.

Well, now that I have made a beginning, I can actually go on.

The Story Proper. A Failure. Trouble Follows Trouble. Brocha-Leah Is Abandoned by Her Husband.

Charity is a great thing, but only for those who hand it out. I don't envy the person who takes charity; he who, alas, must resort to the help of benefactors. I envy my brother, may the Kingdom of Heaven be his, because he died in time and saw no more grief. For the men of wealth who married off the poor bride forgot entirely that Leah was the daughter of a learned Jew and that she was a pure, honest soul. And they chose a bridegroom not all suitable to her position nor, worse yet, to the position of her father. All they wanted was to get her a husband, one who would support her, and thus once and for all loosen the load from their own shoulders.

And they did this without thinking—just so they could get out from under. So they found themselves a lively lad at a cheap rate —a fellow who hung around lawyers. After all, he didn't want a lot, and he was able to support a wife—so they struck a bargain. They got the dowry together, called in the musicians, and staged a wedding—and farewell, good luck!

To tell the truth, this lad wasn't at all to my liking. And my Faiga, God give her health, also remarked that he was far from being good; that he was no great bargain. But since my brother, may the Kingdom of Heaven be his, raised no objections, we in turn kept silent. And this silence was not very wise.

My brother, may the Kingdom of Heaven be his, had hardly set out on his journey when things began to happen. And it followed that everything wasn't as it should be. I found out, on the side, that the domestic affairs of this couple were somewhat awry; they were quarrelling, yelling—the neighbors had to knock on the wall.

I also learned that Brocha-Leah wasn't any too well satisfied;

her husband wasn't pious. And he was threatening to put on modern European clothes and become a lawyer in his own right. And, her husband Moishe was saying that he had been taken in, that they had shown him another better-looking girl as the bride. And he didn't like her clothes, either; they had scraped together a lot of old rags, said he. They had promised to maintain him and his wife, but instead had put one over on him. And he had still another grievance: he had counted on being practically of kin to the well-to-do. He had relied on their influence, but they, having had their fill of fun and stuffing themselves at his poor man's wedding, wouldn't allow him to cross their thresholds now.

I didn't want to become involved at first. These rich gentlemen and my wife, Faiga, wouldn't allow it. And what is all this—is it something new, or what? This sort of thing happens right along. After the wedding, until they get used to each other, frequent misunderstandings take place between husband and wife. But after that—for habit is, after all, second nature—they manage to get along together.

And, actually, I myself had quarreled not a little with my Faiga during our first year of married life. But after that, when the children began coming, and when we were living on our own resources, we dropped this foolishness. I began looking out for some enterprise of my own. I hadn't much luck, and so I became an instructor in Hebrew, and it's not so bad, glory be to God. We manage to live, and may God grant that we get on like that until each of us is a hundred and twenty!

In short, I didn't say anything, not even when, in a short while, Faiga pointed out Leah's altered appearance to me with a look which asked if I understood. Since I am not one of those who have to have everything explained in words of one syllable, I thought to myself, "It's a good sign; everything seems to be for the best!"

Yet things turned out just the other way.

Moishe remained just the same as he had been—or rather, I may say, he became worse. This specimen of manhood possessed one of the traits of Father Abraham: he said little and did a lot. It wasn't enough that he had put on European clothes—he also took to playing cards all night, night after night. Not a night passed but he brought a whole horde of friends into the house, making Leah serve them with tea and vodka and herring, which she had to fix with oil and vinegar because they couldn't eat them plain. And they could eat only white bread with the herring—you couldn't even offer them black bread, God forbid! And if there should be anything lacking—what a row he would raise! On top of that he made sport of her before all of them. And, as if that weren't enough, he reviled and cursed her too.

I saw then that things were in a bad way and that it was impossible to keep silent any longer. I screwed up my courage and went to see him. When I got there I began to talk in a kindly tone, even smiling a little after my fashion. Friendly, as if joking, I remarked that even if he were sinning against the laws of the faith, there was still no great danger in that. And I told him about the things one repentant sinner had done. And I said to him that the merits of Leah's ancestors would help him along the way of reformation. All he had to do was to make a start, to take the first step on the path of repentance. I promised to be good to him, to bring him into the midst of those who were of the same persuasion as myself—the Hasidim, that is. And, if God granted it, and I made a pilgrimage to the Rabbi, I would take him along— and a lot of other things of that sort.

Well, he almost split his sides with laughing!

He made fun of me and of those who believed as I did, and of the Rabbi himself. He would yield all these good things to me, if I would but take Leah off his hands! And, along with this, he used such expressions as one cannot even repeat.

Perceiving that there was no other way out, I began to speak more sternly. I told him that even though he was wearing European clothes, he was an ignoramus just the same and an out-and-out fool. And after that I told him quite boldly and bluntly that if he wanted to reform, well and good; but if he didn't want to, he would be preparing long years of torment in Gehenna for himself.

So he went off into fits of laughter again! Gehenna—what was Gehenna to him? Just as though he'd been there and seen, God save us, that there was no Gehenna at all!

And he wound up, this brazen scoundrel, by showing me the door. What was I to do next? I saw that Leah had turned green. Tears were streaming down her cheeks. So I up and left, and sent him a summons to the Rabbinical Court.

But he refused to show his face there. I waited—I waited a long time. By and by things quieted down—at least I didn't hear anything. But the reason I didn't hear anything was because this arch-transgressor had issued the strictest orders to Leah not to set foot across my threshold, under threat of beating her to death. And as Leah always did as her husband bade her, she now stayed home and shed tears in secret.

I heard nothing, I knew nothing. And just then a misfortune of my own descended upon me. Faiga, my wife, fell ill. The doctor said she had a fever. The neighbors said something else, while I myself was thinking somebody had put the evil eye on her. Now our house was without a mistress. The children were without a mother—and without a father as well, for it was the beginning of the school year, and I still had to go about obtaining more pupils to make ends meet. But that wasn't all. I, myself, was not feeling any too well. Those Warsaw staircases had robbed me of all strength. And at the same time I was beset on all sides. The landlord was demanding the rent. I was half a year behind. The school inspector was insisting that I must rent an additional room for my pupils so there would be more air. May God not punish me, but I was in a daze and almost forgot about Leah! Whenever I did call her to mind I thought that because everything was quiet, it meant that the rascal had mended his ways and that he and Leah were having a second honeymoon. Now it must simply be a case of her living well and not wanting to know poor relations.

One day, however, when I came home tired, with my feet all swollen—may it never happen to you—wanting to wash up, have a bite, and then rest my weary bones, my wife Faiga sprang the news on me. Leah had been to see her and had shed bitter tears, saying that we were no better than monsters, that we weren't at all interested in her miserable lot, and that she was a complete orphan, all alone in the world. She had told Faiga of the unbelievable sufferings her husband Moishe inflicted on her. He beat and tortured her. How many times had be beaten her until the blood came!

I asked my wife if such a thing were possible. Was any man capable of beating his wife—all the more so when she was pregnant? And Faiga replied that Moishe was a madman. He had gone to the dogs entirely. He had no trust in God. He was yelling that he had nothing to live on, and for that reason he wanted

Leah to get an abortion. Everybody did it, he said. The wives of the rich did it. But Leah did not want to do it, so he beat her, cursing her with frightful curses—both her and her father. When I heard that he was cursing my brother—may the Kingdom of Heaven be his!—I boiled over. I forgot everything in the world, and grabbed a stick. One of two things—he would die, or I would. I would cut this dog's throat. And I dashed over to his house with all the strength I had, gasping for breath.

I got there and I saw—oh, what I saw! The door was wide open. The room was in pitch darkness. Our fine bird had flown. No bed, not a dish—he had hauled off everything.

And where was Leah? She was sprawled out writhing on the floor.

A Marvel. My Wife Faiga and Her Deeds. I Am Thrown Out in the Street, and Where I Went.

It is a thing to marvel at, but my wife Faiga has an amazingly level head on her shoulders. When I had seized my stick, yelling that I would kill that dog, Moishe, my wife took the thing calmly. She knows, glory be to God, that I am no cutthroat, that I wouldn't hurt a fly on the wall. She knows that when I am entirely beside myself, the first thing I do is to burst into tears. For that's my way—when I'm in wrath, my tears flow like water. And another thing my wife knows is that even when it comes to my pupils, I do not beat them in the proper way—why, their fathers actually resent me for this. At times, I fear that I please God and men but little in this respect, since corporal punishment is sometimes needed. Forever since the time when one of my pupils went wrong, I have come to believe firmly in the birchrod. However, let's not go astray.

In short, my wife knew that I wouldn't harm Moishe, and for that reason she remained sitting calmly in bed. But then, after an hour passed, and then another, and I was still away, she became frightened. By that time she decided that I had done in this miserable scoundrel and had been put in prison.

Well! She forgot all about her ailments, forgot all about the children, and the house and everything in it. She threw on whatever was at hand and dashed out to look for me. She even forgot to close the door behind her!

I looked over my shoulder. There she was. At once she grasped what was going on. First of all, seeing me standing there gaping, she shouted: "You big fool!"

And right then and there she opened the door and yelled for help. And, as she shouted, the neighboring women showed up on the run. My wife began issuing commands and the women went to work. And one of them, at my wife's orders, just up and shoved me out the door.

Where was I to go? Out in the street, the falling snow was wet; the wind lashed my face, and stole in through the holes in my clothing. So I set out for the synagogue.

There were still people there—men who liked, after the service, to pore a little over the Talmud. I, too, reached for a volume of the Talmud. I needed nothing more. As soon as I opened the book, I forgot all about Leah, and her husband, that montrous blot on all humanity—I forgot all the world. Who had been abandoned by her husband? Who had run off? Who was having such a hard time giving birth? By that time I knew nothing.

My Pupils. Who Is My Teacher? The Torah and the Reward.
The Parable of the Bird. Evil Thoughts, and Doubts.

On occasion when I read the Talmud with ardor, my pupils who have rich parents simply cannot understand, and ask if it is possible that I, too, have to go on studying, and who my teacher is. The foolish ones! They are utterly unaware that God's world is a splendid teacher, that worrying about one's daily bread is a good teacher. Endless sufferings are exceptional teachers. The important thought, "What is there to eat?" which incessantly goes through one's brain is an outstanding teacher. And they themselves, these pupils of mine, and their parents, my masters, are also splendid teachers. Oh, how splendid! Everything in the world compels one to study. But what a reward there is for studying!

I open a book and I have no peer. When I begin on the Talmud, I feel that Heaven is unrolling before me. I feel that the Lord God in His great grace has bestowed wings upon me . . . great, spreading wings. And I soar upon them: I am an eagle. I fly far . . . ever so far. Not only beyond the seas but out of this world . . . out of this world of falsehood, flattery, and great sufferings into a new world, a world filled with goodness . . . and goodness only. A world where there are no potbellied masters, where there is no well-to-do class, a most ignorant class; a world where there is no money, no worry about daily bread. There are no mothers whose labor pains are difficult, nor hungry children . . . and one can't hear the voices of women! And I, a poor, ailing, famished and dried-up *melamed* . . . I, a poor crushed man who is otherwise voiceless as a fish, who is trodden upon like a worm . . . there I am a man to be reckoned with! I am free, my will is free, and I can be creative. I build up whole universes, and I demolish whole universes. I raise up new ones in their place. Newer universes, more beautiful and better. And I dwell in them . . . I fly over them. I am in paradise, in a veritable paradise.

I feel that I know far more than I am able to impart to my pupils . . . even to myself. And I understand things which cannot be expressed in words, which not a single eye beholds and not a single ear can catch. They grow in the heart only and dwell there.

"Two seized hold of a taleth," in this text . . . the way I look at it, and as I explain to my pupils, they are not just Reuben and Simson, but are both ordinary men off the street. And the prayer shawl over which they squabble is not a simple prayer shawl such as one may buy at the shop of Yossel Peshess. No! My understanding of this goes deeper than that.

I swallow the gleams, the bright sparks glittering between the lines; my soul drinks them in like a sponge. I feel that I am absorbing a light which is kept in store for men of righteousness in the future world.

If one could but apply oneself constantly to the Talmud! If one could really study it!

And I must tell you that when I have occasion to call at well-to-do homes and see the people there playing cards all night, night after night, or spending their time in questionable conversations with women and other affairs of vanity . . . or when I walk along a street and look through a tavern's open windows and see working men enveloped in a cloud of smoke, drinking and uttering unseemly things . . . when I see all this, believe me I don't feel angry; I do not condemn them at all. On the contrary, my heart contracts with pity. For looking at it from another angle, what are they to do without the Torah?

As I have already told you, I used to be a *melamed* in a village.

A pupil of mine showed me how toward the end of summer, the little birds flock together and before the coming of winter, forsake our land. I saw how they flocked together in throngs, and how they flew away. . . . The little birds cannot and do not want to remain here during the time of snow and frosts. A little bird cannot live through such a time. And the birds know this; they feel that the winter is coming, that the Angel of Death is drawing nigh.

But once I happened to see an injured little bird, one of its tiny wings broken, hopping and jumping over the chill, sodden earth; it kept squeaking and could not rise up and catch up with the big birds. It was painful to see how the poor little thing could find no place for itself; it kept on hopping, watching the free birds fly away, soaring off far into the heights.

And it was then that I thought, The soul of the ignorant is like this ailing bird. These ignorant ones cannot fly; they have no wings, no knowledge. . . . Give them wings . . . they will fly! They, too, will then soar into the heights above the stars.

But their wings have been broken; they crawl on their bellies. They crawl through the mire. They talk foully. They play cards . . . the rich man in his salon, the poor man in his saloon. . . .

However, let's go back to our story. As I have said, I was sitting over the Talmud. Little by little, everyone left. The sexton was the last to go. What was that to me? I was absorbed; I saw nothing. By the light of the candle in the warm synagogue, a book open before me, I was not afraid; though I was alone. I was carried away, for the Torah, as you know, is like the sea. It wanted to swallow me. But I knew how to swim. Down I went, but at the next wave I swam upwards and reached the surface. At times, the sea would quiet down. Everything would then become beautiful, clear and serene, like the sky. And my soul bathed in the reviving water; it glided along as if over a mirror, with joyousness and delight. The water cleansed my soul of all the stains of this world, until it became pure.

Then suddenly, I felt something burn my finger, and I was left in the dark. The candle that I had been holding went out. When I am alone in the dark, I get frightened. A great fear comes upon me. When it is light, I am not afraid. I feel well. I can see the world around me and I am its master. I see the world, and the world sees me. I know that I am part of the world, that its ruler

309

is my ruler. I know that without His will, not a hair will fall off my head. He would not allow this to happen . . . nor would the world allow it.

But in the dark, when I am alone and cannot see the world, I lose my head altogether. Evil thoughts come over me. At such times it seems . . . may God not punish me for this . . . that I am no longer of this world; neither I, nor my wife, nor my children. We are not in touch with it at all. Then, they'll seize hold of me, of my wife, of my children . . . they will seize us secretly, so that no one will see, no one will ever know.

As soon as my candle had expired, my soul rich in all things and thirsting after knowledge, went up in smoke, and I was left with the frightened, ordinary soul of a poor Hebrew teacher. I was, once more, a nonenity, a lost thing. And my lips babbled: "Lord, have mercy! Lord, have mercy!" while my heart pounded: "Leah will give birth . . . she surely will . . . and to twins, at that. Her mother was known for twins! As if your wife and children were not enough, you've got to have Leah, too, with a child . . . with two or three children, maybe. Zainvel-Jehiel's body is already resting under the sod; his soul is sitting up there in Paradise and studying the Torah, but you will have to go on working, providing food."

And my lips babbled: "Lord, have mercy . . . Lord, have mercy!" And evil thoughts were prompting me: "If God did want to take pity, He could do nothing but send the Angel of Death. To me, or to the woman giving birth!"

Merciful God . . . merciful God! I knew that I was sinning before God, that I was losing faith in Him. I knew that I hadn't the strength to drive these evil thoughts out of my soul. I was helpless when all alone . . . and, in the dark, I was altogether powerless. I knew that the only remedy lay in the Torah, and I wanted to remember it, but I could not! I had forgotten it utterly. I had forgotten the Torah!

And thereupon I began screaming with all my might: "Lord, help me! Help me!"

And a miracle came to pass . . .

A Miracle. The Hidden Light. The Redemption of a Soul.
The Angel of Death. Punishment for Summoning Death.

Later on, when I told this story to one of the Enlightened Ones, a former pupil of mine, he laughed . . . how he laughed! According to him, there had been no miracle . . . no miracle whatsoever. Chance, mere chance, he said, or the power of the imagination . . . or, perhaps, it had been a dream.

However, what does his opinion matter to me? Jethro had seven names, and yet Jethro, the father-in-law of Moses, was but one man. Call it what you will: miracle, chance, imagination . . . the fact remains. All I know is that just when it seemed that I would plunge into the nether world, the whole House of Worship was suddenly flooded with light . . . a soft blue light, like the beams that pour from the sun in summer. A beam . . . as anyone can see with his own eyes . . . is made up of small radiant particles, and each particle within the beam whirls at lightning speed. It was such a beam that filled the synagogue. I immediately calmed down, and my evil thoughts fled.

The whole synagogue was filled with lovely light, and I was brimming over with hope. Everything within me was as clear, as pure as crystal. And when I turned toward the east wall, from where the light was coming, I saw someone. And who do you think it was?

My brother, of blessed memory, in the place where he usually sat and studied! He was seated before an open folio. I could not see his face, since his eyes were shaded by his hands, but my heart told me that it was he . . . that this was my brother Zainvel-Yehiel. I was not frightened in the least, for in such cases the rule is that he who does not fear the living, trembles before the dead. But did that apply to me? I am a miserable worm who is afraid of every living thing . . . why then, should I fear those who have died? And besides, who was I supposed to fear? . . . my brother Zainvel-Yehiel, who during his lifetime was as soft as silk?

I asked him outright: "Is it you, Zainvel-Yehiel?"

"It is I," he answered, and took his hand away from his eyes. And I saw his face: there was such an air of tenderness about it, and his eyes glowed with emotion.

"What are you doing here, brother?" I questioned him anew.

And he answered:

"What am I doing? I am doing a great deal. During my lifetime, as I sat here studying the Torah, the Evil One confused me. Care for daily bread intruded. I passed over many and many a

311

passage, and often I studied without any understanding of the true meaning. Now I am serving my sentence; I am saving my soul. I am studying anew."

"And now, do you go over everything carefully?"

He nodded, and I said:

"Zainvel-Yehiel, are you studying with application because you do not know?"

"How foolish you are," he cut me short with his sweet voice, "Quite the contrary. Since I know, I study with zeal; during my life I knew little and had many doubts. I passed over many things without getting at their meaning . . . since what one does not know is confusing. But now that I know, now that I have no doubts, I learn everything and get the true meaning."

"But you do know that Moishe?"

"Has run off to America? Yes, I know. I know even the name of the liner he took. On that steamer he is eating what it is not permissible to eat . . . I know."

"And do you know that Leah?"

"Is in labor and having a difficult time? Of course I know. I even know that she will give birth to a boy . . ."

"And not twins?"

"No, she won't have twins. But she will be in need of great sympathy: the child will be born a cripple. That villain of a husband knocked her down and crippled the child."

"But do you know what she will live on?"

"That, too, I know," he answered in a pleasant voice. He moved closer, took me by the shoulders, and said: "Look out the window!" I did so. "Well, what do you see?"

"I see someone walking past. He's clad in white. His face glows and he is walking slowly. I feel as if he were a musician playing a melody so sweet that it clutches at one's very soul! There, he has gone."

"That was no man . . . it was an angel!"

"An angel?"

"An angel, and a kindly one . . . most kindly . . . the Angel of Death."

"The Angel of Death?" I echoed, now in fear.

"What are you afraid of? Do you want to run away from him?"

"And where . . . where was the angel heading?"

312

"Where? To Reb Simcha, the rich man . . . his daughter is in labor, giving birth . . ."

"That I know. This morning I was one of a gathering that read the Psalms for her sake and for her child . . ."

"The prayers saved halfway: the child will remain among the living."

"And she?"

"Why, you saw . . ."

"It was to her he was going! And so unwillingly, dragging his steps. Was it out of pity, or what?"

"Possibly. He had no need to hurry; he had not been sent by God."

"What are you saying!" I cried out, aghast. "Who else is there who can command him?"

"A mortal, too, has a will of his own. She herself summoned him . . ."

"She herself?"

"She did not want to have a child . . . she did not want to be a mother! She maimed her child . . ."

"My Lord God!" I exclaimed, and there was great suffering in my voice. "She will die for her sins. But how is the child guilty? The child will be left an orphan. My Lord God . . ."

"Don't shout," and with that, Zainvel-Yehiel took my hand. "Don't shout. Leah will be his wet-nurse. And henceforth know: He Who bestows life bestows the wherewithal to live, also!"

At that same moment, he went off as a mist in space; the beam of light vanished, and the wan light of early morning peered in through the window.

He Who Bestows Life Bestows the Wherewithal to Live Also.

You can't imagine what I lived through at that moment.

I fell face down and stretched out full length; tears welled up in my eyes and streamed down my face. It seemed that they were not tears but stones rising up from the heart. The more tears I shed, the fewer stones pressed against my heart. I was beginning to feel lighter, easier.

Well, the story is coming to an end.

I set out for home. When I got there, I saw that the door, was standing wide open. I entered the room and by the feeble light of daybreak saw that burglars had been busy there, for everything had disappeared from the house!

It didn't matter, I reflected. The children coughed in their sleep, and their coughs were dry. I listened attentively and reflected that there was nothing to be afraid of.

My wife Faiga arrived shortly. "Congratulations!" said she.

"What?" said I. "Is it a boy . . . a crippled boy?"

She stood stock-still:

"Are you a prophet, or what?" And she did not hear the children coughing; she did not see that the house had been emptied of everything. "How do you come to know all this?"

"I know a thing or two besides, my wife," I told her. "I know that the daughter of the rich Simcha has died. (The phrase *passed away* would not come to my lips.) But her child, a boy, is living. And Leah is going to be his wet-nurse!"

"Who told you all this?"

"Well," I answered her, "He Who bestows life, bestows the wherewithal to live also."

And then I told her everything.

Thou Shalt Not Covet...

As you know, every Jew is obligated to fulfill each and every commandment of the Holy Writ. Those he does not succeed in fulfilling in one incarnation he must fulfill in another. And those which he has transgressed against in one incarnation he must make amends for in another, for his soul must return immaculate to the Holy Throne. Those who fulfill all the commandments are abstracted from this world before their time without agony. Great men of righteousness may achieve this in a reincarnation, or perhaps two. A common mortal may experience as many as a hundred and one reincarnations. And there are men who are fated to endure one reincarnation after another until the end of time, the great Resurrection Day, when their souls, so defiled that they seem to hang in shreds, shall be judged in the Vale of Jehoshaphat, or on the Plain of Jesreel. . . .

But that is not what I wish to talk about. I would simply like to show you how at times the most insignificant trifle leads to another reincarnation and how, once men begin to fall, they sink lower and lower. . . .

Once upon a time, a man of great righteousness was due to conclude his cycle of reincarnations upon earth. His soul was just about to take flight to the Holy Throne where it had been shaped as pure as gold, a sanctified thing. And in heaven the hosts of saints were already astir, hurrying to the gates of heaven to meet this pure soul. However, at the last moment a shadow dampened their joyousness.

During its last reincarnation, the soul had been housed in the body of a rather small man; a Jew who tasted not of the delights of this world. He fasted and pored over sacred books; in all his days he had never touched a woman. Dying came very hard to him; the body refused, come what might, to let the soul depart

315

from it and to go its way into the dark grave. "I haven't lived at all!" said the body. "I haven't had my share of life yet!" And each limb battled against the Angel of Death. The heart reasoned: "I haven't felt anything yet!" The eyes: "We haven't seen anything yet!" The hands: "What have we ever held?" The legs: "Where did we go? We never set foot out of the house!"

The angel who had been sent to fetch the soul was forced to back against each muscle and each drop of blood; they were, in a sense, the soul's captors. The angel was faced with the task of freeing the soul, plucking it out, as if it were a frail rose among barbed thorns. The torments of the soul were so great, so extreme, that the body groaned at the final moment of separation. This groan was inspired by envy: the body had felt envious of those to whom dying came easily; it had coveted an easy death! Worse yet, it did not have time to repent of this wish!

And since the man of righteousness had transgressed against the commandment *Thou shalt not covet*—since a Jew must not covet even an easy death for himself—the heavenly hosts melted away, the heavenly portals closed and the soul had to be reincarnated in atonement for the transgression of the body: *Thou shalt not covet.*

Nevertheless there was much sympathy for him in the upper worlds. Some of the heavenly hosts had a grievance against the Angel of Death: why couldn't he have waited a moment more, why hadn't he given the man of righteousness a chance to repent?

It was therefore decided to lighten the term of expiation for this soul, to grant it a life in which there would be no need to envy anyone or to covet anything; also, an easy death was guaranteed.

But the Cunning One listened closely to the decision and smirked. He wasn't letting the man out of his clutches as easily as all that!

The man of righteousness was reincarnated. He began to live in this beautiful world, under the name of Reb Zainvel Purisover. Who was this Reb Zainvel Purisover? A Jew, of course—and may all Jews live no worse than he did! A very important personage he was. Was there one single thing he lacked? Learning? He had more knowledge than any rabbi; he sang better than any cantor; he read the Old Testament before the congregation better than any religious instructor from Lithuania! And his wife was virtuous, his children did well at everything, and he carried on a profitable business in his own house!

What is more, it was the most presentable house in the whole town. And charity poured forth from that house in a stream. Attached to the house was a booth for the Feast of Tabernacles; built of logs, it was hung with palm fronds and fruits from the Holy Land. Who had the best *esrog* [apple of paradise] on the best of silver platters? Reb Zainvel. Who was the most judicious of arbitrators and the wisest of counselors? Reb Zainvel. He had only to say so and he could become a trustee of the synagogue! As it was, not one of the trustees would lift a finger without his advice; without his permission, the sexton dared not make a move!

When Reb Zainvel was sitting at his studies, his eyes glowed and he resembled a sage out of antiquity. When he opened his mouth, pearls poured forth! A handsome old man he was, a king with his white, curling beard, cap of silver-tipped marten, and lapeled kaftan of velvet with silver clasps. In him, learning and grandeur were one.

You would think that this was his last incarnation, would you not? And that is the way things would have worked out—had it not been for the Foul One.

One winter evening, the Cunning One, disguised in the shape of a wanderer, an emaciated-looking young man, stole into the house of prayer before the evening service and sat down near the stove. As a matter of course, Reb Zainvel invited him to his house for supper; he rejoiced over every guest. So the young man went to Reb Zainvel's for supper. Either one of his sons or his son-in-law would start by pointing out some unresolved contradiction in the Talmud; all eyes would turn to Reb Zainvel who would then proceed to solve the question.

Reb Zainvel smiled and offered his guest the honor of the first prayer after the meal. The prayer was said. Reb Zainvel began his explanation with a speech so clear and pure that it was like a straight broad road stretching off into the distance, a road as smooth and level as the top of a table—all one had to do was to harness a carriage and glide away! His sons and son-in-law sat there absorbed, drinking in the wonders of his learning. As for the young man, he sat there too, watching with a leer, his thin lips twisted in a smile. Reb Zainvel noticed this and asked:

"Don't you agree?"

"Oh, no!" the young man answered brazenly.

"Why not?" asked Reb Zainvel, whereupon the young man launched into his speech and the dispute was on!

It took the young man no more than one shake of a lamb's tail to cover all of the Talmud and its commentaries; he inundated his listener with verses of Holy Writ, while his citations from various sources fell like hail. And, as he spoke, the young man grew bigger, and so did his eyes and the malice in them! And with every new utterance his words became more fiery, harsher. It was as if he were encircling Reb Zainvel with a rail of burning thorns. And Reb Zainvel felt the space about him contracting more and more, and there was no way in and no way out; there was no air to breathe. His sons and son-in-law sat helpless while the rail was advancing against him, closing him in. He began to feel mental fatigue, a pain in his heart, a construction in his chest that hindered his breathing.

He got up and stepped outside to catch his breath a little and marshal his thoughts. Since he felt himself to be in the right, he realized that the young man was no more than a thimblerigger, whose words pattered like hail that was bound to melt and turn to nothing, to so much water. All that Reb Zainvel needed was a little time to think.

All this, as we have said, took place on a winter night. And when Reb Zainvel stepped outside, the marketplace was carpeted with freshly fallen snow, while millions of tiny stars glowed in the sky. Reb Zainvel's breath came easier. His brain cleared and he could see the light. And suddenly he saw plainly that the rail of thorns with which the young man had encircled him was swaying. He looked at it more closely and noticed that it was not at all solid, that in many places it had holes. It seemed to him that filling these holes were men of learning, all of them smiling and saying: "This rail is but a deception, Zainvel, it is woven of nothing but spells; come this way—we'll guide you through." And a long road spread out before him. . . .

And Reb Zainvel smiled to himself at the passage open to him. He saw that everything was out in the open; wide spaces, an open world lay before him. And he recalled that such-an-such a sage had said thus and so, that some other commentator had clarified this point or that, while Rashi's commentary on the Talmud spoke clearly on still another point. Reb Zainvel was frightfully pleased; in his mind once again he ran through the Talmud and its commentaries: everywhere there was depth and breadth. Now, he would show his guest what was what! To Reb Zainvel everything was as clear as day; everything glowed like the stars in the sky. But he was not aware that as his mind moved through the worlds of learning his feet were moving, one after the other, across the market place; he went on beyond the market place, further and further over the snow covered road. Soon he was far from the town, where no houses, no roofs were to be seen—nothing at all! He walked through the snow, through open fields where there were no fences, no boundaries.

But suddenly, he stopped in bewilderment.

A heavy cloud stretched across the sky; the stars disappeared abruptly, and a broad shadow fell upon the glittering snow and darkened it. And just as abruptly, the thoughts of Reb Zainvel turned dark and he moved through the snow, astray in his mind concerning the Talmudic problem, knowing neither the way in nor the way out. . . .

Then, in the distance, he caught sight of a slender wisp of smoke snaking under the sky and surmised that there must be a dwelling nearby. Tired, chilled to the bone, his spirits fallen to the very depths of his soul, he went toward the wisp of smoke and managed to make his way to a country inn in an obvious state of decline.

Reb Zainvel entered the inn, the walls of which were grimy with smoke, and stopped near the door; nobody paid any attention to him. He saw the proprietress, an old peasant woman, dozing at the bar over the bottles of wine and the dishes of cold food. A raw, chill wind was blowing through the broken window-panes. Off to one side was the stove in which dry logs were burning, crackling and flaring up into flame. Around the stove sat half-drunk *mouzhiks* each with a mug of vodka in one hand and either a herring or a pickled cucumber in the other. The peasants were drinking; their faces were fiery, their eyes aglow with love and pleasure. From time to time they leaned toward one another, kissing and shedding tears because of their great love, or else reviling one another in abominable language. Then they would drink some more and eat more food. There was no room for Reb Zainvel near the stove, and he could not warm himself.

And Reb Zainvel—who in learning surpassed any rabbi, or any cantor when it came to chanting, who read the Old Testament in assembly better than any religious instructor from Lithuania could, who owned the wealthiest home in town; Reb Zainvel, whose wife was virtuous, whose children were successful in all they undertook, whose booth for the Feast of Tabernacles was the most splendid, whose *esrog* was the best of all—Reb Zainvel, the wisest of counselors, the most upright of arbitrators, the bestower of the most generous charity—Reb Zainvel could not restrain himself at that moment and, as he stood in the middle of the country inn in a fur jacket that hung upon him as if it were cut out of tin (while the wind whispered through it and froze the sweat on his body), he felt envious in the very depths of his soul of each and every peasant sitting around that stove; he felt envious of the *mouzhiks,* drinking vodka out of tin mugs, eating their herring and pickled cucumber, uttering words that were revolting to God. . . .

At that moment a new cycle of reincarnations began for the soul of Reb Zainvel.

Hope and Fear

MY HEART is with you.
My eye cannot feast itself enough on your blazing banner.
My ear never grows weary of listening to your mighty chant.

My heart is with you. Man should be replete and of good cheer.
Man should be sovereign; he should be his own master and have
free scope for his own work.

When you make bold to defy those who would stifle your free
word and strangle your protest, I am delighted; I implore the
Lord to strengthen you. And when you take the offensive against
old Sodom, in order to lay it waste, my soul is with you. Faith in
your ultimate victory warms my very heart, and intoxicates me
like old wine.

And yet—

And yet I am haunted with fear about you.

I fear the subjugated who triumph in the end: they may turn
into oppressors, and every oppressor violates the human spirit.

Is it not already being said among you that humanity must
march in unison like an army, and that you will set the pace for
the vanguard?

Humanity, however, is not an armed force.

In the mighty drive ahead, the warm-hearted can fathom more
deeply, the dignified rise higher—are you not likely to fell the
cedars lest they dwarf the blades of grass?

Will you not spread your wings over the essence of mediocrity?
Will you not safeguard lethargy and foster the gray and drab
herd, each one shorn alike?

I am haunted with fear about you.

You, as victors, are likely to become bureaucrats—doling out
to every man his morsel the way it is done in a poorhouse, allot-
ting each one his task, as it is done with galley-slaves. And you

would trample in the dust the creator of new worlds—the free human will; you would stop the initiative of man—the flow of the purest, most salubrious wellspring of human happiness, the prowess and valor that enables an individual to defy thousands, to challenge whole nations. You would mechanize life, regiment it and have it burned on the town dump.

And you will have your hands full, recording, itemizing, assessing; you will dictate how often a human pulse may beat, how far a human eye may see, a human ear may hear, and in what reveries one may indulge with a longing heart.

I contemplate with great delight your tearing down the walls of old Sodom. But my heart quivers with fear lest you erect on its ruins and debris a new and even worse Sodom—one more bleak and dismal!

There will be no windowless homes—yet mist will enshroud the souls. There will be no empty *stomachs,* yet *souls* shall hunger. No wail of woe shall reach any one's ears; but that eagle, the human spirit, with its wings clipped, will halt at the trough, alongside the cow and the ox.

And Justice, which accompanied you on the thorny, bloodstained road to victory, will desert you, and you will not be aware of it: victors and rulers are blind to such conditions, and you will be in the category of rulers and victors. You will sink in iniquity, yet will be hardly aware of the morass under your feet. Every overlord feels confident and bold—until such time as he stumbles.

You will build jails for those who will call your attention to the abyss toward which you are heading. You will pluck out the tongues that admonish you, of those who would supersede you, and overthrow you and your gross injustice.

With a vengeance you will defend the equal rights of the herd to the grass under their feet and to the salt over their heads; and your foes will be the free individuals, supermen, erudite inventors, prophets, saviors, poets and artists.

Whatever occurs, does so in space and time.

The steadfast, the firmly-established, already exists in space; therefore *this day and age,* petrified, and frost-riven, shall and must become extinct.

Time is synonymous with change, metamorphosis, evolution;

322

time is perpetual burgeoning, interminable blossoming—an eternal tomorrow.

And when the morrow for which you all yearn, will come to pass, you will become the champions of the bygone day, of the sands of life that are running out, of the extinct. *You* will trample the buds of the coming dawn, you will crush its blossoms—you will discourage the spirits of the masterminds of prophecy, vision and new hope.

Today is unwilling to expire: every sunset is invariably red with the hue of blood.

I yearn and clamor for your ultimate victory—yet I am haunted with fear about its consummation.

You are my fervent hope. You are my fear.

Do Not Follow Me

DO NOT FOLLOW ME, beloved child. The road the lonely wanderer follows is hard and dreary.

And if, at times, I languish, if I weaken with longing, if I stagger under affliction and prostrate myself before you to plead tearfully: "Come with me!" do not listen to my entreaties.

The road the lonely wanderer follows is depressing; it is bordered by weeping willows and their shadows darken it.

They were rejected by heaven but the earth welcomed them.

A sunbeam among these mournful trees is deprived of its joy and radiance, and if a ray seems to fall on the wanderer's road it is only the weak and lifeless shadow of a ray.

The road the lonely wanderer follows is not for you, my dearest.

In the leaves of the mourning willows which never behold the sky, in their branches which the birds shun when they are searching for a place to nest, your troubled soul will yearn for warmth and song. For there are no flowers in bloom along their somber way. Your wistful eyes will seek them in vain. Do not follow me, my child.

Do not extinguish the sparks of mercy in your eyes. The road the lonely wanderer follows is thorny; he has to run the gauntlet of the weeping willows, and hear the sinister midnight murmur of their drooping leaves and branches, a murmur echoing with laments silenced long ago that Heaven failed to heed, with the maledictions and gnashing of teeth of the repudiated and the accursed. At midnight, this rustling resounds and blends with the wail of sinful souls that wander in vain search of a heaven.

Dawn ushers in no solace. A sun as wrathful and crimson as blood peers through the ashes of cremated souls, souls interred without rites. That road is not for you, my child. Do not follow me.

Skulls are strewn along the road—the skulls of human beings

who died long ago and lie still unburied. Their hollow sockets seem to cry out mutely: "Why? Why?"

And my way carried me over graves forgotten and overgrown with thorns. They are the tombs of recalcitrant angels who rebelled against the Throne of Heaven. Eventually, vanquished and cast out of Heaven, they sought forgetfulness and solace in the arms of the daughters of men, and in due time expired like candles. The earth claimed them, yet could not assimilate them. And listen, my child! Often, at midnight, those thorny graves burst open, and the angels emerge, array themselves once more and glower with fierce hatred at the heavens, shaking their fists menacingly—only to bite their fingers in anguish and shame the next moment. Oh, why are their arms so short?

Do not follow me, my child! I implore you not to heed my pleas to do so, to shake off my entreaties as you would a green caterpillar that might drop from a tree upon your bosom. Shadows of the unborn lurk in that realm, phantoms that know no rest and who recklessly strike for light and life against God's will, before He has seen fit to invest them with flesh and blood. Those rebellious spirits are lusting for life and woe to whomever crosses their path! They drain the color from one's cheeks, extinguish the light in one's eyes, and suck out the very lifeblood . . . they are thirsty for life.

The road the lonely wanderer follows is not for you.

And should I ever lose heart, should I be overcome by gnawing pain and beseech you on my knees: "Come with me—do not forsake me!" heed not my plea! Smother those sparks of compassion in your eyes and uproot the longing I may have planted in your heart. See how the skies scowl upon me and how the unlucky stars are dogging my tracks!

Behold the storm clouds looming on the horizon for me! Through the trees, through the appalling darkness, your quiet, cozy home casts a friendly gleam of light. It beckons to you gently, warning you: "Stay clear of this, my child! Get back to your haven!" The elements are lashing the sky into fury. Go to sleep and lift your innocent eyes in prayer to the Lord. Implore Him to disperse the black cloud now threatening to blot out your spotless heaven. May the seeds of unrest and longing which I, with my sinful hand, have planted in your tender heart be uprooted.

And let the shadow which I have cast upon your immaculate soul vanish.

Beseech the Lord, my child! Providence is not angry with you, and will answer your prayer.

Do not follow me, my dearly beloved child!

A Journey in Time

I TOSSED ABOUT IN BED; a single idea was tormenting me and would not let me fall asleep. In my half-sleep it tangled all my dreams. . . .

"We live in time and space."

Space does, after all, yield to the pressure of our will: we can stay in one spot or move about—we can shift in space.

Our relation to time is an altogether different thing: we move in it against our will; even religions are subject to this motion!

In space, we can distinguish three dimensions: we can move forward and backward, up and down, to the right and to the left; here we can set definite limits and points of departure.

But time is a line without any direction except forward and backward.

The historians look back by means of imagination, sometimes as far as the time of Adam and Eve; they behold the first man and woman strolling about naked and chewing grass.

On the other hand, prophets and dreamers gaze only ahead; they often leap over into the far distant future, to the Last, Great Day, when a young herdsman bearing a staff blossoming with roses shall herd a wolf side by side with lambs.

These are exceptions, however, and most of the time seers are content with the soap-bubble of a simulation of life rather than the real thing. But all of God's people, the enormous mass of humanity which moves step by step, among whom I dwell, sinner that I am—what are we to do? We want to live, and not to dream, and the remembrance of comfort and pleasure is dearer to us than the sweet reveries of rivers flowing with milk and honey. And I am tormented by the problem: Why do we not move independently in time?

We have always found new means of overcoming space. We are progressing! At first, we moved from one place to another on foot, or even crept on all fours; then, we used horses to carry us; finally, someone invented the wheel—we harnessed the horse to it and off we went: soon, steam came and crowded out the horse; electricity is competing with steam and winning. Now, planes have appeared, and we are off, soaring into the stratosphere.

But how can we deal with time? There is no means of overcoming it!

My eyelids are heavy as lead; I cannot keep them open, yet thought continues to torment me.

"When one place becomes too cold, I can fly from the cold, if I have the money. I can move from darkness toward light, from winter to summer. If I like, I can have only spring, all year round, hear the song of birds, delight in the countryside. But if I feel chilled by time, there is nowhere to fly! There is no means of escape: neither steam nor electricity nor any airplane would be of any use!

Yet, I cannot stand still; I am forced to move with time, at a definite speed.

To go backward with the historians, I cannot—the generations whose linen went unstarched disgust me. To prophesy, I also cannot—only little children are capable of doing so. Yet, I do want to travel in time!

I dozed off and it seemed to me that to travel in time was not altogether impossible. One must but will it; everything depends on the will—and I do desire, I strive with all my strength, with all my soul.

And suddenly I was soaring off in time!

Grain was no longer being sown. Land had ceased to be property of landlords and of the people. Chemistry produced food from thistles and the only creatures we had to war against for this food were the asses. One felt sorry for them, of course, but there was no alternative. For hundreds of years, we had starved while they were sated; now the pendulum had swung the other way. Grain, however, was not the only thing being created by chemistry; meat, and fish, and game were produced as well—only as far as sensations of taste were concerned, of course. The potbelly disappeared; the large intestine, which had been inseparable from man for thousands of years, vanished without a trace. And we no longer ate —we just drank, except in Paris where even drinking was considered quite vulgar—there, food was inhaled. The British carried sacks, no bigger than tobacco pouches, filled with nutrient snuff: if they felt like eating they would sniff a pinch of it and their hunger was stayed. People's mouths were still there, but only because it was still necessary to flatter women and to flirt with them. . . .

Free love prevailed: jealousy did not exist, nor was there such a thing as infidelity.

The husband did not support his wife, as was customary in the twentieth century, nor did the wife support her husband, as was customary in the thirtieth century. Every man and woman had his or her own sack of nutrient snuff, and therefore no special rights or privileges were necessary.

"And who are you?"

"Me?"

"Yes, you."

"I am the driver."

"What sort of driver?"

"I steer the Wheel of Time. You wanted to go ahead to get into the future—didn't you?"

"Yes, yes! Lead me to the shepherd who herds wolves."

We rushed onward.

"What epoch are we in now? What is it called?"

"It has no name yet; it has just been evolved."

"Drive on!"

I saw people dashing about in all directions, shouting:

"What are we to do? How can we occupy ourselves? There are no beggars to whom we can hand out bread; there are none whose thirst we can slake, nor any who go naked for lack of clothing; there are none who are ill, whom we can nurse. There are none who are unhappy, none who are crushed, none who evoke our compassion."

All mankind lived and died normally on schedule. While they were alive, they were always sated. When they died, it was simply from old age.

All the organs shriveled by degrees, becoming smaller and smaller and, finally disappearing—all the organs deteriorated at the same tempo—entirely according to Mechnikov, without any pain or discomfort. Body and soul died together. There was no living soul in the dead body—and no dead body with a living soul. There was no will to surmount obstacles and no obstacles that could surmount the will. There were no unfulfilled needs, no hidden energy attempting to express itself! Even lovemaking was forgotten: desire cannot exist without energy.

There were no discussions, for there was nothing to discuss. Opinions no longer provoked any interest; speeches were colorless —one sensed in them neither wrath, indignation, humor, nor sarcasm. I attended a literary soiree; there were readings from the works of a famous humorist of the twentieth century—no one ever smiled; the audience was yawning.

Gradually, yawning had become the malady of the epoch—the all prevalent malady of the universe.

"And whatever became of the dream about the shepherd who herds the wolves together with the lambs?"

"What do you want with him—may the devil take him!"

Reptiles and wild beasts had long since been electrocuted. Even the toads had gone to the Kingdom Come!

"You take earthquakes, now—there has not been one for years!" an old man complained—and yawned.

"Get going!" I cried out in horror to my driver. "Lively now!"

"What is this—a fair?"

"God forbid—what trade could there be nowadays?"

"What is it then—a coronation?"

"People have long since forgotten about that sort of thing."

"Let's take a look."

The street was crowded with people. Some of them told me what had happened.

When the Jesuits were expelled from France, one of them was so griefstricken that he drank himself blind on chartreuse. In his drunken stupor, he collapsed near a cask in the wine cellar and remained asleep until today. Without the Jesuits, France rotted, just as Spain had done after the expulsion of the Jews. The land was submerged in filth, and finally an earthquake turned it into a heap of ruins. And today, a certain yawner, as he was digging a grave in which to bury himself alive, happened to stumble upon this Jesuit. He was carried into the city and brought back to consciousness.

No sooner had he been awakened than he was surrounded by a crowd. Everyone was interested in knowing whether people used to yawn in his day.

"Yes," answered the Jesuit. "The English lords used to yawn constantly; so did American billionaires."

"But what about the common people?"

"No. Apparently they didn't."

"What did they do?"

"Before the expulsion of the Jesuits, the common people of all nations prayed; they glorified God, they sang hymns to Him—"

"That is how they frittered away their time, you mean?"

"They also rejoiced over the rising of the sun and its setting— particularly the poets."

"We have neither morning nor evening. The nocturnal electric sun gives a brighter light than the sun in the heavens."

"There used to be concerts given for charity!"

"We have no charity—there are no poor people."

"There were hurdy-gurdies playing in the streets—"

"We have buttons: press one and you hear the finest music."

"Oh, yes!" the Jesuit recalled. "Some people, just to amuse themselves on a cold winter night, would stick a foot out from under the blanket and then tuck it in again."

"We have no frosts, no winter. There's a subtropical climate now all over the earth."

"Wait a minute; give me a chance to remember," said the Jesuit wearily. "Do you happen to have a bit of wine?"

"No. But we have some distilled snuff."

"There used to be soldiers marching through the streets behind a military band, and the people ran after them—"

"What are soldiers?"

"People dressed in uniforms, and armed—"

"And just what is a uniform? What's the meaning of armed?"

"Let me have a little more wine; my memory has become very weak."

They let him have another sniff; his memory returned at once, and he described uniforms and arms in detail.

"That sounds magnificent," the people decided, and immediately soldiers appeared, uniformed and fully armed. But as the soldiers goose-stepped through the streets, they never stopped yawning, nor did the people watching them.

"You have fooled us, Jesuit!"

"No—such a thing never entered my mind. However, they are not soldiers."

"They're in regulation uniforms, aren't they?"

"You're perfectly right!"

"And they're fully armed, aren't they?"

"Yes. But—"

"What's all this *but* business?"

"They have never shed blood; their faces are devoid of war-like expressions."

"Shed blood!" screamed the frenzied throng. "Slash away and shoot!"

"Slash and shoot whom?" asked the general.

"Us! All of us! Anything is better than yawning! Shoot away!" thundered the people. And the people are, after all, the supreme law-making body.

"Fire!" commanded the general.

That was when I awakened.

Eternal Peace in the Land of Somewhere

HERE IS WHAT a little fairy tale has to say about the Land of Somewhere:

There was a tall mountain in the Land of Somewhere. Mighty eagles built their nests on the summit of this mountain, and riotous winds frolicked among its expanses. The summit constantly beheld almost all of the horizon over the Land of Somewhere. Each morning it admired the most wondrous sunrise to be found in that land.

And the summit was bathed in the clearest light, for it was the summit of the highest mountain in the Land of Somewhere. There was nothing to screen it from the sun, and no shadow fell upon it.

This was a mighty mountain: the crags were its sinews, the lodes of copper and gold were its veins. The wild goat knew all this, the wild goat that scrambled over rib-like ridges of the mountain.

That is what this little fairy tale had to say.

The mothers heard this little tale. They made up a lullaby about it and lulled their little ones to sleep with it, with this cradle song about the Land of Somewhere, and about the great mountain in the Land of Somewhere.

But then, the child would grow up and forget the dear song. At school, and at play it was forgotten; it was forgotten during the business of living—in love, in suffering, and amid the hurly-burly of this world.

Yet somewhere, within some hidden cranny of the heart, the string would still be vibrating—and this cradle song about the mountain summit in the Land of Somewhere would ring forth. But life would be plashing all around one; it would be bubbling, coming to a boil—and the vibrating string of the song could not be heard.

Years went by—year after year.

And then, this would come to pass:

A youth might be spinning the golden thread of his life—when Fate would stretch forth its pitiless hand and sunder the thread. The youth would withdraw from life into loneliness. And suddenly, amid the quiet of this loneliness, he would sense that something was quivering, that something was ringing within the hidden cranny of his heart. He would pause, hearkening. . . .

A youth might be playing the happy song of love on the golden harp of his youth. Evil Fate would hear it, then creep up on him, stretch forth its evil hand, and snap his strings, one after the other. The harp would fall silent; the heart would grow quiet in dread. And, suddenly, amid the silence that had fallen, the cradle song would ring forth—the song about the great, tall mountain which is in the Land of Somewhere.

Or else, on some quiet moonlit night, the song would come to someone in a dream, would suddenly ring forth in his ear—and that man would awaken.

Or then, again, a man would fall into deep thought, a pensive mood coming suddenly upon him—and he would be drawn into the Land of Somewhere, to the tall mountain which is in that land. The Land of Somewhere drew him, beckoning. . . . And he would go off wandering.

In all times, by various ways, from all ends of the earth, people trudged, wandering toward the Land of Somewhere.

Some actually succeeded in reaching it.

Yes, some did manage to make their way there. But not one of these wanderers knew about any other. They traveled by different roads. They came from different ends of the earth, without meeting.

The little fairy tale spins along.

They spin it out of moonbeams on quiet nights, on nights flooded with moonlight.

And this tale continues:

At the foot of the tall mountain, which is in the Land of Somewhere, lay lands that knew freedom—fertile lands of black loam;

thick forests that had not been disturbed for ages grew there; streams purled, flowing rivers circled in the great mountain.

Travelers, upon reaching the mountain which is in the Land of Somewhere, would settle at its foot. Afterward, hunters would journey to the forest with bow and arrows; fishermen would sit beside the clear pools with rod and net; the tiller of the soil would work his plow; the shepherd would drive his flock to the rich meadow. Settlements sprang up in the lowlands.

Yet, vast and expansive as was the base of the mountain, one settlement was out of sight of the next, knowing of no other.

Each settlement created for itself a separate world of its own and then arranged this world to suit itself. Each made up its own holy of holies for its "only" god, and then bowed down to the "only" Sovereign of the Universe.

And each inhabitant of each settlement lived his life, and died when his time came—in accordance with the will and law of the "only" god.

They prayed to their god, and conversed in the "only" human tongue. And they worked, and multiplied and, step by step, climbed up the slope of the mountain they desired. Slowly, sowing wheat, oats and rye, came the tiller of the soil; he would be overtaken and left behind by the grower of the grape; higher up, trailing the wild goat, the shepherd leaped over the rocks and crags, while the miner stubbornly followed each lode of ore.

But, there were some who attained to even greater heights.

They were the ones who, even when all things were going well, could find no rest. For their souls were far too turbulent; they longed far too greatly after the height—after the highest height! In their hearts, far more so than in the hearts of others, rang the dear song, the cradle song. They would lay aside, on impulse, the bow and arrows, the rod and net, and leave the forest or the pond; they would let the scythe and the honing stone fall out of their hands, forget the sickle, leave the plow and throw aside the ax; they would abandon their vineyards, or lose themselves in gazing, out of the depths where the lodes of ore lay, at God's world; they would leave the wild goat to its own devices and clamber upward.

The summit of the mountain drew them.

In every settlement there was such a yearner; in some settlements there actually were many—and lo, they were striving upward.

They strove upward.

And the higher they went, the narrower became the ridge of the mountain. Now and again, during their wanderings, they would encounter each other.

And when they did—

The little fairy tale becomes sad at this point—sad and frightening.

The tales it tells are fraught with gloom; they are tales of bloody battles!

The little fairy tale spins along.

In each settlement there is one who yearns, and in some settlements there are many yearners.

It is the height they yearn for—and the winds, the strong winds, the mighty eagles, the sky, far-flung and free, and for the clear bright light, for the wondrous sunrise. . . .

The summit draws them.

Each one sets out alone. They pace along the boundaries of the fields. They come out of the shelters that the growers of the grape build. They glide along the edges of the mine-shafts. They spring over rocks and crags, heading off the wild goat. With yearning gaze fixed upon the lofty height they wander about, their ears on the alert for the sounds that the heights make—and, on occasion, they encounter one another.

They meet and are frightened.

Having halted distrustfully, they look at each other in astonishment.

They had come from different quarters; they had followed different ways, and each of them differs in dress; their hair is not cut alike, and each one wears a different head-covering.

As they greet each other they stammer:

"Peace be unto you!"

Each one utters this in his own tongue, his "only" tongue. This sounds alien to the ears of the hearer—somehow harsh and inhuman. To each it seems that the other one is threatening. "He is insulting, he is berating me."

And this is the point at which they clash.

"If you are a man, you must believe in—" at which each calls upon
the name of his god, the "only" god.

Two divine names are uttered in two tongues. And each man is
thinking about the other: "His speech is not human, and besides,
he does not believe in God—"

And they get ready for battle. Before doing battle each calls
upon his god for help. They speak different languages. They call
out different names, and each one thinks secretly: "He is mocking
me, and blaspheming besides!"

Or: "He worships another god—not the real god but an evil
one!"

Their hatred blazes up, and they fight. Their fight is a fight to
the death. And one of them comes off victorious—with his "one"
god.

As for the vanquished, he either blesses or curses his god and
falls dead.

The body of the vanquished man rolls downward, and becomes
a bloody trail upon the slope of the great mountain. As for the
victor, he, having offered thanks to his god in his own tongue,
climbs higher.

Every day in the settlements brings an increase of those who
yearn, and encounter one another on the slope of the mountain,
and enter battle.

The yearning that drives them higher also intensifies the wrath
against the barbarian encountered on the way—against the wild
beast who does not believe in God, whose god is not the real god
and who babbles in some sort of a tongue that is not human.

And each time a man rises higher he carries his wrath with him
—and together with the man, strife and battles rise.

Each time the battles come closer to the summit of the mountain. More frequently, and from a greater height, the bodies
of the vanquished hurtle down the slopes. Catching on the sharp
rocks and crags, they shatter into pieces of bloody pulp. More and
more often blood spurts and stains the crest of the mountain, and
streams down the mountainside.

As they roll down, the mutilated corpses of the blasphemers make
the soil at the mountain's foot more and more fertile; the ears of
wheat and rye grow ever fuller, ever more generous; ever more succulent grow the grapes and ever sweeter the juice of their clusters;

thicker and thicker is the grass under the hoofs of the wild she-goat, ever richer the milk that she yields to the shepherd.

But the yearning victors thank the Lord their God and climb ever higher. . . .

And the little fairy tale also tells us:

The settlements at the mountain's foot increased and multiplied. The number of those who yearned after the height grew; so did the number of those who climbed upward.

Ever more dangerous is the road upward leading to the mighty eagles and the free winds, to the sunrise and the wide expanses of heaven. There are more and more of the babbling barbarian blasphemers on the mountainside. And now, when men climb there, they go armed. And more and more often do the armed bands clash. At every encounter battles take place, and all this in the name of God, in the name of the "only" God.

The herdsman emerges from his hut of branches, the miner from his pit, the vineyard keeper runs out of his vineyard, the tiller of the soil hastens from his plow, the fisherman from his pond, and the hunter from his virgin forest. And all of them bear arms.

The battles occur more often, and are always more embittered.

The mountain rumbles from the ceaseless strife, from the ringing of arms, from war cries and . . . the name of God, whom all call upon in various tongues.

And the corpses roll down, smashing against rocks and crags. And rivers of blood flow down the mountainside, swirling and foaming.

Each time the bottomlands grow more fertile, more swollen the ears of wheat, oats and rye, still sweeter and more fiery the wine; ever more nourishing is the grass the wild she-goat grazes on among the rocks and crags, and ever richer the milk that she yields.

On one occasion, however, (so the little fairy tale tells us) two men in the heat of battle suddenly found themselves on the crest of the mountain, and were plunged into a sea of light—that brightest and clearest of lights, the light of the heights.

At once, unexpectedly, they not only heard but understood each other, and each recognized the other as a human being; each heard from the lips of the other the self-same name of God, and they flew into each other's arms.

And following them came others, bathed in the light of the heights; and after them came many more, and they all began to speak the only human language—the language of light.

And great joy prevailed.

But suddenly the noise of battle reached their ears from below; the mountain echoed with the din of strife.

What was bound to happen in the lowlands, did happen. Just as the turbulent individuals had come into conflict near the summit, so did the settlements at its foot: in the end they clashed among themselves.

The settlements had increased and multiplied; they had spread out and grown. The free forests and the fields, that at one time had been so spacious, had become narrower and more crowded. Clashes occurred between hunter and hunter, between one tiller of the soil and the next, and underground, between miner and miner.

"The outlanders have come! The strangers are tilling our soil, the newcomers are fishing in our ponds! The barbarians are sinking their teeth in our soil! The unbelievers have seized our vineyards, the worshipers of false and evil gods have captured the wild goat!"

Such were the cries that went up in the lowlands. And war flared up on all sides.

It was then that those who had become brothers upon the summit of the mountain hastened to the lowlands:

"Quiet down! Away with arms! All men are equal here. There is but one human speech and one only—the speech of light."

And that (so the little fairy tale tells us) was the beginning.

The beginning of eternal peace. Of eternal peace in the Land of Somewhere, at the foot of the great tall mountain.

At this point the little fairy tale smiles—the little fairy tale beams. . . . It beams for all the world like the sun rising in the east over the summit, the lofty summit of the great mountain in the Land of Somewhere.

For the fairy tale knows full well that a little song, a cradle song, will come into being, and that it will be sung by mothers, each crooning the song over her most beloved child as it lies in its cradle.

And, in the heart of the child this little song will ring forth, and later on, will grow into yearning.

Into yearning for the Land of Somewhere, for the land of peace, with its only human speech—the speech of light.

It will mature into a splendidly beautiful yearning and a wondrous one. . . .

APPENDIXES

My First Meeting with Peretz

by SHOLEM ASCH

IT IS a curious fact that Mendelssohn's translation of the Bible into German, printed in Hebrew characters, opened the way to the German classics for many a *yeshivah bochur* whose mental horizon had been bounded by talmudic and rabbinic lore—opened the way to Schiller, Koerner, and Goethe, as well as Shakespeare in German translation. But these were, in the final analysis, only extraneous books. The lacunae left by loss of religious faith and belief in the Messiah still remained. There was no substance to cling to, there was no purpose to aim for. Hebrew, Polish grammar, the elements of arithmetic, German—these subjects were only a means to an end. But what practical end was to be envisaged? Our hearts remained empty and gnawed by a vague longing. Yet we were young and craved for something to live by.

Just then a young man came to town from Lodz, bringing with him Peretz's "Shtreiml" (Fur Mitre) and "Bontche Shveig" (Bontche the Silent). We had known Peretz only through his collection of Hebrew poems entitled "Ha-Ugav" (The Organ), which we had read and memorized, not so much for the love about which it sang as for its Hebrew diction. And here was Peretz now in the "Yiddish jargon," printed in little story books, the kind servant girls and journeymen borrowed from book-hawkers at three copecks a week.

We read them and were powerfully affected by them. They taught me three things: first, as regards language, that there was no need of waiting until I could write grammatical German or Hebrew, but that I could say things now in the simple idiom that I and all others around me spoke. Secondly, I learned that the story need not deal with barons or princes, as in Schiller and Koerner; or cruel Jews and bands of robbers, as in Smolenskin; or Palestinian Jews, as found in Mapu's "Ahavas Zion." Why not a present-day story about people I knew and saw daily? And it was borne in upon me that I could do it; I had but to reach for the pen and write. Thirdly and most important, I found that there was always an idea behind the story that Peretz wrote. He demanded, for example, some great act of justice for his heroes—for the girl for whom "the heavens were a nuptial canopy," and for Bontche who was silent all his life.

From then on I longed for No. 1 Ceglana, Peretz's address.

I went there and walked up and down the steps a few times, my heart beating audibly. Finally I took courage and rang at the door bearing a brass plate with the inscription "I. L. Peretz, 3 to 5."

I regretted my boldness now and should have liked to run down, but it was too late; I heard footsteps. The door opened and I saw before me I. L. Peretz, resembling the photograph that appeared in his booklet "Ha-Ugav," showing Peretz wearing a fur cap. He looked a trifle older, however.

"Whom do you wish to see?"

"Does I. L. Peretz live here?' I asked in Hebrew. I did not dare address a man like him in ordinary Yiddish.

"Right here," Peretz replied in Hebrew, barely concealing a smile behind his bushy moustaches, and led me into a room at the end of the corridor, into his study.

In a corner by the window sat a pale-faced young man with a pensive and weary expression. He was holding in his hand an exercise-book with writing in it.

"What do you wish?" Peretz asked me.

"I wish to speak to you, sir," I stammered on in Hebrew.

"Maybe you'll find it easier to speak Yiddish," Peretz suggested.

"I have brought along something I wrote in Hebrew, and I'd like to know—"

"That's the way to talk. Fine. Sit down a while and listen," he replied, indicating a chair.

I sat down and the pale-faced young man resumed reading out of his exercise-book. My arrival had apparently interrupted him. Peretz sat behind the table, listening with closed eyes.

The young man was reading a story about trees being cut in a forest and about a big-eyed child listening to them crashing to the ground.

The language and the tone of the narrative fascinated me so completely that I sat as if chained to my chair. I all but saw the forest and heard the rustling of the trees. What impressed me most, however, was the voice of the young man with the pained face. There was a ring of such sincerity and earnestness in his voice, that I was moved to tears. The youth was Nomberg; he was reading his story "Di Oigen" (The Eyes).

When he finished reading, Peretz turned to me:

"And what have you brought along?"

Shy and frightened, I took out of my pocket a sentimental piece written in Hebrew and handed it to Peretz. I realized how juvenile and how inferior it was to what I had just heard read.

Peretz's eyes ran over it. My writing was hard to read and my Hebrew was faulty. He laid it aside, pondered a while and then turned to me:

"There is something in it. But you can't say what you want to because you aren't at your ease in the Hebrew language. Go home and write something in a tongue in which you can express everything you wish; I mean Yiddish. Send it to me and I'll know what you are trying to say."

I did not feel disheartened. I don't know why.

"Do you smoke?" he asked. "Have a cigarette." He handed me one out of a box. I took it and held it in my hand, not knowing what to do with it. Was I to smoke Peretz's cigarette? I wanted to keep it.

"Where do you come from?" he inquired. "Did you say from Greater Poland, from Kutno? Poland is beginning to make herself heard." The last remark was addressed to Nomberg.

"Why don't you smoke?" he asked me, noticing that I could not make up my mind what to do with the cigarette.

"I don't feel like smoking your cigarette," I replied shyly. "I'd like to keep it."

"Cigarettes are made to smoke and not to keep," he replied, giving me a light.

Soon his wife came in from an adjoining room and beckoned to him: dinner is served.

"Well, if you write anything, send it to me. I'll answer you," Peretz said as he bade Nomberg and me good-bye.

"Come along with me. We'll have some tea," Nomberg suggested to me as we went down the steps.

We walked along the streets of Warsaw that I was seeing for the first time. I stopped every now and then to look at things. On the way, Nomberg asked me a lot of questions about the provincial town I had just come from.

He was living on Pawia street, in a tiny room on the third floor. He showed me into his room and made some tea on a small cooker. Soon another young man joined us. He was tall and thin. He asked Nomberg inquisitively:

"Well, what did he say? Did Peretz like 'The Eyes'?"

The young man spoke with a Lithuanian accent, rarely heard in small Polish towns.

"A new talent from the province," Nomberg said, introducing me. "And this is Abraham Reisen, a Yiddish writer. Have you heard of him?"

"Abraham Reisen!" I exclaimed enthusiastically. I had read his poem "My ko mashma lon" which had appeared in a periodical and which had impressed me enormously. I had also come across some other things by him in the then new journal "Der Yud."

"A new talent!" Reisen called joyfully. "What do you write, poems, stories?"

"He writes Hebrew," was Nomberg's reply.

"Better write Yiddish. Then people will read and understand you," Reisen counselled me. "Well, has there been any talk in the province about my "Twentieth Century"? What, you haven't seen it yet? Here's a copy. Nomberg appears here for the first time. A great talent. Take it and show it to people in your town." Reisen handed me a copy of "The Twentieth Century" which he had pulled out of a bundle he was carrying. The same bundle, however, also contained bread, butter, and herring. He laid out the food on the table and my new friends asked me to eat with them unceremoniously.

"Don't be bashful, do have something. We all belong to the same family here," Reisen coaxed me. "Nomberg, why don't you ask him to have some tea," he reprimanded his friend.

"It's on the table. Let him drink some if he wants to; he needn't drink any if he doesn't want to. Here we don't coax anybody," Nomberg replied dryly.

"You're mean. Come now, have some tea with us."

It was so good to be with my new chums, that I said to myself that I would not go back home and would stay on with them. But I had left without saying a word about it to anybody and without even taking any baggage along.

That same evening the Vistula carried me back to my home town. I wrote something in Yiddish, a story entitled "Mottele," and sent it on to 1 Ceglana. Weeks lengthened into months without word from Peretz. I could not bear staying in town. I used to take along solitary hikes across the fields, while yearning for Warsaw. I must admit that I yearned even more for Pawia (that is for my new chums Nomberg and Reisen) than for Ceglana.

I waited until after the holidays, passing the Feast of Tabernacles in a dreary mood. Immediately thereafter I made for Warsaw, determined to stay there, whatever betide.

I found no one on Pawia street. Nomberg and Reisen had moved; nobody knew where to. But 1 Ceglana was a permanent address. One Saturday afternoon I was standing at Peretz's door again. This time my heart did not pound so violently. I carried in my pocket "Mottele" and "Moshele" written in a language which I knew and could pronounce.

I found at Peretz's house my two new friends Nomberg and Reisen, as well as Dr. Lurie, editor of "Der Yud" and others. Old Dyneson was there too, busily occupied making cigarettes.

This time Peretz received me as an old acquaintance. "So you've come back," he said with a smile.

"Since you didn't answer me, I simply had to call for the answer myself," I replied, speaking more boldly than at our first meeting.

"Who in the world can read your writing?" Peretz answered, picking up my manuscript which lay on his desk. Apparently he had tried to read it without success. "Now that you're here," he continued as he handed me the manuscript, "read it to me yourself."

"I wanted to answer you, but you didn't give any address," old Dyneson said with a laugh. "What address are we to write you to?"

A glance at the manuscript showed me that I really failed to indicate my address.

"Never mind, let him read it himself," Peretz suggested as he called for attention. "Gentleman, a new talent!" he added introducing me.

I took my seat and began to read. My diction was that of Greater Poland and my pronunciation such that only Polish Jews could understand me, those of Lithuania with difficulty.

"Take this and print it in your paper!" Peretz said when I had finished reading, and handed my manuscript to Dr. Lurie.

I looked at Peretz and then at Dr. Lurie as he took the manuscript.

"Come to my office tomorrow for your honourarium," the latter said to me.

I could not believe my eyes and ears. Was I witnessing a miracle?

"Have you anything else?"

"Another story, 'Moshele'."

"Read it."

"You can print this too," Peretz said passing the manuscript to Dr. Lurie.

"I'll print this one first, I like it better," Dr. Lurie replied.

"Moshele" actually proved to be the first thing from my pen to be published; it appeared in the "Yud" in the fall of 1897. And the following morning I received the first four roubles I ever earned for Yiddish literature.

I lived with Reisen and saw Nomberg daily. Everything that any one of us wrote was first read to the others. Nor did we have anything published without first reading it to Peretz. Occasionally he suggested alterations, giving his reasons. It must be said, however, that Peretz thought very highly of writers with a mind of their own who did not follow his advice blindly. He did not like unreasoned obedience.

He had one great gift which helped him to discover new talent: he seemed to sense the "soul" of everything that was read to him. That was precisely what he was looking for, and the moment he penetrated the intrinsic significance of a piece of writing, he was willing to overlook many external flaws due to technical inexperience. That enabled him to distinguish between what was individual and new, on the one hand, and commonplace and done by rote, on the other hand. Peretz often spurned beginners who evinced maturity of form while lacking individuality. He loved the spring breeze wafted by groping immaturity. I know of those whom Peretz discouraged and who later appeared in print and attained a measure of success. But they never rose above mediocrity, never set foot on any but the trodden path they entered from the first. And Peretz loathed this mediocrity all his life.

Nomberg, Reisen, and I used to call on him every third day.

The day we visited him was a holiday to us, as eagerly looked forward to as Passover by a Jewish boy.

Each of us wrote a fair amount—a story a week. There was, however, no journal to publish our work in. The only Yiddish periodical of the time, the weekly "Der Yud," carried in each issue a short story, a poem, and an installment of a long story. Its contributors included Mendele, Sholom Aleichem, and Peretz. There were also contributions by Frug, Rovnitski, and Ben Ami. This left little room for young writers. Peretz was our only protector. He tried to get our work published. Often he even withheld his own stories to make room for us. I remember on one occasion Dr. Lurie asking for a chassidic story for his weekly, a story that Peretz had read to him. Peretz knew, however, that Dr. Lurie had on hand some stories by Nomberg and me and would not let go of his story until the editor had used our work.

We all used to look forward to Saturday; for on that day we used to call on Peretz and stay on until late in the evening. In addition to us young writers, Dyneson and Dr. Lurie, his callers often included visitors that were passing through Warsaw. For if an out-of-town Jewish writer or public man happened to be in Warsaw on a Saturday, he was sure to go and see Peretz. As a result, one could meet in Peretz's home almost everybody that was active in Jewish life. The house on 1 Ceglana became the centre of Jewish radical thought. It was there that the foundation of neo-Yiddish literature was laid, not as a means but as an end in itself. From that house issued forth the idea of Yiddish, the poetic renaissance of Chassidism, the love of the folk song and the folk story.

In the Sabbath twilights we used to sit singing folk songs, while the light faded into darkness. Inspired by the deep emotion that inheres in the Yiddish folk song and by its simple form, Peretz taught us how to penetrate into the inner recesses of the Jewish soul.

There appeared at the time in St. Petersburg a collection of Yiddish folk songs without music. Some of us remembered their melodies as we had heard them sung at home, or else we sought out the tunes in the Warsaw courtyards and repeated them to Peretz at our Saturday reunions. Then there was many a "transmigration of a tune." The street song had a solemn ring in Peretz's house and put us in an exalted mood in the Sabbath twilights. Peretz's magnificent essay on the folk song, entitled "Jewish life according to the Folk Song," belongs to that period.

The cultivation of the folk song in Peretz's home began in the following manner: when Peretz had been placed under arrest for alleged political activities, Nomberg composed a song—to which he fitted a melody—opening with the words, "Es yogn, es loifn shvartze Volkn" (Black clouds are seen speeding and racing). The song was first sung in Peretz's house on a Saturday evening when we met there. From there it spread to the street. A few weeks later it could be heard in workshops and factories. Since the author's name was unknown, it came to be regarded as a folk song. Thus Nomberg's song led to the custom of singing folk songs at Peretz's on the Sabbath.

Everyone sang the songs he knew; Peretz wrote them down. Then the idea of collecting these folk songs was hit upon. At about that time, a young man named J. L. Kohen was touring the country gathering folk songs, which were subsequently published in New York. Peretz received him enthusiastically and encouraged him to go on collecting this material.

Peretz used to be especially fond of a certain chassidic song consisting of just one word, the word "rebbenue," meaning "dear rabbi."

> Rebbenue,
> Oy, oy, rebbenue ...

The word is repeated over and over again in the song and the melody keeps on gaining momentum. We used to sing this song at Peretz's house every Saturday. He was so fond of it that whenever he paced up and down his room, absorbed in thought, he constantly hummed it to himself. The song never left his lips to the very last.

The first winter I came to Warsaw, preparations were under way for Peretz's fiftieth jubilee. Dyneson headed a committee that issued a one-volume edition of Peretz's collected works. The celebration took place on Leg Ba Omer. The enthusiasm exceeded anything Jewish Warsaw had ever witnessed. It was an especially memorable holiday for us young writers. We clubbed together and bought Peretz a golden pen. He was very happy over it. At the banquet we young writers were given seats at the very rear. The seats of honour were reserved for dignitaries and members of the Community Council in whose employ Peretz was.

When he came in, he looked us up and had us seated at his table, saying: "They really belong to my family."

On the occasion of his jubilee, he made me a present of a volume of his works with the following inscription:

> I hear it peck;
> It pecks so loud:
> Who knows?—
> A crow, or else an eagle.

"A crow, or else an eagle"—I say to myself every time I write anything or do anything.

How I. L. Peretz Wrote His Folk Tales

by A. MUKDONI

I. L. PERETZ was always surrounded by young writers. I had the good fortune to be one of them and to learn something about his creative method which I am about to describe. His house was the rendezvous of young men and reechoed with the din of their literary disputations. For he was everlastingly young himself, scurrying and bustling and buoyant.

Older writers used to avoid Peretz. Jacob Dyneson was the outstanding exception. Yet there was something poignantly tragic about the fast friendship of the two men. The tragic element of this friendship was hardly ever alluded to, least of all by Peretz himself. Not that he was not keenly alive to it but because it was too painful a subject.

The bold facts of the case are that Dyneson's fellowship with Peretz meant the end of his career as a writer. His literary aspirations now merged with, or became subservient to those of Peretz. He came to identify Peretz's literary ambitions with his own, so that whenever Peretz wrote anything new, Dyneson took greater delight in it than the author himself and never tired of reading it aloud to all and sundry, his old little face radiant with joy.

Yet before the flowering of this friendship, Dyneson had been a writer of considerable talent, with an individuality of his own, and an assured place in Yiddish literature. All this ceased with his intimacy with Peretz. His literary work was henceforth limited to memoirs, written listlessly and without his old-time fervor.

Young writers, on the other hand, drew inspiration from their proximity to Peretz. Under his powerful influence no inconsiderable number of them became authors of note for he showed genuine concern in their work and knew how to stimulate them. He easily warmed up to these young men and became their sworn friend.

The older writers manifested something akin to a dislike of him, shunning him and dreading him. It was an unreasoned dread; they felt a premonition of danger in his friendship. Maybe the case of J. Dyneson had something to do with it.

One day, however, another older writer appeared at his house and immediately became his warm friend. His name was S. An-sky (the pseudonym of S. Z. Rapoport). He had met Peretz before, somewhere in Russia, and was drawn to him irresistibly. He visited Peretz in Warsaw, then came to his house again and again, like a pilgrim to a shrine.

The first time I met An-sky at Peretz's home, he was in company of his young and beautiful, but obviously spoilt, wife. The sight of this bowed, elderly man with a radiant, coquettish, young woman at his side was somewhat repugnant to all of us. There was something grotesque about the relationship. That the marriage was not a happy one was borne out by later events: one fine morning An-sky's young wife left him.

She was young and fickle and had a feminine weakness for celebrities. An-sky was popular even though he was but a mediocre writer. It is not easy to explain his popularity. It probably stemmed largely from the fact that he began his literary career in Russian. To the half-baked Jewish intellectuals of the time a Russian writer, no matter how ordinary, seemed a very exalted personage. Moreover, An-sky's revolutionary activities had greatly enhanced his prestige. Added to all this, his extremely lovable personality won him a host of admirers.

Among them was the young girl who became his short-lived wife. She had been dazzled by the prospect of being introduced into the Russian literary world and presiding over a literary salon. She was, however, soon disillusioned by her husband's poor material circumstances and the want of pomp in his literary environment. The result, as we have seen, was a brief but intensely dramatic period in the life of An-sky. This dramatic episode and the ensuing tragedy were not only known in Peretz's home, they were veritably lived through.

I recall An-sky's entries into Peretz's house, his cordial, grandfatherly smile and his Russo-Jewish warmth. After embracing and kissing each other in Russian fashion, Peretz would ask: "Are you bringing along any wares this time?" We knew what wares he was talking about.

S. An-sky was touring the country in the interests of the Jewish Historic-Ethnographical Society of St. Petersburg, collecting Jewish folklore material, stories, legends, songs, melodies, old Jewish ceremonial objects, and manuscripts. Hence he was an inexhaustible source to Peretz for his own matchless *"Folkstimliche Geshichten"* (Folk Tales). He never tired listening to him, urging him on to tell more and more.

After their cordial greeting, Peretz would sit down beside his friend and with his big smiling eyes fixed on him, he would exhort him: "Well, out with those wares of yours!" then An-sky would produce a little notebook, search through it and begin narrating. Peretz was all ears.

Occasionally he would manifest disapproval of the material by interrupting the narrator: "This is false, this is foreign. Find something better. What district does it come from, Bessarabia? It sounds too Wallachian." An-sky used to smile like a father whose precocious child has caught on to his attempt to fool him.

At other times Peretz's eyes would sparkle and he would burst out enthusiastically: "That's what I call genuine. Let's hear it the way it was told to you. That's good, that's very good."

Once I was present when An-sky recounted a folk tale he had heard (if my memory serves me rightly) somewhere in Volhynia. Peretz hung on every word and when An-sky had finished, he began pacing up and down the room, then resumed his seat beside An-sky, smiling blissfully.

I was rather surprised at this show of unusual interest in a story that struck me as neither peculiarly new or original; on the face of it, of a piece with the thousand and one folk stories that could be heard in Peretz's home. For it was a veritable clearing-house for folklore material of every kind.

It so happened that this homely and apparently common-place story enabled us to see Peretz in his laboratory in the act of distilling his folk tales. This came about in the following manner:

During the years of 1912–1913 Peretz flung himself with renewed zeal into communal cultural work, as was his wont after a spell of activity. He now turned to the "Hazamir," at the time a half-dormant, half-defunct organization, devoted in the main to Jewish music. This predominant interest was due to the musical predilections and virtuosity of its chairman, Dr. Gershon Lewin. An admirer of Peretz, he had persistently tried to attract him to the "Hazamir," knowing that if his enthusiasm were fired, he could blow the breath of new life into the organization. He knew, too, that Peretz was not the man to be won by artificial inducements or by influence exerted from without. Unless there was an inner compulsion, Peretz held aloof.

In the period under discussion, Peretz drew close to the "Hazamir" of his own accord. He went so far as to accept its chairmanship and bring into the executive committee a number of his zealots, writers and artists. He became fairly wrapped up in the new venture.

The fact of the matter is that Peretz wanted to satisfy his longing for an audience, for living men and women whom he could look at and who could look at him. Such direct contact was essential to Peretz. Readers of periodicals and books were too abstract for him. He always craved direct human relationship, direct reaction to his artistic work.

The need for an audience in the flesh was probably one of Peretz's weaknesses. He just could not visualize his readers. Hence his occasional unconcern for them and his consequent not uncommon disregard of clarity. If his sentences were incomplete, if his meaning was only partially expressed, it behooved the reader himself to seek further clarification of the subject matter. He was, however, never obscure when in direct touch with his auditors. A look at them would tell him whether he was being followed or not; and he saw to it that he made himself clear.

The period referred to saw the origin of the famous "box-evenings," so called because of the written questions posed by members of the audience and put in a box to be answered by Peretz and others. It goes without saying that most of the questions were directed at him. Consequently he was either the spokesman or the chief speaker at these meetings.

Peretz used to answer with amazing readiness, sharply, clearly and captivatingly. When he warmed up, he rose to great oratorical heights. He was especially adept in pathos, humour and satire. When at his best, these were well balanced in his speeches, which were variegated in tone and dazzlingly colourful. As secretary of these question-and-answer meetings, I was frequently electrified by his flashes of thought, his sound logic and deep insight. Yes, insight, for Peretz did not possess great erudition or a well rounded education. He was too full of the zest of living and too impulsive to be poring over books or trying to follow an involved subject to its ultimate conclusion. And so there were times when, on hearing him expound and clarify some intricate philosophical problem of which he had but the vaguest knowledge, I did not believe my own ears.

On one occasion somebody asked if there was a God and, if so, what were his attributes. Peretz replied in a speech that lasted all evening. He revealed himself as an intensely faithful Jew. He also betrayed the mystic, not the other-worldly type but one deeply rooted in reality—the creator or reinterpreter of folk and hasidic tales.

This was the first time that Peretz had championed the Jewish religion and religious mysticism, to the chagrin of the Jewish radicals. He had done so before in writing, but his spoken words carried greater conviction and proved more offensive to the agnostically-minded. One Saturday afternoon, shortly after this address, as Peretz was strolling through the Sachsische Garten, he was accosted by two young workers who handed him a little psalter with the remark, "That's all you need now." Peretz accepted the psalter, thanked the young men and advised them to procure a similar book of Psalms for themselves. "You will learn something from this book," he added, "something that you don't seem to know yet."

Peretz possessed an excess of energy that was exhausted neither by the question-box evenings, the concerts, nor the executive-committee meetings of the "Hazamir." The idea then occurred to him to organize "Monday Evenings," especially for Jewish writers, to enable them to read their latest works and to hear them discussed and dissected. Few writers, however, cared to subject their products to the scalpel, especially if it were handled by Peretz himself, for despite his kindliness and indulgence for young colleagues, he could also be very biting. Consequently they were hesitant about exposing themselves to his criticism, Peretz had no choice but to fill the program either with his own latest writings or with talks. Thus the purpose for which these evenings were instituted was only partly realized.

No one, however, minded Peretz's personal share in them. Quite the contrary. And no one was happier than Peretz himself. It always gave one a feeling of sheer delight to see Peretz in good spirits; his big, penetrating eyes looking as gentle as a child's, his broad, somewhat stern face slightly flushed, his mighty lower lip expressing abundant delight.

At one of these meetings, when no one offered to read anything he had recently written, Peretz sat down at the table and said simply: "I am going to tell you a folk tale, a story that was told to me a few days ago by a friend." He told the story orally, without a scrap of paper before him; he told it as one would a personal experience. An-sky was present. Peretz looked at him mischievously now and then in the course of his narrative. An-sky listened spellbound, without missing a syllable and staring into Peretz's eyes in amazement bordering on disbelief. Peretz kept on telling, simply, clearly and intimately, while his listeners wondered why he had gone to the trouble of memorizing such a lengthy tale, for there could be no doubt that he had memorized it. What an extraordinary feat! The story was a masterpiece. There was not a flaw in descriptive nuances or narrative and stylistic subtleties. How could he remember it all? As the narration progressed, we all became increasingly absorbed in it and drew closer to Peretz, forming a solid circle around him. He kept on reciting without seeming to improvise, without inserting a superfluous word, without pausing in search for one.

Unlike Sholom Aleichem, Peretz was no adept in mimicry or any other phase of the histrionic art. He was not fashioned of the stuff that goes to the making of great actors. He was too outstanding and too clear-cut a personality to mask his own features. He was too effervescent not to betray his true self.

Here was a virtually new oral narrative style, quiet and without theatrical tricks. He told a simple tale without oratorical or rhetorical flourishes, with here and there a flash of humour or a bit of touching piety and simple moving faith. All the magic of Peretz's written folk tales was transferred to his oral narrative, with the added charm of the spoken word.

When Peretz finished his story, An-sky threw his arms around him, kissed him, hugged him and asked him in utter bewilderment: "When did you write this story, how could you have found time to write it? Why, I told it to you only a few days ago."

Peretz, beaming and deeply moved, answered simply: "I haven't written it down yet. I've just got it in my head. I'll be easy enough to transfer it from my head to paper, just as soon as I can find the time." But An-sky's amazement did not abate. It was past his understanding how his colourless, sketchy story could have grown into such a colourful, detailed folk tale. Peretz then told us that for years now he had followed this method of treating his folk tales. This type of story was of its very essence an oral one, not meant to be committed to writing. He could best preserve its viva voce characteristics by not fixing it in written form until he had shaped its oral version. This curiosity of Peretz's method was for a long time the talk of literary circles.

I looked for an opportunity to get more information on the subject from Peretz. I found him quite willing to be drawn out. He expounded to me ungrudgingly, his theory on the writing of folk stories. The thing to remember, he insisted, was that the common people did not write stories, did not know the art of writing. What they did know was how to tell stories by word of mouth, a form of art from which professional writers had much to learn. Ordinary folk had an uncanny understanding for content and style. The content and style of their stories were twins.

The style was as reverent and as unaffected and had the same overtones as the story. The very simplicity of the style made it difficult to imitate. It could be learned only by a slow process of absorption. Peretz emphasized that there was a wide divergence between the written and the spoken word. That was why writers were at times unable to read to others simply and clearly what they had written themselves, for writing and speaking were different branches of the art of expression. Peretz admitted that he had learned this simple truth somewhat too late, when most of his folk stories had already been written.

"Now that I have learned what should always have been obvious to me," he added, "I take my time in writing down a folk story that I hear from a collector of folklore or directly from a man of the people. I first fashion it as an oral narrative. I bear in mind, too, that every folk story is told differently by every narrator, depending for one thing on the degree of narrative skill that he possesses. When I hear several versions of a story, I can tell the true and the beautiful from the false and the ugly. Poor dear An-sky, for example, kills the stories that he hears, by trying to give them a literary polish. I get them from him in that vitiated form. All he thinks about is the moral of the story, as if ordinary folk were constantly in search of wisdom and considered the plot as of secondary importance. An-sky's stories give me a lot of trouble. I first have to peel off their literary rind, and restore them to their oral version. I try hard to find another variant of the same tale before deciding on its final shape.

"It so happens that the story I told on Monday evening was told to me well by An-sky. Apparently he received it, so to speak, in good condition, undamaged by unskilful narrators, and this time he didn't spoil it himself either. Its only fault was that it was too short, so short that very little was left outside the core, the epitome, the basic moral of the story. But the abridgment concealed a complete folk story. It was just a matter of rediscovering it and that I did."

Shortly after that we read the same story in two installments, in the "Freint." Its essentially oral character was clearly evident, something that Peretz's previously published folk tales had often lacked.

Ever since, whenever I hear a folk story of Peretz read, I miss the viva voce quality that is so basic to folk stories. This quality seems largely submerged in its literary style and in the ethical idea underlying the story.

I have tried to bring home to a number of elocutionists Peretz's view of the essential nature of the folk story by letting them peer into his literary laboratory. But I have always had the feeling that they did not grasp the central thought I was trying to convey.

Maybe I shall have more luck with the foregoing exposition and that both those who read Peretz's folk stories aloud to others and those who read them silently to themselves will get a clearer notion of how they should be read. In any event, they will learn something about the manner in which Peretz handled his folk tales in his latter years: that his writing of them was subsidiary and subsequent to his oral composition of the stories.

A Psychologist Evaluates Peretz

by A. A. ROBACK

FORTY YEARS have elapsed since Peretz was found dead at his desk, after completing the second line of a children's song indited for the war refugee children's home founded by him. In the interval the world has been shaken, and yet reshaken. Movements, social, political and cultural, have been inaugurated; others have gone the way of all flesh—and spirit too. An all but tottering world had regained a measure of equilibrium only to flounder again. The literary complexion of the world, including that of its Jewry, has changed under the onslaught of a myriad of experiences, both exhilarating and frightful. Great and terrible things have happened during this period.

Yet throughout these tense decades, the personality of I. L. Peretz still stands out not only as an illustrious symbol of the golden period in Yiddish literature, but as a banner assembling under its device the constructive forces of a forward-looking Jewry. It seems to many of us as if his genial features, his reassuring smile and beaming eyes, were still beckoning to us encouragingly to throw off the shackles of despair and, as he had done, to forge our weapon of resistance with renewed vigour, so as to withstand the lure of assimilation, on the one hand, and the menace of annihilation, on the other, at the same time spreading the gospel of progress, justice, and peace in every corner of the globe.

To many of our own generation, Peretz has become a legend. There are still those who knew him, ready to puncture this legend. His shortcomings and weaknesses have not been spared. Some of his coevals have even gone to the extent of exaggerating his foibles. Yet the halo still surrounds him; and in the course of the century, unless Jewish culture declines, it is likely to take on an even more luminous character.

Thirty years is a long time to reconsider values. We can now

begin to speak in the name of posterity. Has Peretz actually de-
served the encomium showered upon him by Jewish leaders
throughout the world? Are his contributions to Yiddish and Hebrew literature such as would accord him a place in non-Jewish
literature? Is there any *genre* of writing in which he stands out
as foremost? Did he play the part of an innovator or leader in
Jewish life? Unless we examine these questions we are apt to indulge in mere hero-worship.

Without resorting to invidious comparison, we cannot help seeing Peretz not so much in the light of his own age, when his rivals
were Mendele and Sholom Aleichem, but in that of the distinguished representatives of the literature today.

After all, Mendele did not proceed far beyond Kabtzansk,
Glupsk, and Tuneiadevke. It was as the first stylist in Yiddish, the
first classicist to invest his stories with artistic form, that he rose
to the rank of greatness. Sholom Aleichem's fiction, moreover,
was until recently regarded as entertainment rather than as art;
hence Peretz had the advantage over him when they were both
alive. Peretz would have had more to vie with today, since the
erstwhile epigones have made their mark in the world both quali-
tatively and quantitatively. Each one of his close proteges, of one
time or another, Asch, Pinski, Reisen, Schneour, and a few of
those meteors, like I. J. Singer, whom he scarcely knew, have out-
stripped him in some one department, securing popular acclaim
and all that goes with it.

Sholem Asch has certainly, since painting his Polish townlet,
acquired an undisputed place as one of the world's leading novel-
ists, even before his name resounded from one end of Christendom
to the other. Peretz had never even so much as attempted a full-
length novel, and compressed nearly all his talent into the short
story, frequently spending himself in fragments, sparks, so to
speak. As to poetry, besides *"Monish,"* with which he made his
literary debut, and a few shorter speciments of good verse, he
turned out very little that could take its place beside masters like
Rosenfeld, Yehoash, and Bialik, unless we include in this field his
dramatic poems and versified dramas. It is, indeed, problematic
whether Peretz could have reached the top rung in our own
poetically fruitful decade. It is likewise with drama. So little did
he accomplish in this sphere, that Pinski, with his dozens of plays,
is easily his peer as a playwright. Even Peretz Hirshbein, with

whom Peretz is often confused among American and Canadian Jews, can lay claim to at least as much accomplishment in the realm of the stage. Peretz's main excellence lies in the short story, but even there he has competitors who have written not only a larger number of tales in Yiddish, but who have a surer instinct for the purely narrative pattern.

It will not be necessary to extend this miniature survey. We shall grant that, just as a very attractive woman, when we begin taking her features apart, so Peretz is at a disadvantage when we start to analyze his specific contributions. He can receive his proper evaluation only when we scan his literary physiognomy as a whole.

It was Peretz's inveterate adversary, David Frishman, who, in his obituary on the dead lion, wrote the following: "When I saw Peretz for the first time some twenty-five years ago and perceived the powerful imp with his glowing eyes and heard him articulate the terse sentences and *ex cathedra dicta* which he, as a rule, would disavow in the next breath—and contemplated his intense emotions, together with his lack of patience to clarify them in his mind and to realize his wishes—it dawned upon me that no matter how great this man might be as a *litterateur,* as a personality he ranks, out of all proportions, higher. His literary activity is in reality nothing but an epiphenomenon, a slight accessory, an insignificant supplement. The chief thing in him is after all the man. As a writer, he has given us probably more than was in his power, but as a personality, less. He who is acquainted only with his literature and has not known him personally, knows only a small fraction of him. He is a hundred times more powerful and infinitely mightier than the whole community of people who surrounded him. That is why he dominated them so forcefully, so tyrannically; and that is why, too, he loomed as a great writer to them. But what prevented him from becoming a truly great writer was simply his impatience. He did not have sufficient endurance to become an artist. He was burnt up by an uncontrollable passion to be—no matter what—so long as he was to be somebody. He was one of those who could not exist for a moment without applause . . . Incidentally, he also became a great writer."

Incidentally, a man does not "incidentally" become a great writer, as Frishman nonchalantly asserts—unless the observation is intended for subtle sarcasm. Endowments are not distilled out of mere circumstances, even if they may gain in scope and depth as a result of them. Is there not more than a grain of pride and prejudice concealed in the ambivalent eulogy? Yes, and a germ of truth is to be found there too; for Peretz's personality decidedly overshadowed his works. Indeed, his works will be understood only in the light of his temperament and cultural sweep.

Everyone who had come in contact with him was fascinated by his dynamic and buoyant qualities. At the Yiddish Language Conference in Czernowitz, in 1908, he was hailed as a national hero. It was he who steered the discussions, geared the delegates for action, inspired the audiences by his impromptu addresses, devised effective slogans and mapped out the cultural projects for the future.

It must not be supposed, however, that I am diverting attention from indifferent literary achievement to a striking personality. All that is postulated here is that Peretz's personality is so interwoven with his work that we cannot understand the one without the other. We shall have occasion to see that in spite of a relatively meagre output, his personal equation means so much more when added to the content—which brings us to the positive features of his literary configuration, clearly distinguishing him from other Yiddish and perhaps, too, Jewish writers in general.

In the first instance, he was a pathfinder, what the Germans call a *Bahnbrecher*. It is curious that his very name *Peretz* (the Hebrew for "breaking through") symbolically signifies just this. Even his compeers, Mendele and Sholom Aleichen, keen as they were in their detailed perceptions, browsed in a ghetto. Peretz broke the barriers between East and West, between Jew and Gentile, thus Europeanizing the literature which up to his time had seemed impervious to influences from without, and supplied a lofty conception to the whole framework.

Critics said he was under the sway of this Russian or that Polish writer, just as other cavillers spoke of Sholom Aleichem as an imitator of Chekhov, but it mattered not. Peretz demonstrated that Yiddish could be set on a cultural plane alongside French, German, Russian, or Polish, although he did complain of the dearth of poetic expressions, thus betraying his inadequacy in this domain. He never had cause to deplore the poverty of Yiddish diction in writing his deeply moving folk tales and sparkling feuilletons.

Peretz not only blazed the trail by introducing new themes and a fresh style. He exploited his subjects in an original manner. He was original in setting the problems and in disclosing relations, even if he did not explain their *quale*. That did not detract from his individuality, since much of what was then vague and inarticulate began to take on a definite shape and hue as the years went by, just as Beethoven's symphonies mean much more to us today than they did to the privileged first auditors.

There can be no question about Peretz being a creative mind, even if many of his products were not finished. Schubert's "Unfinished Symphony" is great music in spite of its incompleteness. Together with Schiller he would rather be in constant quest of objectives than actually attain them. And herein lies another fundamental trait of Peretz's literary personality. He was the perpetual seeker—of new forms, new ideas, new outlets of expression. His mercurial nature was an obstruction and at the same time a release—an obstruction to his literary reputation, and a release to the urges of his inner self.

Many of his opponents placed him in the category of a chammeleon, but he did not assume the colouring of the environment. Rather did he take the initiative in transforming it. That is one reason why he could not be a realist or a naturalist. It would be necessary for him to remain on one plane; it would spell stagnation for him. He must transform the mere sense-data into an ideological entity, trying out various approches.

In the process of his transformation, like his own *"Gilgl fun a Nign"* (Incarnation of a Tune), he passes through various layers. Sometimes he descends like a diver into the depths of history, bringing to the surface his find, and without resting on earth, he soars with it to Olympic heights where it is purified and crystallized into a literary creation. It is perhaps in this respect that he differs from both his predecessors and successors.

While they could retreat to some one period in Jewish history and make a study of it for their particular purpose, all that Peretz needed to do was simply to take a plunge, and he grasped the entire age *uno intuitu*. Perhaps without being aware of it, he possessed the formula of *kfitzas haderech* (seven league boots).

In many other writers, the passage from one story to another, from one play or novel to another, is accompanied by or mediated through the change of interest and mentality. Each of Peretz's writings, however, is merely a chip off the old block. It is Peretz objectified into a tale, poem, or *feuilleton*. The true literary picture of the artist can be envisaged only after all these items, fragments, and even aphorisms are welded into an integrated whole; and we must not lose sight of his great versatility in this connection: correspondence, memoirs, epigrams, publicisra, allegories, poetry, drama, essays, travel pictures, criticism, popular science—all capped by his insinuating folk tales and chassidic stories.

Peretz himself thought more of his drama, "The Golden Chain," than of anything else he wrote. His more objective friends knew that his inimitable "Folk Tales" will always live in the memory of his people. A number of his narratives like "The Incarnation of a Tune," "He Who Gives Life," "In Times of Pestilence," "The Messenger," "A Chapter of Psalms," "The Bass Viol," "Domestic Bliss," and "Precipice" require a cultural background of the reader. Perhaps that is why the pointed stories like "If Not Higher" and "Bontche Shveig" have been singled out as the most characteristic and most valuable of his writings. They are fine to cite as illustrations, but remind us of Bartlett's "Familiar Quotations," as compared with a volume of, let us say, Emerson's "Essays."

Another conventional practice is to give the gist of one or two of Peretz's tales, including the folk legends. It would seem futile to condense into a paragraph of ordinary prose a poetic gem, the setting of which is by far more important than the plot or the moral. In other words, in order to enjoy Peretz one must read him. Unfortunately the English-speaking reader has yet to discover him. There are only two volumes in English translation (much of which is duplicated), one of them awkwardly translated and the other, while done adequately as to diction, somewhat inaccurately translated.

Of his poems, *"Monish"* is unequalled as a ballad in Yiddish literature, while "The Sewing of the Wedding Gown" is a powerful indictment of human exploitation in dramatic form.

To my mind, the eerie drama "Beinacht oifn Altn Mark" (The Old Market at Night), is his great masterpiece. It is a Jewish conception of Faust with a "Walpurgisnacht" originally conceived on a ghetto scale, narrow but deep. In rhymed verse, it shows us the Peretz we might have had, were he working under propitious circumstances. That, indeed, is what we always have in the back of our mind when we pay homage to the man who had so many facets, each of which shone as if it were of a different water. We honour him for his potentialities as well as for his actualities.

Peretz not only was the foremost writer in Yiddish. He was a pillar in Hebrew literature too. His poetry, in contrast with the didactic and moralistics trends of the day, introduced an erotic note and appealed to the aesthetic sense. His sketches and playlets in Hebrew are, in part, variants of some of his Yiddish writings, sometimes preceding them. A series of fantastic pictures of "The Eighth Compartment of the Inferno" is his most ambitious contribution to Hebrew literature.

Considerations of space preclude a discussion of Peretz as an editor, as a publisher, as a theatrical promoter. He was the "nervus vivendi" of Warsaw Jewry—one might almost say, of Polish Jewry. Hardly a beginner in the Yiddish or Hebrew literary field but sued this Nestor for a word of encouragement. It was he who introduced Nomberg, Abraham Reisen, Sholem Asch and others to the world. When the last-named now world-famous man of letters read to him his first fruit in Hebrew, he was advised to bring him something in Yiddish. Peretz spotted his talent at once, and was reported to have remarked to a friend, "You see this young man? He is going to be Sholem Asch some day."

His sudden death during the Passover week in 1915 plunged not only the Warsaw Jews but all Jewries into deep mourning. It is estimated that more than 150,000 people participated in the funeral. The streets were thronged, and there was scarcely a Jewish organization in Poland which did not send a delegation to represent it.

Thus lived and died, and yet continues to live, a beacon light in Jewish culture, a warrior and an artist at the same time, a creator of lasting values, and an illustrious son of his people.

I. L. Peretz—the Man and Writer

by DAVID PINSKI *and* MELECH GRAFSTEIN

IT WAS a slow road that Peretz travelled in search of himself, slowly learning the nature of his own powers. It was slower yet that recognition came. He began writing when still very young, but it was not until he was forty that he attracted the attention of the Jewish world.

He was the bright boy of the family, a strictly observant middle-class household in Zamosc, Poland. Unlike most devout Jewish parents of the time, however, his father permitted him, while studying the Talmud, to familiarize himself with Polish, Russian and German, and to read secular books. The lad became a diligent reader; this he remained to his end. He also took to writing. At first it was poetry, but despite the fact that he read Heine, it was not love poetry.

Girls used to fall in love with him, especially with his large, beautiful eyes; but his heart was not awake. He was married off to a girl he had not chosen, only to part with her after a few years. Love came into his life with Helena Ringelheim, to whom he wrote verses and who was later to become his second wife. The boy gained in wisdom and insight and his large open eyes saw men and events increasingly clearly. They furnished him with poetical themes for special occasions.

In order not to offend his extremely religious mother, Peretz did not proceed to a secular university. Hence, when the traditional period of dependence on his father's support was at an end, he had no gainful occupation. He was a "jack of all trades, but master of none." He took by turns to brewing, to teaching Hebrew, to operating a flour-mill, and to practising law. He finally secured employment as official or bookkeeper with the Warsaw Jewish Community or "Gmina," a post which he held for the rest of his life.

He experienced both comparative prosperity and extreme want, but his economic situation left him unaffected; it was something extraneous to his true self. The true Peretz was in quite another world, ever groping—a great unrest within him. It was a creative unrest, the desire for expression.

Hebrew literature in those days was still in the grip of the "Haskala" or movement of enlightenment. This movement tore down much in Jewish life, but created little. It was foreign to Jewry, for it came from without. It lacked warmth. But in young Peretz it touched off a spark, and awoke the builder within him. In his poem "Nagniel," the twenty-five-year-old Peretz reproached the Hebrew poets for using only empty rhetorical expressions which led nowhere, and did nothing for the Jewish masses. He insisted that words had a purpose, to uplift the soul of the reader, stir him, lead him on. And this young person sought within himself for such words as would convey his own restlessness to his reader, his own desire for a better life.

Modern Yiddish literature was in the course of evolution at the time. Mendele Mocher Sforim and Linietsky, new creators in Yiddish letters, were also chastisers, and held up Jewish life to ridicule, as grotesque and absurd. But they offered no solution leading to a better and more beautiful life. They wished to lead, but whither? To be sure, young Peretz too began with satire, derision and sarcasm, but he had a goal both for himself and the Jewish masses.

Where there is darkness, light must be introduced. Where the blight of ignorance exists knowledge must be disseminated. Pity and love must replace poverty. His large bright eyes looked round and saw that "there is nothing to be done with the old Talmudists and bourgeois. There is nothing to hope for in them." They could not be changed. For them no program would avail. They would remain as they were. They could only be scoffed and satirized. But there were the large working masses, the poor, those lacking in life's necessities, but rich in spirit. Here could be found idealism, a desire for a new life, a yearning for enlightenment. This class was sadly neglected, scarcely taken note of. To them he would direct all his energies. He would speak to them in their own language.

He organized evening classes for Jewish workers and lectured to them on Jewish history. Let them begin, he thought, by knowing their own history, something about their own people. To this period belong his beginnings as a Yiddish writer.

When he made his debut in Yiddish with several contributions in Sholom Aleichem's *"Yiddishe Folks Bibliotek,"* he caused little stir. To be sure, his poem "Monish" was read with some interest, as was also his "Venus and Sulamith," but nobody was especially concerned with their author. Those who knew him by his Hebrew works did not think too highly of him. The Hebrew literary authority of that time, "Criticus" (S. Dubnow) of the Russian-Jewish journal "Voskhod," who had angrily attacked one of his Hebrew poems a year or two previously in "Heasif," now treated his "Monish" most unkindly. But Peretz soon attracted the attention of the Jewish youth who accepted him as their own. He introduced a new and refreshing tone in Yiddish letters. They anxiously waited for more of his writings and welcomed with joy his "Familiar Pictures" a small book consisting of three short stories and published by his friend Jacob Dyneson. The first volume of his *"Yiddishe Bibliotek"* was likewise received with genuine enthusiasm.

The organizer of evening courses for the people in Zamosc now made use of the printed word to spread his ideas on education for the masses, rousing Jewish public opinion and, most important of all, the Jewish youth. He found many adherents among them. He was surrounded by Jewish students of the Warsaw University who were anxious to help him in this sacred work of spreading knowledge among the masses. Popular scientific books under his editorship were projected. If nothing came of this undertaking it was through no fault of his. He was heart and soul in this "holy work." But his co-workers, the students, failed him in what they had undertaken to do. They even brought financial ruin to the project.

Peretz did not throw up his hands in despair. He continued his work. Then came the years of the "Yomtov Bletlech," "Literatur un Leben," "Yiddishe Bibliotek," volume three—three eventful years (1893–1896) full of work and the joy of accomplishment. His voice was heard, he had attained something; at least he played a part in the driving-force which awakened and stirred the Jewish working classes.

After the storm of these three years came the calm. He did not keep up with the advancing multitudes of the working classes, but withdrew into himself. Was it only the awakening of the Jewish workers that he sought? Was it not rather the rousing of the entire Jewish People? He began searching within himself.

He felt that he had been floating only on the periphery of Jewish existence. Within him was another truth, the central truth of the Jewish soul, of Judaism. For some time he had been aware of this. From time to time it had pointed toward something. He had not fully grasped its meaning. Was he discovering it now? At the time he addressed the working-class meetings, he wrote his "Cabbalists." Many of his readers considered it as a farce, as they did also his "Dowering of the Bride," and were pleased to laugh over the chassidim.

At the turn of the last century, when he was nearly fifty, he realized what he had within him to contribute to the Jewish people. He began to delve deeper into himself. He brought forth "Chassidic" stories and "Folk Tales," works which embody the age-old prophetic spirit which sees true Judaism not merely in outward piety but, as Peretz expressed it in "At the Death-Bed," in "uplifting the fallen, healing the sick, feeding the hungry, giving drink to the parched, seeking and restoring the lost," even though it should mean going through the fires of hell.

He revealed himself as a great Jewish spirit, the embodiment of our people's soul. In his works, both big and small, in his stories, dramas, and poems, as well as in his journalistic writings he dealt with the essential heritage of our people, its morality and ethics, its sense of mercy and justice, its regard for man and human dignity, and its longing for a better world and a day of unalloyed sabbatical peace.

Peretz became the central pillar of modern Yiddish literature, its mainstay and hope. He laid bare what was noblest in the Jewish soul. He gave to the new generation of writers a love and zeal for their people. They learned from him the joy of true Jewish creativity.

On the third of April, 1915, the third of the intermediary days of Passover, in the Jewish calendar year of 5675, he died suddenly at his desk. It is thirty years since his pen fell from his hand, but it is as if he were still sitting at his desk. For his works are a never-ending discovery, abounding in what is new in content and fresh in form, as new and as fresh as the spirit they portray.

The Legacy of I. L. Peretz

by S. NIGER

A MAN BEQUEATHS to his children: (a) what he had; (b) what he was.

The second type of bequest is the surer. It is also the more effective and the more dynamic.

The *estate* that one transmits to his heirs may soon dwindle away or leave no trace at all. Not so the *person* of the deceased—his physical and spiritual characteristics, his build, his facial features and traits of character, his inborn tendencies and aptitudes. To whatever extent these are inherited by his offspring, they are preserved in them; they live on in them. These are the things that a parent leaves not *for* his children and their descendants but *in* them. It is himself living on in them. That is his life after death, his continuity, his "eternity."

What one *is,* rather than what one *has,* is the thing that binds one generation to another. In each generation, however, it is manifested in a peculiar way and to a varying degree. This kind of heredity, though appearing fixed and stable is, in very truth, highly mutable.

In other words, what remains of a man's physical and spiritual *self* after death is both more tangible and more vital than his estate. This is true, however, only of men who leave behind them nothing but ponderable possessions. The man bequeathing to us not material but spiritual wealth—say literary works—belongs to a totally different category. Of him it cannot be said that what he *was* is more important than what he *had.* His assets—his spiritual life-work—are the revelation of that which he *was.* In his case *having* equates *being.* Furthermore, what he incorporates in his work is more durable than what he *is.* The best and most beautiful part, for example, of that which Leo Tolstoi *was* died with him, whereas that which he *had*—his works—remain immortal. His own life after death depends on the life of his works.

Nevertheless there are some authors regarding whose legacy one might confidently assert what has been asserted regarding that of other non-creative men—that what they *were* is even more enduring and more valuable than what they *had*. Those are the authors that leave us with the impression—and such an impression was left also by I. L. Peretz—that they had much more than they succeeded in putting into their works.

I. L. Peretz is one of those writers who are even more remarkable, even more scintillating and even more brilliant than what they write.

What has been said is not meant to imply that Peretz strove to achieve more than he did. This is certainly not true of one portion of his work, for example, his best "chassidic" and "folk" tales. As regards those works in which his powers actually fell short of his talent, that sort of thing happens to almost every author unless he is a dull mediocrity. What I have tried to say is that Peretz was decidedly greater and had greater creative potentialities than came to light in the totality of his creativeness.

Like a sower in early spring Peretz went about the—as yet ill-plowed—field of Yiddish literature, scattering handfuls of seed, or rather throwing it away. Much of it fell on fertile soil, took root, came up, put forth shoots, blossomed and bore fruit. Some seeds were borne away by the wind. Others found or will find their way to the soil of his spiritual children or grandchildren.

Peretz lives not only in his own works. He lives and breathes in the speech and literature of the generations that followed him. He has a silent share in nearly everything that has been achieved in our literature during the last three or four decades. He will have a share in many subsequent achievements. We should, indeed, thank and praise him not only for what he has given us but will yet give us through his disciples.

Other writers endure in the consciousness of the people and in the creative work of its gifted children only through their actual accomplishments. Peretz, however, has lived on and continued to exert an influence also by means of his heroic strivings, his mute innuendos, his daring attempts, and stimulating challenges. Things that he initiated have been or will be completed by others. But it was he who initiated them. Appetites that he roused have been or will be satisfied by others. But he has been and still is the active stimulus.

Let us not hasten to make a *classic* of Peretz, the writer said in a hastily written obituary (in "Yiddishe Velt," Vilna) when the sad news of Peretz's death arrived. He is one of us, I insisted in the name of the then young literary fraternity. His work is not done, his epoch is just beginning . . . "I have sown the seeds, give heed to the vegetation that will sprout forth!" That, it seemed to me, was Peretz's testament, and I called: Let us tend the green vegetation! The great spiritual thirst that Peretz awakened in the people has not been quenched; we must continue Peretz's great educational work. The bridge that he was building between the intellectuals and the people is not completed; we must have new and trusty builders! Peretz did not say to the people: "This is for you." He said: "I am with you. If I should feel crowded in your house, you and I will try to enlarge it." He entrusted his entire self to folk culture and folk speech; he came to the masses like an equal to equals; he never talked down to them. They permitted him to be what he was, and although they did not understand everything he said in his works, they were deeply beholden to him.

We cannot achieve the results that he achieved because we do not possess those abundant spiritual means that he possessed. But his way must also be ours. We too must come to the people with everything we have, with our entire spiritual personality; and we too must drink thirstily from the spring from which he drank so eagerly. Peretz's life must be lived on by us. We must think of him not as a *classic,* but as a great neophyte suddenly snatched from us. We are not orphans, we are heirs, responsible heirs . . .

We are responsible for his entire heritage—both for what he had, that is his works, and for what he was, that is the dynamic force of the hidden potentialities of his spiritual self.

Limitations of space preclude an appreciation or even a characterization of his works in this essay. Just a few words will have to suffice.

In the portraits, sketches, stories, and belletristic essays of his first period he raised to a higher level what had been present in Mendele and Sholom Aleichem. He refined their homely realism. He condensed their realistic popular style, he modernized it to a degree; simultaneously he individualized their psychology (adding to their mass psychology that of the individual). That was a great achievement, but he achieved even more in the second period when he heightened the style of, or rather, lent a characteristically Peretzian style to chassidic and other Yiddish folk stories. It was then he gave us something that had practically not existed in modern Yiddish literature—sublimated idealization and romanticism. It was then, too, that he evolved the style of his essays—the style of modern Yiddish prose. In this way, and also by other means, he helped Yiddish speech and Yiddish literature to rise above the position of the common people's language and the common people's literature and to strive for the level of a national language and a national literature.

As has been indicated, however, considerations of space do not permit a more concrete characterization of the literary legacy bequeathed by Peretz. I shall therefore pass on from what Peretz *had* and *we* have now to what he *was* and what his heirs, after his death, have wanted to be.

He was the *leaven* that caused to ferment and rise the stuff from which the new Yiddish literature was kneaded.

He was the urge, the momentum, the yearning, the dream-come-true of our creative spirit. (I should not like this to be taken as a mere figure of speech.)

He said himself in his memoirs: "If instead of using a pen for describing, I had used a pencil for drawing, I should have made the following caricature of myself as a boy: puny, skinny; arms and legs like spindles, a large head; an undersized forehead; big, searching, painfully questioning eyes."

Nor is this altogether a caricature: Peretz was, in very truth, the big, searching, painfully-questioning eyes of Yiddish literature.

Whereas others before him, in our spiritual world, gave answers (or thought they did), Peretz boldly asked questions.

He taught us to ask questions—to have the courage to ask questions, not to be afraid to proclaim our doubts.

Questions and *doubts,* it will be objected, are perhaps not a particularly useful legacy. To *question* and to *doubt* is, however, a useful and necessary art, especially since Peretz began to teach it to us at a time when the all-wise Haskala (enlightenment) was still quite sure of its naive answers, at a time when the dogmas of all kinds of catechisms were still held to be sacred and their precepts immutable.

Jewish writers—and not only the adherents of the Haskala but also their heirs, the folkists and the socialists—were in the habit of coming to the Jewish public as a doctor comes to a patient; they were accustomed to feel his pulse, to sound him, and to write a prescription. Peretz felt his own pulse. He did not ask: "What ails me?" He said: "I am ailing." He came as a patient, not as a healer. For the first time there was a certain intimate air in Yiddish literature instead of the former austere atmosphere of the hospital, or the pulpit.

"Not *knowing* but *reflecting* is the thing," says one of Peretz's heroes. This might have served as a motto for the greater part of his writings. Even when he was minded on giving us knowledge he was primarily interested in reflection. Even when he came to us —and he came very often—with new ideas, he was not so much concerned with the *ideas* as with their *newness*. "Ideas are neither true nor false, but fresh or stale, blossoming, or withered . . . If an idea is presented to you, put your nose close to it; take fresh ones and pin them to your breast, cast away old ones. . . ." This Peretz told us in all that he wrote and not merely in the aphorism just quoted.

Peretz was fond of the vague searchings of the romantic spirit, he liked twilight dreaming and musing. He was romantic, but his romanticism did not hark back to old things, but, on the contrary, to new things. Even his glorification of Chassidism was because it lent itself to modernization. He loved old stories just because it was such a joy to revive them. Archaic style became dear to him only after he had infused into it his own life-breath.

In contrast to Mendele and Sholom Aleichem, Peretz was not the summation of what had preceded, but the first page of a new account.

To Peretz the past served merely as material for some structure of the future. He was all in all, it might be said, the futurity of Yiddish literature. He was Yiddish literature *in the making*. Although all his works are full of things of the past, they are not the balance of a life that is being liquidated, but an attempt to balance forces contending for a new life, and to synthesize ideas seeking a new lease of life.

It is as though Peretz were minded to leave legatees rather than a legacy.

For evermore a spokesman for juvenescence, he set store by the *journey* rather than the *arrival,* the road rather than the destination, the quest rather than the discovery.

The searching and investigating spirit of the Jewish world, Peretz was neither its dimension of *breadth,* like Sholom Aleichem; nor of its *depth,* like Mendele; but of its *height,* ever striving upwards—"Maybe Even Higher," in the concluding words of his story by that name.

What Peretz *was*—that stirring, variable, hot, seething, more latent than kinetic energy, the energy that makes Peretz's creative stream so restless, so stormy and effervescent—is that portion of the legacy that is as dear to us as, or even dearer than, what Peretz *had.*

What he *was* he left behind him *in,* not just *for,* Yiddish literature. By means of his turbulent restlessness, his burning ardor, his searchings and yearnings, his visions and presentiments, he so roused and stirred and inspired Yiddish literature that it became a sequel of what he was rather than of what he had. It became a sequel of his work, rather than of his works, of his strivings rather than of his goal.

It goes without saying, however, that what he *was* was strongly reflected in what he *had.* It goes without saying that the impatience and restlessness of his *work* left traces in his *works.* The spiritual goods that he bequeathed to us in both our languages, his poems, stories, essays, and aphorisms, have in them something mobile and moving.

Just try and read his poems, especially his early ones, look into his early prose-miniatures, those he termed "ma'aselech," take the humorous or polemical essays he published in the "Yomtov Bletlech," in "Ha-mailitz," and you will see that although a considerable number of them—particularly those written in prose—have preserved the sharpness of tone and the freshness of relish that they had half a century ago, their distinguishing features are their atmosphere of restlessness and feverishness, the quaver and tremulousness to be found in almost everything that Peretz wrote. It will become manifest to you, if you will look into his words once more, that the greatest significance of his writing, as of his speech, lay in the tempest that he raised. Nothing that was touched by his hot breath ever remained still. Things stirred and were set in motion. "The fatty, glistening, green" film of the stagnant water was torn asunder, the water bubbled and began to flow and stream.

There appeared a new Yiddish personality, a new Yiddish style.

It differed from the preceding personality (and mode of writing) as the fast and restless city differs from the slow and quiet townlet (and as the nervous and breathless urban center differs from the calm and staid rural point.)

Peretz himself once casually indicated his main achievement when writing (a long time ago in "In Honor of Passover") about the Jew of olden times: "What conception did he have of life? It looked to him like a calm, limpid, and noiseless brook, flowing out of the gate of the Garden of Eden, and would have flowed on thus calmly, limpidly, and noiselessly, but for the evil inclination and sensual appetite of man who throws a stone into the water, shattering the clear mirror and stirring up ripples and waves . . ."

Peretz's pen was the "evil inclination" which threw a stone into the still water, shattered the clear mirror and stirred up ripples and waves.